THE DOCUMENTS IN THE CASE

THE DOCUMENTS
IN THE CASE

Dorothy L. Sayers
and Robert Eustace

NEW ENGLISH LIBRARY/TIMES MIRROR

First published in Great Britain by
Victor Gollancz Ltd. in 1930
Eleventh impression 1958

First published as a Four Square edition 1964
Reissued as an NEL edition January 1969
New edition June 1970
Reprinted April 1973
New edition April 1975
New edition January 1978
This new edition May 1981

NEL Books are published by
New English Library Limited,
Barnard's Inn, Holborn,
London EC1N 2JR.

Made and printed in Great Britain by
Hunt Barnard Printing Ltd.,
Aylesbury, Bucks.

0 450 05341 5

CONTENTS

INTRODUCTION

Paul Harrison to Sir Gilbert Pugh
[Letter covering the attached documents.]

REDGAUNTLET HOTEL, BLOOMSBURY, W.C.
18th March, 1930

DEAR SIR,

I am obliged by your letter of yesterday's date, and hasten to send you, as requested, the complete dossier of documents. When you have read them. I shall be happy to call upon you at any time convenient to yourself, and give you any further information that may be within my power.

All the points I specially wished to make are, I think, fully covered by my previous letter. But since that letter has now served its original purpose of arousing your interest in the matter, I feel that it would be better forgotten, as far as possible. I would rather you came to the present documents with an entirely open mind. To me, who have been working over them for the last six or seven months, they seem to point clearly to one and only one conclusion, but I suppose it is possible that both Sir James Lubbock and I may be mistaken. You will judge for yourself. I only most earnestly beg of you to give the case your most careful consideration. You will realise that it is of vital importance to me to have the matter fully investigated.

You will, I fear, find some of the letters and statements very diffuse and full of irrelevancies. I thought it best to send the originals, complete and untouched, exactly as they stand. Many of the incidental details, though unimportant in themselves, throw useful sidelights on the situation, and will, I think, help a stranger, like yourself to understand exactly what took place in my late father's household.

I have arranged the papers, as nearly as possible, in chronological order. My own statement (Number 49) explains fully how the various documents came into my hands.

Trusting to hear further from you in due course,

I am, dear sir,

Yours faithfully,

PAUL HARRISON

SECTION ONE

Synthesis

1. *Agatha Milsom to Olive Farebrother*

15, WHITTINGTON TERRACE, BAYSWATER
9th September, 1928

MY DEAR OLIVE,

Thank you very much for your letter and kind inquiries after my health. I like my new doctor very much indeed. I think he *understands me a great deal better* than Dr Coombs, and he has put me on quite a different treatment. He says I am just going through a 'difficult phase' at present, and that if only I can hold on and not let things get on top of me for the next year or two I shall come out of it quite all right. But I am not to have a rest-cure! It seems Dr Coombs was all wrong about that – of course he didn't exactly *say* she was wrong, it wouldn't be professional, but I could see that he *thought* it! Dr Trevor says that rest-cures only 'turn you in upon yourself', and that makes things worse. He says I must get right away from myself and my feelings, so as to 'sublimate' all these repressed urges and turn them into some other sort of energy. He says it was quite all right to start with to have my dreams and subconscious betrayals analysed, so as to know exactly what was the matter with me, but that *now* the time has come when I must learn to throw all these bottled-up desires *outwards*, and give them something to do. He explained it all *most* clearly. I said, 'I suppose it is sex, doctor, isn't it?' (Of course, one gets quite used to asking things perfectly frankly, and one doesn't mind it a bit.) And he said, well, largely; and, of course, that was a thing most people suffered from one way and another, and in these days one couldn't always take the obvious and direct way out of a condition of sex-repression, because it would often be socially and economically inconvenient. I said that with two million extra women in this country it didn't seem possible, certainly, for everybody to get married, and he smiled and said: 'My dear Miss Milsom, half my patients come to me because they are not married – and the other half because they are!' We had quite a laugh about it. He is very nice and rather good-looking, but he doesn't seem to think it necessary for all his patients to fall in love with him, like that odd man I went to see in Wimpole Street, who suffered so dreadfully from halitosis.

Well, anyway, he asked me what I was interested in, and I said I'd always had an idea I should like to *write*. He said that was an awfully good idea, and I ought to encourage it by trying my hand at a little sketch or article every day, or by just putting down my observations of people and things as I saw them. I'm sure I get subjects enough in this house, as far as *matrimony* goes, anyhow. Indeed, my dear, from what I see of men, I'm very glad there are *other* ways out of my troubles than what Dr Trevor calls the *direct* way!! Do you mind, please, not throwing my letters away – just stick them in one of the drawers in my old desk when you've finished with them, because I think I might use some of the funny little incidents that happen here to work up into a novel some time. One puts these things down when they are fresh in one's mind, and then one forgets about them.

Well, we are jogging along here in our usual placid way – with the usual little outbreaks, of course, when a meal goes wrong, as they will sometimes, with all my care. Mr Harrison is such an expert, you know, that it is very hard for a person with only one pair of hands to keep everything up to his high standard. And, fond though I am, and always shall be, of dear Mrs Harrison, I do sometimes wish that she was just a *little* more practical. If anything at all is left to her to do, she is so apt to lose herself in a book or a daydream and forget all about it. She always says she ought to have been born to ten thousand a year – but who of us could not say that? I always feel myself that I was really meant to 'sit on a cushion and sew a fine seam' – you remember the games we used to play about being princesses in the Arabian Nights, with a train of a hundred black slaves, carrying alabaster bowls filled with rubies – but alas! life is life and we have to make the best of it. And I do sometimes feel it a little unfair that so *much* should come upon my shoulders. Women do want romance in their lives, and there is so little of it about. Of course, as you know, I do feel for Mrs Harrison – her husband is such a dry sort of man and so lacking in sympathy. I do what I can, but that is not the same thing and it is very worrying. I must learn to detach myself. Dr Trevor says it is very important to cultivate detachment.

When I was shopping this morning I met Mr Bell, who told me the top maisonette was let at last – to two young men! I said I hoped they wouldn't be noisy (though anything would be a relief after that awful woman with her children), and he said they seemed quiet, gentlemanly young fellows. One of them he thinks must be some kind of artist, because they were so interested in the top back room which has a big window with a north light – you know, the one Mr Harrison always covets so much. Though, of course, it is not nearly so convenient a house as ours in other ways.

I have started on Tom's stockings. They are going to be *very* smart. I have worked out an original design for the turnover – a sort of swirly pattern in fawn, brown and black, taken from the coat of the kitchen cat – tabby, you know. Mr Perry saw it the other day when he called. He thinks I have quite a talent for that kind of thing.

Give my love to Ronnie and Joan. I hope you are taking care of yourself.

Your loving sister,
AGGIE

2. *The Same to the Same*

15, WHITTINGTON TERRACE, BAYSWATER
13th September, 1928

DEAR OLIVE,

I really think it is *very unkind* of you to suggest that I like Dr Trevor simply because he is a *man*. I am the last person to imagine that a woman doctor is necessarily inferior. Quite the contrary. Other things being equal I much prefer a woman, but if the man happens to be *right* and the woman *wrong*, it would be absurd not to admit it. I do feel that Dr Trevor's treatment is doing me good, and I am not the least little bit prejudiced by the sex question one way or another. I daresay Tom has been airing his opinions, but that does not impress me at all. Men never ever get out of their heads that the whole world centres round their high-mightinesses. I'm not blaming Tom, but *all* men are self-centred. They can't help it. Dr Trevor says that it is a necessary part of their psychological make-up; they have to be self-regarding, just as women have to be other-regarding – on account of the children and so on. But I do beg you will not take Tom's pronouncements for Gospel where I am concerned.

I read such a clever article the other day by Storm Jameson, in which she said that all women, in the depths of their hearts, resented men. Now I do think that is so true. It is so maddening, the calm assumption of superiority that a man puts on when he is talking to a woman. We had quite a little dispute the other evening – about Einstein, of all people! Mrs Harrison started to talk about an interesting account of him in the Sunday paper, but Mr Harrison only grunted and went on reading something tedious about the Government. However, she went on asking him questions till he simply *had* to answer, and then he said, quite snubbingly, that he considered the man was a charlatan who was pulling people's legs with his theories. I said I didn't think all these professors would believe in him and have him down to lecture and so on if it was just that. So he said, 'Just you ask my old friend, Professor Alcock, if you won't believe me.' Mrs Harrison said she couldn't ask Professor Alcock, because she had never seen him, and why didn't Mr Harrison sometimes bring somebody interesting to the house? That seemed to annoy him, though I thought it was very much to the point, but, being only a paid subordinate, I said meekly that we were all entitled to our own opinions. So he smiled sarcastically and said that perhaps *some* of us were better qualified to judge than others, and that the Sunday Press was not always the best guide to knowledge. 'But *you* read the papers,' said Mrs Harrison. 'When I'm given the chance,' said he.

If I had been in Mrs Harrison's place I should have taken warning from the way he rattled *The Times,* but one cannot expect old heads on young shoulders – or perhaps mature heads would be fairer to myself. But she is perhaps a little tactless now and again, poor girl, and said if she didn't read the papers how was she to improve her mind? Of course, I knew exactly what the answer would be – the virtues of the old-fashioned domestic woman and the perpetual chatter of the modern woman about things which were outside her province. It is the fatal subject, and somehow or other it always seems to crop up. Mrs Harrison was very much hurt, and said of course she knew she couldn't possibly come up to the perfections of Mrs Harrison No. 1. Then, of course, the fat was in the fire. It was just like a woman to take it personally. Mrs Harrison began to cry, and he said, 'Please don't make a scene,' and went out and slammed the door.

What I wanted to do was just to go up to Mr Harrison and say, 'Now do be a little human. Make a fuss of her. Let her cry if she wants to and then make it up and be friends.' But he isn't the kind of person you can very well say things to. He would think it impertinent of me. And it's true that it never pays to interfere between husband and wife. But if only he would listen to me, I know I could put matters right. In my kind of life one gets plenty of experience – lookers-on see most of the game, you know – and Mrs Harrison would be so ready to attach herself to him, if only he would give her the chance. Often and often

I've known her work herself up for hours to make an appeal to his feelings, but he receives it so coldly. Somehow it never seems to be the right moment. He is always absorbed in his painting or his natural history or something. How true it is that men live for Things and women for People! To pin one's heart to a Person always means suffering in this world, if one has an acutely-sensitive nature. You are to be congratulated, Olive, on not being sensitive. Temperament is a great gift, but a very unhappy one, as I know so well from my own experience. I really *admire* Mrs Harrison – she never loses hope, but goes on, day after day, trying to be brave and devoted and to keep up her interest in life. And she has such a vivid alert mind – she is keen on everything, even on things like Einstein, which are so very modern and difficult. But I do not see how one can go on being keen about things with so *very* little encouragement.

No, my dear! No men for me! It's different for you, I know. You have the children, and I'm sure Tom is attentive in his man's way – but Mr Harrison is such a *stick*. And then, of course, he is a lot older than she is.

So you see you are quite wrong in your ideas about me. Naturally, I am interested in the new tenants, because, after all, we share the front hall and the staircase with them, and it does make a difference whether people are pleasant neighbours or not, but that is all! By the way, it's quite true that one of them is an artist. We saw the men carrying in the lay-figure this morning – a life-sized one. It came out of the van not wrapped up at all – a most naked and indecent sight – and was carried up the path by Carter Paterson's man, looking like the rape of the Sabines! You should have seen the heads popping out of the windows all down the street! Quite an excitement in our calm neighbourhood.

I am just turning the heel of the first stocking, tell Tom, and hope to get the pair done before you go down to Norfolk. Mr Perry is the vicar – I'm sure I have told you about him before. Such a nice man, only rather High Church, but not at all bigoted. I always enjoy a chat with him.

I must stop now and get the joint in the oven for dinner. His lordship is coming in to prepare his special mushroom dish with his own fair hands!! So you see we have a treat to look forward to!

Ever your loving sister,
AGGIE

3. *The Same to the Same*

15, WHITTINGTON TERRACE, BAYSWATER
20th September, 1928

DEAR OLIVE,

You ought to thank your lucky stars, my dear, that you *are* the sort of person for whom 'a good husband' is enough. But then, of course, Mother never brought us up to be brainy. We always lived so quietly at home, and what you've never had you don't miss, as the saying goes. I can't say I should have cared for an office job myself, though perhaps it would have been better for my health if I had had something to occupy my mind. But I am really feeling much better now, and I am getting free of that dreadful sensation of being obliged to go back and see if I really have done things when I know perfectly well I have. I know you say everybody feels like that sometimes, but you don't know what it's like to be *compelled* to do it! The other night I got the idea that I had left the beef out on the kitchen table, and though I really remembered quite clearly shutting it up in the meat-safe, I simply *had* to creep downstairs in my dressing-gown and make sure, otherwise I shouldn't have got a wink of sleep. Still, that has been the only relapse for about a fortnight now.

As a matter of fact, we have had quite a lot of thrills this week – very good for us – occupies our minds, you know. The upstairs tenants have arrived!! Two young men – the artist and a poet! They came in the day before yesterday, and oh, my dear, the bumpings and noises! They brought a grand piano – I only hope they won't be playing it all night, because I'm simply good for nothing if I don't get my sleep before midnight – and there's a gramophone

15

as well. Why can't people be content with the wireless, which shuts down at a reasonable hour?

I haven't properly seen the poet yet, except that he's rather tall and dark and thin. I've only caught glimpses of him running in and out of the front door, but the artist came in the first night after dinner to ask about the coal bunkers. He is quite exciting looking - very young – not more than twenty-four or five, I should say, with a lot of thick hair and one of those rather sulky-handsome faces. He has very nice manners, and didn't address *all* his conversation to Mr and Mrs Harrison and leave me out in the cold, as most of these young men do. Mr Harrison, even, was quite gracious to him and offered him a drink, and he stayed talking for quite a little while. His name is Lathom, and he has very little money and has to take afternoon classes in an Art-school, but, of course, that is only to make money until he gets recognised. He has exhibited pictures in Manchester (I think he said), and some other places up north, but he didn't talk much about his work. He seems nice and modest about it. I think Mr Harrison is rather pleased that there should be an artist in the house. He started laying down the law about art at once, in his usual way, and brought out some of his water-colours for Mr Lathom to look at. Mr Lathom said they were very nice indeed, which rather surprised me, because I always think they are rather wishy-washy. However, I suppose he couldn't very well have said anything else, as he was drinking Mr Harrison's whisky and he had never seen him till that moment.

Mrs Harrison seemed rather nervous all the time, and she said afterwards she thought Mr Lathom was quite a pleasant young man, but she did wish George wouldn't inflict his painting on everybody. It must be very humiliating to be ashamed of one's husband's manners.

I have a dreadful confession to make about Tom's stockings! With all my care, one of the turn-overs has come out slightly larger and looser than the other. It *is* so tiresome! Why should one's knitting vary so from day to day? I suppose as long as one is a human being and not a machine one must get variations in one's work, but I thought I had

16

been so careful. I simply can't face unpicking it all, and it isn't really very noticeable. Tell Tom, if he can manage to put up with the trifling difference for a few weeks, it will probably even itself up in the wash.

I went out to Virginia Water on Sunday on a 'bus and had a lovely walk. I have been trying to put down my impressions in a little sketch. Dr Trevor thinks it is quite good, and says I must certainly persevere. He says my power of *feeling* things so intensely ought to make me a really good writer, when I have mastered the technique of putting it down on paper.

Best love to you all. Give the children each a hug from their Auntie. I hope you are keeping free from colds.

Your affectionate sister,
AGGIE

4. *The Same to the Same*

15, WHITTINGTON TERRACE, BAYSWATER
29th September, 1928

DEAREST OLIVE,

I am so glad Tom finds he can wear the stockings all right. Yes, I am a wee bit proud of the pattern. And there's one thing about it – it's quite original. He couldn't have brought anything like it in a shop, and that's something in these machine-made days! Mr Perry was tremendously impressed with the finished result, and he said that if I cared to do that sort of thing as a little business proposition, he thought he could get me quite a number of commissions among his parishioners. I was rather relieved, because he introduced the subject so delicately, I was afraid he was going to ask me to make him a present of a pair! – which would have seemed rather pointed, especially as he is unmarried! Anyway, I said I should like very much to do it, only, of course, I couldn't undertake to do any big orders against time. I haven't the leisure, for one thing – and besides, inventing patterns is artistic work and can't be done to order. Mr

Perry *quite* understood, and asked how much I should charge, so I said ten shillings a pair. I think that is fair, don't you? They take ten ounces of double-knitting, not counting the small amount of coloured wool for the tops, and then there is my work to be considered, and the invention. You would have to pay *at least* fifteen shilling for anything of the same quality in a shop. I dare say with practice I shall be able to get both legs the same.

Yes! I have at last made the acquaintance of the poet. I slept very badly on Friday night, and I thought I'd like an early cup of tea, but all the milk had been used for rice-pudding, so at seven o'clock I slipped out in my kimono to take in the morning delivery, and there, if you please, was the young man coming downstairs with nothing on but a vest and shorts! I couldn't escape, so I carried it through as unconcernedly as I could – and really, in my pyjamas and kimono I was far less indecent than he was. I just said, 'Oh, I beg your pardon, Mr Munting' (that's his name – what a name for a poet!), 'I was just taking in the milk.' So he picked it up and offered it to me with a tremendous bow. I had to say *something* to the man, so I said 'Where are you off to?' and he said he was going to run round the Square to keep his figure down. I'm sure it doesn't want keeping down, for it is all joints and hollows, and I think he only said it to attract my attention to his charming person, for his eyes were looking me up and down all the time in the most unpleasant way.

He is very sallow and what Mother would have called bilious-looking, with black eyes and wrinkles at the corners, and a sarcastic mouth, and he smiled all the time he was speaking, in a way that makes a woman feel most uncomfortable. He looks a great deal older than his friend – I should put him at well over thirty, but perhaps it is only due to leading a fast life. I didn't say much to him, but got in as quickly as I could. I didn't want everybody to see him exposing himself there with me on the doorstep. I saw him afterwards from my bedroom window, rushing round the Square like a madman.

Mr Harrison has been more amiable lately. He has bought a wonderful new box of paints, on the strength of knowing a real artist, I suppose, and spends his time working up some of his holiday sketches. He is very excited about a new scheme for fitting up his studio, as he calls it, with some new kind of electric bulbs, which give a light like daylight, so that he can work in the evenings. So we shall get less of his company than ever. Not that it makes any difference to me, personally, only it seems such a very unsatisfactory idea of married life, to be out all day and shut himself up every evening. I have written a little sketch, called 'These Men—.' Dr Trevor thinks it is very promising, and says I ought to try it on some of the evening papers, so I have sent it to the *Standard*.

I'm so sorry about Joan's bad throat. Do you think she wraps up enough? I will make her one of my special scarves, if you will tell me what coloured frocks she is wearing.

With best love,
Your affectionate sister,

AGGIE

5. *John Munting to Elizabeth Drake*

15A, WHITTINGTON TERRACE, BAYSWATER
30th September, 1928

DEAR BUNGIE,

Forgive me for this rotten series of scraps and post-cards, but I'm a lazy devil, and there hasn't been a place to sit down in for the last fortnight. Lathom's things are all over the place, and when I fling myself into a chair in exhaustion, after hours of shifting furniture, I'm sure to get up with one of his tubes of Permanent Blue adhering to my pants.

This place isn't too bad – rather Bayswatery, but there is a good north light for Lathom's doings, and that is the essential. We have the two top floors in this mid-Victorian skyscraper, and share the hall and staircase with the people downstairs, which is rather a blight on our young lives, but I daresay we shall survive it.

Unfortunately, Lathom, who is one of those companionable blighters, has gone and struck up acquaintance with the Harrisons, and yesterday evening I was hauled down to see them. Apparently Mr H. goes in for dabbling in water-colours, and wanted Lathom's advice about some lighting for his studio. Lathom grumbled a good deal, but I told him it was his own fault if he would go about being so chatty.

I didn't think much of Mrs H. – she's a sort of suburban vamp, an ex-typist or something, and entirely wrapped up, I should say, in her own attractions, but she's evidently got her husband by the short hairs. Not good-looking, but full of S.A. and all that. He is a cut above her, I imagine, and at least twenty years older; small, thin, rather stooping, goatee beard, gold specs and wears his forehead well over the top of his head. He has a decentish post of some kind with a firm of civil engineers. I gather she is his second wife, and that he has a son *en premières noces*, also an engineer, now building a bridge in Central Africa and doing rather well. The old boy is not a bad old bird, but an alarming bore on the subject of Art with a capital A. We had to go through an exhibition of his masterpieces – Devonshire lanes and nice little bits in the Cotswolds, with trees and cottages. Lathom stuck it very well, and said they were very nice, which is his way of expressing utter damnation – but Harrison didn't know that, so they got on together like a house afire.

They've got an appalling sitting-room, all arty stuff from Tottenham Court Road, with blue and mauve cushions, and everything ghastly about it – like Ye Olde Oake Tea-Roomes. Harrison is fearfully proud of his wife's taste, and played showman rather pathetically. They keep a 'lady-help' – they would! – a dreadful middle-aged female with a come-hither eye. She cornered me at the front door the other morning, just as I was popping out for my daily dozen round the houses. She was prowling round the hall in rose-pink pyjamas and a pale-blue *négligé*, pretending to take in the milk. I dawdled on the stairs as long as I could, to give her a chance to run to cover, but as she appeared to be determined, and the situation was becoming rather absurd, I marched out, and was, of course, involved in a conversation. I made myself as repellent as I could, but the good lady's curiosity would take no denial. Last night was like a friendly evening with the Grand Inquisitor. I told her all she wanted to know about my income and prospects and family, and Lathom's ditto so far as I knew them, and by that time she was chatting so archly (lovely word!) about the young ladies of the neighbourhood that I thought it best just to mention that I was engaged. That worked her up into still greater excitement, but I didn't tell her much, Bungie, old dear. I've got a sort of weakness about you, though you mightn't think it, my child, so I said nothing. Hadn't I got a photograph? No, I didn't approve of photographs. Well, of course, they were only mechanical, weren't they? Hadn't Mr Lathom painted a portrait of my fiancée? I said that, though I had few illusions about any of my belongings, I couldn't expose you to the ordeal of being painted by Lathom. So she said how like a man to talk of his belongings, and she supposed Mr Lathom was very Modern (capital M). I said yes, terrifically so, and that he always painted his sitters with green mouths and their noses all askew. So she said she supposed I wrote poems to you instead. I replied that poems to one's fiancée were a little old-fashioned, didn't she think so, and she agreed, and said, 'What was the title of my next volume?' So I said at random 'Spawn,' which I thought was rather good for the spur of the moment, and it rather shut her up, because she wasn't quite sure of the right answer, and just said that that sounded very modern too, and she hoped I would present her with a copy when it was printed. Then I got reckless, and said I feared it never would be printed, because Jix had his eye on me and opened all my letters to my publishers. You'd adore these people, my dear – they are like something out of one of your own books. How is the new work getting on?

I must stop now, old thing; I've been quill-driving all day on the *Life*, and I'm just about dead. But I had to write you some sort of yarn, just to show I hadn't been and gone and deserted you.

Yours, Bungie, if indeed anything of one's self can ever be anybody else's which, as an up-to-date young woman, you will conscientiously doubt, but, at any rate, with the usual damned feeling of incompleteness in your absence, yours, blast you! yours,

JACK

6. *The Same to the Same*

15A, WHITTINGTON TERRACE, BAYSWATER
4th October, 1928

DEAR BUNGIE,

Yours to hand, and your remarks about middle-aged spinsters noted. I will try not to be (*a*) catty; (*b*) mid-Victorian; (*c*) always imagining myself to be truly run after. I did not know I was all those things, but, being a modern woman and a successful novelist, no doubt you are quite right. Also, of course, you are quite right to speak your mind. As you say, married life should be based on mutual frankness.

In return, may I just hint that there are some sides of life which I, as a man, may possibly know more about than you do, merely through having lived longer and knocked about more. I assure you I can size up some types of people pretty well. However, it may give you pleasure to learn that Mrs Harrison, at any rate, is not out for my scalp. She has read *Deadlock* and is disgusted with its coarseness and cynicism. How do I know? Because I was in Mudie's when she went in to change it. The girl said, no, it wasn't a very nice book and she was afraid at the time Mrs Harrison wouldn't care for it, and would she like the latest Michael Arlen? Which she did.

Our place really looks very jolly now; I wish you could come and see it. The Picasso is over the studio fireplace and the *famille rose* jar is in my sitting-room, and so are the etchings. They give my surroundings quite a distinguished-man-of-letters appearance. I wish I could get rid of this damned *Life* and get back to my own stuff, but I'm being too well paid for it, that's the devil of it. Never mind – I'll pretend I am the Industrious Apprentice, working hard so as to be able to marry his master's daughter.

Glad the book seems to be working itself out amiably. For God's sake, though, don't overdo the psycho-analytical part. It's not your natural style. Don't listen to that Challenger woman, but write your own stuff. The other kind of thing wants writing (forgive me) fearfully well if it's to be any good, and even then it is rather dreary and old-fashioned. Glands, my child, glands are the thing, as Barrie would say. Pre-natal influences and childhood fears have gone out with compulsory Greek.

> *A Don who encountered a Maenad*
> *Was left with less wits than the Dean 'ad;*
> *Till the Dean, being vexed by a Gonad,*
> *Was left with less wits than the Don 'ad:*
> *This shows what implicit reliance*
> *We may place on the progress of Science.*

Talking of Science, I have brought up all standing by Nicholson's book on *The Development of English Biography*. According to him, 'pure' biography is doomed, and we are to have the 'scientific biography,' which will in the end prove destructive of the literary interest. There are to be nothing but studies of heredity and indoctrine secretions, economics and aesthetics, and so on – all specialised and all damned. This is where I get off; I only hope this infernal work will get itself published before the rot sets in. So back to the shop, Mr Keats!

Yours, while this machine is to him,

JACK

On looking this through, I seem to be rather in a scolding mood. But it's only because I think so highly of your stuff that I don't want you to get sloppy and psycho. That kind of thing is all sentimentality, really. *Tout comprendre, c'est tout pardonner; tout pardonner, c'est tout embêter.*

7. The Same to the Same

15A, WHITTINGTON TERRACE, BAYSWATER
8th October, 1928

DARLING OLD BUNGIE, OLD THING –

All right, damn it, no! I don't want to hector and lay

down the law. You carry on in your own way, my child, and don't pay any attention to me. I quite see what you say about taking things for granted – so we'll lay it down quite clearly for future guidance that, although I am always right, I must never be so ex officio and because I am a man and a husband. No doubt it is irritating. I hadn't quite looked at it from that point of view, but possibly there is something in it. Signed Jacko, the almost-human Ape.

Making a strenuous effort to adopt this feminine view-point, I am beginning to wonder whether my neighbour goes quite the right way to assert his position as head of the household. I fancy he must have read somewhere that women like to be treated rough and feel the tight hand on the rein and that sort of thing. Unfortunately, nature did not design him for a sheik part, having made him small, dry, and a little bald on top.

We were just starting off to dine with Lambert the other night, and were waiting in the hall for a taxi, when Mrs H. came in, rather flurried and very wet. She was hanging up her waterproof, when Harrison came charging out on the landing and called down:

'Is that you, Margaret? Do you know what time it is?'

'I'm sorry – I won't be a moment.'

'Where on earth have you been?'

'That's a secret' (in the tone of voice of someone who wants to have the secret teased out of her. She was laughing to herself, and had a fattish parcel tucked under her arm).

'Oh! I suppose it's all the same to you if the dinner's un-eatable.'

Evidently no interest was to be taken in the 'secret'. The next effort was along the lines of cheerful common sense.

'Why didn't you begin without me?'

'I don't choose to. This is my home – or supposed to be – not a hotel' (in a tone of peevish protest).

She had gone past us up to the first-floor landing, and, like the Wedding-Guest, we could not choose but hear.

'I'm sorry, dear. I was getting something for tomorrow.'

'That's no excuse. You've been chattering to some of your office friends in some tea-shop or other and forgetting

24

all about what you were supposed to be doing. No, I don't want any dinner now.'

'Oh, very well.'

He came running downstairs then and saw us. I think it gave him a shock, because he pulled himself up and smiled and said something vague. Then he turned and called up the stairs again:

'All right, my dear, I'll be up in a minute.' His eyes were unhappy. There's something wrong in this house – something more than a little misunderstanding about dinner time. I shouldn't wonder if she gives this man a devil of a time – probably without meaning it, that's the rub. Lathom, who is at the chivalrous age, was all for youth and beauty, of course, and wanted to hop out and sling the old boy into his own umbrella stand, but I told him not to be an infernal ass. Why shouldn't the woman come home in time for meals? It's not much to do, and I don't believe she has any other job in life except to sit reading novels in the front window all day. I know, I've seen her at it. All the same, I do wish we had a separate staircase. It's a bore to have people fighting out their matrimonial quarrels on one's front doorstep. I'm a man of peace, I am.

I heard afterwards (per Lathom, via Miss Milsom) that the mysterious parcel was a present for Harrison, the next day being their wedding-anniversary. The row in the hall rather spoilt the sentiment of the occasion, I gather. Lathom says the man is a brute. But I don't altogether see that. He couldn't be supposed to know, and anyhow, what is the good of giving a person a lavish display of affection with one hand and rubbing pepper into his eyes with the other?

Oh, Bungie, it's the silly little things of life that I'm afraid of. Don't they frighten you, too, competent as you are?

Yours always,

JACK

8. *The Same to the Same*

15A, WHITTINGTON TERRACE, BAYSWATER
12th October, 1928

DEAREST BUNGIE,

Things are looking up. This *Life* will be finished by Christmas, I hope. I am rather stuck at present over the chapter on 'Religious Convictions'. It is difficult to bring one's mind into sympathy with that curious Victorian blend of materialism and trust in a personally interfering Providence. It's odd how they seem to have blinded themselves to the hopeless contradiction between their science and their conventional ethics. On the one hand, an acceptance of the Darwinian survival of the fittest, which ought to have made them completely ruthless in theory and practice; on the other, a sort of sentimental humanitarianism, which directly led to our own special problem of the multitudinous survival of the unfittest. They seem to have had a pathetic belief that it could all be set right by machinery. I don't know, come to think of it, that we are in a much better position today, except that we have lost the saving belief in machinery. Which doesn't stop our becoming more and more mechanical, any more than their having lost their belief in anthropomorphism stopped them from becoming more and more humanitarian. Compromise – blessed word! – Chesterton speaks somewhere of the great Victorian compromise – but why Victorian, more than anything else? At any rate, they had the consolation of feeling that this earth and its affairs were extremely large and important – though why they should have thought so, when they were convinced they were only the mechanical outcome of a cast-iron law of evolution on a very three-by-four planet, whirling round a fifth-rate star in illimitable space, passes human comprehension. It would be more reasonable to think so today, if Eddington and those people are right in supposing that we are rather a freak sort of planet, with quite unusual facilities for being

26

inhabited, and that space is a sort of cosy little thing which God could fold up and put in his pocket without our ever noticing the difference. Anyhow, if time and space and straightness and curliness and bigness and smallness are all relative, then we may just as well think ourselves important as not. 'Important, unimportant – unimportant, important,' as the King of Hearts said, trying to see which sounded best. So, like the Victorians, we shall no doubt compromise – say it is important when we have a *magnum opus* to present to an admiring creation, and unimportant when it suits our convenience to have our peccadilloes passed over.

Forgive me wandering away like this. It's just a sort of talking the thing out with you before I talk it out in the book. Because, for some reason, it does seem to me important to do this job as well as I can – not merely because it will do me good with publishers, and make it possible to embark on the important triviality of marriage, but for some obscure and irrational motive connected with the development of my soul, if I may so allude to it. I am increasingly not clear whether I am a mess of oddly-assorted chemicals (chiefly salt and water), or a kind of hypertrophied fish-egg, or an enormous, all-inclusive cosmos of solar-systematically revolving atoms, each one supporting planetfuls of solemn imbeciles like myself.

But, whatever I am, I must finish the *Life* and then get on to *our* life, Bungie, because that somehow does count for something too.

JACK

9. *The Same to the Same*

15A, WHITTINGTON TERRACE, BAYSWATER
15th October, 1928

I knew it, Bungie – I knew it, I knew it! I knew we should be asked downstairs to tea. And we've been! Down among the Liberty curtains and the brass Benares ware! Three young women, two bright youths, the local parson and the family. Crockery from Heal's and everything too conscientiously bright. Mrs Harrison all radiance and very much the centre of attraction.

No sooner had I got there than I was swept into a discussion about 'this wonderful man Einstein.' Extraordinarily interesting, wasn't it, and what did I make of it? Displaying all my social charm, I said I thought it was a delightful idea. I liked thinking that all the straight lines were really curly, and only wished I'd known all about it at school, because it would have annoyed the geometry master so much.

'But you do think there's something in it, don't you? My husband says it is all nonsense, but what do *you* say?'

There was a little stir of triumph about this, and I somehow gathered that the Einstein topic had been deliberately chosen for a purpose. I said guardedly that I believed the theory was now generally accepted by mathematicians, though with very many reserves.

'It really is, is it? Really true that nothing actually exists as we see it? I do hope so, because I have always felt so strongly that materialism is all wrong. There is something so deadening about materialism, isn't there? I do so wish I knew what life means and what we really are. But I can't understand these things, and you know, I should so like to, if only I had someone to explain them to me.'

'As far as I can make out,' I replied, 'you are *really* only made up of large lumps of space, loosely tied together with electricity. It doesn't sound flattering, but there it is.'

She frowned attractively.

'But I can't believe that.'

'Why do you want to believe it?' said Harrison. 'It's all words. When it comes to doing anything practical you have to come back to common sense. My friend Professor Alcock –'

'Yes, yes, I know.' She waved the interruption aside impatiently. 'But the idea is the real thing, isn't it? Haven't they come round to thinking that poetry and imagination and the beautiful things of the mind are the only true realities after all?'

'Of course beauty is the only true reality,' said Lathom eagerly. 'But it isn't always what ordinary people think of

28

as beauty. I mean, it's not pretty-pretty. When you think a thing, then you create it and it exists. What's the use of arguing what you make it *of*? That doesn't matter to the thing itself, any more than the stuff paints are made of matter to the picture.'

'It matters a good deal in practice,' said Harrison. 'Now the Pre-Raphaelites understood that – though, mind you, I don't think much of the Pre-Raphaelite school myself. Some of their pictures are so remarkably ugly, and so exaggerated in colour. Take that thing of Holman Hunt's, now – '

'Darling,' said Mrs Harrison, with emphasis, 'you're side-tracking.'

'No, I'm not. I'm coming back to that. What I mean is that the Pre-Raphaelites, especially William Morris, knew a great deal about the material of their paints. They used to get the right stuff and grind it themselves, so as to be sure it wasn't adulterated. Now I'm all of their opinion. I say they were quite right. I get my colours from a man up in town, a wholesale dealer – '

'My husband is always so literal,' said Mrs Harrison, taking the whole company into a confederacy to condemn the unfortunate man. 'But I didn't mean that at all. Mr Lathom understands what I mean – don't you, Mr Lathom?'

'Yes,' said Lathom, 'and, of course, it's true in a way. But you mustn't think that the form of the thing doesn't matter, too. Whatever the world is made of, there it is, and it's ours to make something of.'

'It must be marvellous to paint great pictures!' said one of the young women.

Lathom scowled frightfully, and, ostentatiously ignoring her, continued his remarks to Mrs Harrison in an undertone.

What a conversation, my God! Harrison faded out and I don't blame him, and I took the opportunity to tackle the parson, a fellow by the name of Perry. He turned out to be an earnest and cultivated middle-aged spike from Keble, and I took the opportunity to mention the *Life* and the difficulties about Victorian materialism.

'Yes,' he said, 'we've rather got past that stage now, haven't we? I've got one or two books that I think might be

29

useful to you, as giving the point of view and all that. Shall I send them over?'

I said it was very good of him (not expecting much from it), and, by way of a leg-pull, asked him what *he* thought of relativity.

'Why, I'm rather grateful to it,' said he, 'it makes my job much easier. We'll have a chat some day and go into it. I must be going now.'

He oozed competently away, and the party rambled on till I could stand it no longer and rambled out into the passage, where I met Harrison.

'Hullo!' said he, 'come and have a pipe in the studio. And a whisky-and-soda or something. Better than tea.'

I went in, expecting him to talk Art, but he didn't. He just sat smoking in silence and I did likewise. I had an idea I ought to say something to him, but nothing presented itself. If I had said what I felt like saying, he would have been angry with me.

So much for social life in Suburbia. I had a letter from Jim on Wednesday. He is thoroughly enjoying himself in Germany, and begs to be remembered to you. He is reading hard – or so he says – and he'd jolly well better, the young cub, since if he fails in his tripos there's no money to give him another year there and he'll have to go as an apothecary's apprentice or something. I haven't looked up Cynthia or the Brierleys yet, but I will pull myself together and do it before long.

Love to everybody. Wish I was up north with you among the burrns and birrds. Give the Guv'nor my love. Has he had good sport? I suppose the hills are beginning to look a bit grim again now, bless their granite hearts. Remember me to all the artist fraternity.

Ever and ever yours, funny-face, old dear. I'd like to see your cheery grin now and again. I must be damned fond of you – sometimes it positively puts me off my stroke. Damned inconvenient. I shall really have to see about this marriage business. I cannot have my work interrupted in this way.

Yours deeply injured
JACK

10. *Agatha Milsom to Olive Farebrother*

15, WHITTINGTON TERRACE, BAYSWATER
15.10.28

DEAREST OLIVE,

I am so sorry I have not written for such a long time, but I have been feeling anything but fit. This household is *most* trying to live with, and I really feel that in my present nervous condition I am hardly fit to cope with my work here. I have been to Dr Trevor and put the whole situation very fully and carefully before him, and he agrees that I certainly ought not to be subjected to so much emotional strain. On the other hand, I know poor Mrs Harrison does cling to me so much for sympathy and support that it seems almost wicked not to hang on if I can possibly manage it. She has no one else to confide in at all, and I do at least feel that here I am being of real use to somebody. Dr Trevor says that if only I can lose sight of my own difficulties in helping her with hers, it will be good for me to make the effort, provided I do not let the atmosphere of the house get on my nerves. I have started a little exercise on Coué lines. Every morning I say to myself: 'I am cool, strong, confident,' twenty times, and at night I say: 'I am satisfied and at peace,' also twenty times. Dr Trevor thinks these are quite good phrases to say.

I *did* hope, a few days ago, that the difficulty was going to solve itself. Mrs Harrison announced that she was going to take up office work again. The idea of it seemed to brighten her up tremendously, and I think it would be the best thing she could do. But, of course, the Bear played his old trick again. When she first announced her decision, he pretended to agree, and said she could do as she liked, so was awfully pleased, and rang up one of the people at her old office to see if they had a vacancy there. As it happened, they had, and she practically arranged to start work next week. Then Mr Bear started off. 'All right? Well, I suppose it is all right if you think so. But don't you think it's a trifle hard on me,

31

my dear, having a wife out all day, fagging herself to death in an office and coming home fit for nothing? I give you a good home, and I rather expected, or hoped, you would like to make it a home for me to come back to. That is the usual idea, isn't it? But I suppose the modern woman thinks differently about these things. If hotel life is your notion of happiness you ought to go and live in America.'

It is too bad to work upon the poor girl's feelings in that selfish way. She tried to reason with him, but, of course, the end was that she made herself perfectly sick with crying, and wrote and told the people that she couldn't manage to take the job after all. And now he goes about saying it's a pity she can't find something better to do with herself than reading trashy novels all day. I spoke up. I said, 'Mr Harrison, excuse me, but you ought not to speak to your wife like that. She gave up the work she wanted to do, *entirely* to please you, and I think you ought to consider her a little more and yourself a good deal less.' I daresay he wasn't best pleased, but I thought it my duty to say it. I felt most terribly exhausted after this trying scene. It is such a drain upon one's personality, coping with outbreaks of this kind. One is giving, giving, all the time. I am asking Dr Trevor to prescribe me a tonic. A curious feature of my malady at the moment is a craving for shrimps. Our fishmonger keeps very good ones, but sometimes I have to go quite a long way to get them, because I am afraid he will think it funny if I buy shrimps every day.

I am sure I don't know what we should do if it were not for Mr Lathom. He often drops in of an evening now and cheers us up immensely. The Bear is always dragging the poor man off into his studio, as he calls it, to twaddle about art, but Mr Lathom has most delightful manners and puts up with it heroically. He thinks my scarf-patterns and stocking-tops show great talent, 'a very good sense of design.' He is a real artist, so I am sure he wouldn't say so if he didn't think it.

We do not see much of the objectionable Mr Munting, I am glad to say. He often doesn't come home till very late. You never know what these men are after. It is a good thing that he shares the maisonette with Mr Lathom, who I am sure would not allow any undesirable goings-on under our roof.

I hope darling Joan is quite strong again now. Give her my love, and say I have started on the scarf. I am doing a pattern of purple and white clematis, which will be very chic, I think.

Your loving sister,
AGGIE

11. *John Munting to Elizabeth Drake*

15A, WHITTINGTON TERRACE
19.10.28

Damn it all, yes, Bungie – I suppose you are right. Our ideas are always ahead of our actions, or rather, askew to them, and we move lop-sided, like a knight on a chess-board. We get somewhere, even if it isn't the place we thought we were aiming for. By the time the next generation has come along, the ideas which were new and strange to us have become part of its habitual commonplace. It goes straight along them, even when it imagines it is rebelling against them.

And after all, this business of imagining that one is one kind of thing and *being* actually another – we all do it, all the time, so why shouldn't whole nations and periods do it? Have you read J. D. Beresford's *Writing Aloud*, by the way? It is enormously fascinating, and I delight in the bit where he tells how, in his callow youth, he had a 'passionate impulse' to 'save' a young prostitute he had talked to, and then prayed desperately to be delivered from the sin of hypocrisy and be made single-hearted and all that – only to be delighted, later on in life, with the discovery that he was 'not one person but fifty'. One imagines – one dramatises oneself into the belief that one is going one way, and lo and behold! the path 'gives itself a little shake' like the one in *Alice* and one finds oneself walking at the front door again.

Our friend Mrs Harrison is a perfect example of this

dramatisation business – and is quite capable of dramatising herself in two totally inconsistent directions at once, rather like the Victorian age. Any attitude that appeals to her sense of the picturesque she appropriates instantly, and, I really believe, with perfect sincerity. If she reads a 'piece in the paper' about the modern woman who finds spiritual satisfaction in a career, she *is* that woman; and her whole life has been ruined by having had to give up her job at the office. Capable, intelligent, a comradely woman, meeting male and female on a brisk, pleasant, man-to-man basis – there she is! If, on the other hand, she reads about the necessity of a 'complete physical life' for the development of personality, then she is the thwarted maternal woman, who would be all right if only she had a child. Or if she gets a mental picture of herself as a Great Courtesan (in capital letters), she is perfectly persuaded that her face only needed opportunity to burn the topless towers of Ilium. And so on. What she really is, if reality means anything, I do not know. But I can see now, what I didn't see before, that this power of dramatisation coupled with a tremendous vitality and plenty of ill-regulated intelligence, has its fascination. If ever she found anyone to take one of her impersonations seriously, she would probably be able to live very brilliantly and successfully in that character for – well, not all her life, perhaps, but for long enough to make an impressive drama of it. Unfortunately, the excellent Harrison is not a good audience. He admires, but he won't clap, which must be very discouraging.

'You will gather from this that I have been seeing a good deal of the Harrisons. Quite right, Sherlock, I have. When you once make up your mind to look on people as social studies, you can get quite reconciled to their company. Mrs H. cornered me in the artistic sitting-room last night, while her husband was telling Lathom about aerial perspective, to tell me about her own personality. She feels cramped in her surroundings, it seems. Her mentality has no room to expand. It is so hard for a woman, isn't it? Perhaps the only way is to express herself through her children – but then – if one has no children? She said she always felt she could have made herself a happy life by living for and in others.

I did not say that she would probably end by devouring her hypothetical family, though I could very well see her doing it. I felt mischievous, and said that there were other forms of passionate altruism, and that I could see her in a cloister, walking serenely among the lilies and burning her soul away in contemplation. Could I really? Well, yes, there was something very wonderful about the life of devotion. I ought to write a book about it. At this point I became a little alarmed, and turned the conversation to new books. We had a little difficulty, because her idea of an important writer and my idea are not exactly identical; however, we agreed that *The Constant Nymph* was a very good piece of work, and, encouraged by that, she tackled the awkward question of *Deadlock*. I tried to explain what I had really meant by it, and she proved quite adaptable. She said she did not mind a book's being 'powerful', provided it was filled with a 'sense of the beautiful'. She thought *Sweet Pepper* was powerful, but nevertheless there was something about it that redeemed it. What a pity it was that Hutchinson hadn't written another book like *If Winter Comes*. She thinks that if only I wouldn't be so harsh and mocking I might write a book as strong and really beautiful as that.

These are the people who read the books, Bungie. And what are we to do about it, you and I, if we want to live by bread?

Next day I met her in the hall, dressed in a demure grey frock, with a long veil swathed nun-like about her cloche hat. She saluted me with a grave and far-away smile. I grinned cheerfully, and mentioned that I was going to watch a football match.

Your not-very-well-behaved and rather malicious.

JACK

12. *The Same to the Same*

20.10.28

MY DEAR BUNGIE,

Don't be a silly ass. I thought you had more sense than the ordinary futile sort of woman. I am not in the least fascinated by Mrs Harrison. She quite simply interests me as a type – a personality, that is. It is my job to be interested in people. I might want to use that kind of person in a book some day.

Good heavens! If I was 'fascinated' by her, I shouldn't be likely to analyse her in that dispassionate way. She is essentially a suburban vamp, as I think I said before, if you have thought any of my remarks worth remembering. And I never said she was beautiful. Her mouth is sloppy and bad . . .

Later: Saunders Enfield burst in on me when I was writing this, and hauled me out to lunch with him. On returning, with the better part of a bottle of perfectly good Corton inside me, I realise that the brilliant line of defence I am taking up is exactly the one I should equally have taken if the accusation had been true. I should have said just those things, in exactly that tone of exasperated superiority, and I should have elaborated them with such a wealth of detail that you could not have failed to disbelieve every word of it.

My first impulse (after lunch, I mean) was to destroy the incriminating paper, and to ignore your observations altogether. But I think that would probably have a highly suspicious appearance also. Upon my word, I don't believe there *is* any convincing reply to such a charge.

Except to tell you that I honestly don't care a damn for any woman in the world except one. And if you don't believe that, my child, then it doesn't matter what you think of me, because I shall be beyond caring.

I believe you're only pulling my leg, anyhow. Blast you! Don't do it again.

36

And believe me (as the business people say),

Yours faithfully,

Jack

13. *The Same to the Same*

Hullo, Bungie, darling! My God, but I'm played out! I've been sticking to the accursed *Life* like a leech, and have finished the religious outlook. Having ground it out with incredible sweat and travail, I read it through and thought it so awful that I was in two minds about chucking the whole thing into the fire. However, I didn't, but instead went over and joined Jim in Paris for a week, on his way home, as you saw by my post card. We had a mildly riotous time in that cheerful city, restraining each other in a brotherly way from the more perilous kinds of exuberance, and reached home feeling fit for anything. I took up the infernal religious outlook, read it through again, and came to the conclusion that it was bloody good stuff, after all! So now I am pressing forward with shouts of joy and encouragement to the critical estimate, which is the only part of the thing I really want to write at all. Dilkes, the dear old man, to whom I explained my troubles, talked to me like fifty fathers, and said extraordinarily nice things. He thinks, by the way, that the flippant and imaginative kind of biography has had its day, having been too much imitated, and that the time has come round again for solid facts and research. 'The great humility of science, in face of the infinite and valuable variety of Truth.' Isn't that an exquisite Victorian remark? 'We should pray,' said he, making me feel like a very grubby fourth-form infant, 'to be delivered from cleverness, because very clever people end by finding that nothing is worth while.' So I said, rather ungraciously, that probably nothing *was* worth while, and he gave the funniest twinkle from under his thick eyebrows and replied: 'You must not think that, or you will become a bore.'

My parson turns out to be rather an enlightened person. It appears he took a mathematical tripos among other things, which is one up to him. He also has read Eddington, and, moreover, took it for granted that I had read Jeans and Japp and one or two other fantastic scientists whose names I had never heard of, which was two up to him. Also, he seemed quite delighted about the whole thing, and said he was thankful to find that scientists would at last allow him to believe what the Church taught, which in his young days they wouldn't. I should have put this down to the usual shifty ecclesiastical clap-trap, but for the obvious fact that he knew what he was talking about, and I didn't, so, feeling a fool, I put a good face on the matter and asked his advice about the religious outlook chapter. He gave me some really very useful stuff about Victorian materialism, which you will find in the book when it's finished. We ended by discussing, with much laughter, some incredibly silly letter from correspondents in the *Daily Dispatch*, one of whom said: 'Sir, Genesis says that God made Adam from the dust of the earth. God is the initial cause and dust is protoplasm. Yours faithfully'; while the reply observed briefly, 'Sir, Dust is not protoplasm, Yours faithfully.'

Dearest, do you really want to be married to the sort of unsatisfactory bloke I am? It is extraordinarily brave and dear of you. You will have a devil of a time. I want to warn you now that when I say I want you to keep your independence and exquisite detachment, I don't really mean it. I shall try to mould you into the mirror of myself, fatally and inevitably. When I say I am not jealous, either of your work or friends, I am lying. When I promise to look at things from your point of view, I am promising what I cannot perform. When I declare myself ready to discuss everything fully and freely and have a *situation nette,* I am pretending to be more honest than a man ever is or can be. I shall be reticent, inconsistent, selfish and jealous. I shall put my interests before yours, and the slightest suggestion that I should put myself out to give you peace and quietness to work in will wound my self-importance. I know it. I shall pretend to give you freedom, and make such an unholy martyr of myself that you will take up your chains for the sake of a quiet life. You will end by hating me, and leave me for some scamp of a fellow who knows how to handle women. And you will be quite right, from your point of view. I have been trying to look honestly into the thing, and I want to warn you. You think I am 'different', but I am not. With all your theoretical knowledge, Bungie, you haven't had experience. You are generous, I know, and think you are willing to risk it, but I must try and make you understand the facts. Don't think that I am wanting for one moment to cut our engagement out. I want you as I have never wanted anything. I want you terribly. But do try and understand that it won't be what you think. I don't want us to end in a ghastly sort of muddle.

I know you will say that you understand, but you don't. You have an idea – all women have – that you can enter into a man's point of view. You can't; any more than I can enter into a woman's point of view. Don't, for God's sake, tell me to cheer up and it will be all right. Don't be sweet and understanding – be brutal, if you like – I shall not take offence at anything you may say, but I want you to realise what you are in for.

Yours ever,
J<small>ACK</small>

P.S. This is arrant hypocrisy. I am bound to take offence, whatever you say, and we shall have one of those painful and acrimonious arguments. If you say nothing, I shall be offended at that, too. But for God's sake don't chuck me, Bungie.

14. *The Same to the Same*

DEAREST AND MOST WONDERFUL BUNGIE,

Forgive me for writing such a foul letter, and bless you for answering it so promptly. The alarming list of faults which you have produced in answer to mine relieves my mind a good deal. Thank Heaven for a woman with a sense of humour. I was feeling rather awful that day, being thoroughly fagged, and had, I suppose, a grouch against civilisation. But I quite agree about the innocent 'animal' business; I can imagine nothing more tedious. All the same, I feel very strongly, in my more honest moments, that love has got to be happy, for fear it should become all-important. I can't expect you to understand this, and you would be an unnatural woman if you did, and I should hate you for it. But I do feel that the old 'not long will his love stay behind him' attitude is degrading and horrible. I don't want to feel that anybody's life and happiness is bound up with mine. What dignity is there in life if one is not free to take one's own risks? It doesn't matter whether it's a wife or a parent or a child or a brother – people should set their own value on themselves and not 'live for others' or 'live only in their children', or whoever it is. It's beastly. And yet – if I heard *you* say that – I don't know, but I expect I should go off the deep end like poor old Harrison.

I think Lathom is rather getting on my nerves. If I had known he was such a gregarious devil I don't think I should have agreed to set up housekeeping with him. Fortunately, as he is merely an acquaintance, and *not* my wife or my father or my brother, I can more or less ignore his vagaries. He is always 'running down' to see the Harrisons, and having them up here. You can't get on with your work when people are everlastingly coming in and out. I just chuck it now, and sit tight in my own room, and let them get on with it.

I like the old boy, though – and, by jove, he does know

40

how to cook! Yes, cook! He has a passion for cookery as a fine art. I must get him to show me how to make omelettes – I don't believe *you* know anything about it, do you? Also rump-steak, on which his views are very sound. He also has a fungus-complex – thinks the poor peasants ought to go forth and cull his grub from the hedgerow, and all that. He knows a tremendous lot about edible toadstools, and delivers lectures on them to Lathom, for whom he has taken a great fancy. As a matter of fact, Lathom is one of those offensively healthy people who shovel down anything that is set before them, but Harrison doesn't see that, and enthuses mildly on in a sort of resistless river of speech that forces itself past all interruptions. Mrs H. yawns, Miss Milsom yawns, Lathom yawns and I do my best not to yawn, because I'm the only person here who has any real sympathy with the subject, so it's up to me. I'm not sure, though, that his monologues aren't better than her intense duets. However, Harrison has now gone away into the country on his lonesome, so perhaps we shall be free of visitors for a bit.

I have been round to see Merritt & Hopkins, and this time saw the great Man of Merritt himself. He was very genial, and encouraged me to dig my old novel out of its sepulchre, in a last forlorn effort. You know – the one I wrote just before I met you, and which no one will have anything to do with. He has promised to read it himself, which was so decent of him that I hadn't the heart to suggest that a younger man might look upon it with more sympathy!

I have just been reading the *Messenger's* interview with you, my child. How entertaining! What grand publicity! And how damnable impertinent. I suppose I shall be expected to put up with everybody's having the right to comment on My Wife in public. We shall have rows about it; I see that inevitably. I shall sneer first and then lose my temper, and if you once give in you will be a lost woman.

Are you still quite sure you want to risk matrimony with

Yours infuriatingly,

JACK

15. *George Harrison to Paul Harrison*

THE SHACK, NEAR MANATON, DEVON
22.10.28

MY DEAR BOY,

This month I must begin by wishing you very many happy returns of the day, and I trust that the mail will live up to its reputation and deliver my letter in time for the auspicious occasion. God bless you, my dear boy, and send you all happiness and prosperity. You are now thirty-six years old – still a very young man to hold the responsible position you have made for yourself. Yet to me it seems strange to think that when I was your age I had been married and settled for sixteen years! I was only a boy of twenty when I married your dear Mother! Her memory is very near and dear to me at this time, as indeed, at all times. You must never think that, because I have formed other ties of late years, I do not think of her with the deepest affection. But I know you do not think so. You know that there is room in my heart for both: and it is a great happiness to me to have a son whose face recalls, even more vividly as the years go by, that of my dear first wife.

I was greatly pleased to have your letter and to know that the work goes so well. Yours is a great opportunity. I know how proud and happy I should have been at your age to have the advantage of working under so distinguished a man as Sir Maurice. In my opinion he is the greatest engineer of his day. It is most gratifying that he should entrust so much of the responsible work to you. Be very careful to check *every* figure and test *everything*, no matter how small, before it is put in place. The most brilliant calculations will not compensate for a defective bolt. Dolby's is a first-class firm, but it is a sound rule to take nothing for granted.

As you see, I am down in the old shack for my usual holiday. I was obliged to take it rather late this year, as I could not be spared from the office till we had got the new power-station through. However, the weather is fortunately very favourable, and I have been able to do a good deal of sketching as well as rambling after fungi. I missed our old Puff-ball friend, *Lycoperdon giganteum*, of course, but I gathered a beautiful dish of the little *Amethyst Agaric* yesterday, and tomorrow morning I am going out in search of *Amanita rubescens*, which I intend to try very slowly and delicately stewed in beef broth, or in a mock-beef gravy of *Fistulina Hepatica*, if I can find one in good condition. I do not know whether any one has ever tried this combination of two fungi. If it is a success I shall give the recipe in the little book I am writing on *Neglected Edible Treasures*. Messrs Hopkin & Bigelow are interested in my 'operculum', and I rather think they mean to publish it.

I am sorry you are not here to go a-mushrooming with me. Margaret, of course, does not care for this kind of camp-life – I could not expect it of such a thorough little town-bird as she is – so I have had to become an old bachelor for the time being. I am hoping that young Lathom will come out with me sometimes on sketching expeditions. He seems a very decent, friendly young fellow, and it is very pleasant to have a fellow-artist in the place, with whom to exchange ideas. He runs in and out of our flat frequently of an evening, and we are always glad to see him. His lively chatter seems to amuse Margaret, and it is nice to have some young life about the place. We do not see quite so much of his friend Munting. He is reserved and quiet and talks modestly enough, though I believe he has written a book of very *risqué* verse and a rather salacious novel. Margaret says she dislikes his sarcastic manner, but I cannot say I have found him in any way objectionable. Miss Milsom seems to have taken offence at something he said to her, but then she is not a particularly sensible woman. Nothing I can say will stop her putting dripping in the pan when frying a steak, which is a great nuisance. She has no real feeling for cookery.

Well, my boy, I have written rather a long letter, and I must stop now, as I see the lad approaching with the bread, and I must secure his services to take this to the post. I enclose a little cheque, as an offering which is always suitable in every season and country, and remain,

With every good wish,

Your affectionate Father,

GEO. HARRISON

16. *Agatha Milsom to Olive Farebrother*

15, WHITTINGTON TERRACE, BAYSWATER

25.10.28

DEAREST OLIVE,

We are all breathing again! The Bear has taken himself off for one of his camping holidays, complete with painting outfit and half a dozen scribbling pads. He is actually going to write a book! – telling people how to live on nettles and toadstools and that sort of thing, and how in case of another Great War we could support the entire nation on boiled hedgehogs or some such nastiness. My dear, it is such a relief to get him out of the house! Of course, he couldn't go off without creating an unpleasantness. He was absurd enough to suggest that Mrs Harrison should go with him – the idea of it! in a horrible little shack, *miles* from anywhere – damp as a well, I shouldn't wonder, with no proper water or *sanitation* or anything. Did you ever hear of such a thing? Naturally, Mrs Harrison said she didn't think she would care about it – what did the man expect? He didn't say anything more about it *then* – I think I've taught him not to bully his wife when I'm about! – but he took it out of her when they went upstairs. She came in crying at 12 o'clock at night to sleep with me because she couldn't stand it any longer. 'My dear,' I said, 'why do you take any notice of it? If he wants your company so badly, why can't he sacrifice himself for once and take you to Brighton or Margate, or some nice cheerful place? He just likes to make people miserable, that's all.' So then I told her a little about what Dr Trevor said about the people who enjoy inflicting torture on others. I said, 'You must just look on it as a kind of disease and not resent it if you can help it. Build up a

44

wall of protective thought about yourself and determine to be quite detached about it.' We had a very interesting little talk about repressions, and I have lent her my handbook to Freud. It is so important to get a healthy angle on these things.

Mr Lathom has been very nice, coming in almost every evening to keep us company. It must be a relief to him not to be bothered with the Bear's everlasting drivel about Art. He is going to paint our portraits. Mrs Harrison is going up for her first sitting tomorrow. It is to be a blue, green and bronze colour-scheme – blue dress, green background and a big bowl of those bronze chrysanthemums. It gave Mr Lathom a great deal of trouble deciding it. Of course, Mrs Harrison is very attractive-looking, but you couldn't exactly call her *pretty*, with those greeny eyes and her rather pale complexion. I haven't decided what to wear. I asked Mr Lathom, but he said he thought I should look nice in anything and he could safely leave it to me. I think I shall have it done in that orange thing with the square yoke – the one which Mr Ramsbottom said made me look like a Pre-Raphaelite page – you remember? – and have my hair waved and curled under all round to carry out the idea. I pointed out to Mr Lathom that my face wasn't the same both sides, and he laughed, and said no human being ever was the same both sides – Nature never worked by rule and compass.

I am doing well with my stockings, and have had several orders for scarves. Don't forget to tell anybody who wants one that I am quite ready to undertake the work. I am experimenting on some calendars, made like the old-fashioned tinsel pictures, with the coloured paper-wrappers off chocolate creams. Some of the designs are simply beautiful. You might send me any you get. I think I might get some Christmas orders for them. I've thought out quite an original idea ...

[The remainder of this letter, which contained only some designs for needlework, has been detached.]

17. *John Munting to Elizabeth Drake*

15A, WHITTINGTON TERRACE
28.10.28

DARLING BUNGIE,

Just a line to say I am running down to Oxford to stay
with the Cobbs for a week or two. It is simply impossible to
work in this place at the moment – the downstairs menagerie
swarms over us all day. This is the last time I'll think of setting up housekeeping with a man on the strength of a school
and restaurant acquaintance. Of course, it's financially useful – but, damn it all! money isn't everything, even when
one's hoping to get married. Lathom will insist on being a
little ray of sunshine about the place. Damn sunshine. If it
hadn't gone joggling up the perfectly good and placid atoms
in the primeval ooze, they would never have sweltered up
in this unsatisfactory world of life and bothersomeness.

The great idea now is to paint a portrait of Mrs Harrison
as a surprise for Harrison on his return. Knowing Lathom's
style, I should say it would be a very great surprise to him,
indeed. It will probably be a very fine work – the man can
paint – but I wish they could get on with it quietly by themselves and leave me alone. That poisonous old woman is in
and out the whole time. I daren't emerge from my own room
for a minute without being collared and asked some imbecile
question or other. Impertinent old bitch. She's a dangerous
woman, too. In Harrison's place I'd give her the sack. She
had the damned sauce to edge into my room after me yesterday and ask whose photograph that was on my table, was
it my best girl's? I said, No – it was my last mistress but
three or four, I had lost count. (It was Brenda's, as a matter
of fact.) I was told I was a dreadful man and that Miss
Drake ought to know the way I behaved. I was furious. I
don't know how the devil she got hold of your name.
Lathom's damned chattiness, I suppose – confound him! She
wound up the interview by saying, really, she didn't think it
safe to be in the same room with me, and leered her way out.
Disgusting fool! Fortunately, I was only revising 'Birth and

46

Childhood', or I should have been too irritable to work for the rest of the day. I hope, for your sake, I am not becoming neurotic – that would be the last straw.

Anyway, the Cobbs's invitation came at the exact right moment to prevent my doing something regrettable, so I'm barging off. Otherwise I should probably have had a row with Lathom, which would have been a nuisance, as I've paid the rent up to Christmas.

No news from Merritt yet. Probably he has slung the poor old MS into a drawer and forgotten about it. It could write its memoirs by this time: *Pigeon-holes I Have Lived in*. How goes your latest?

My love to the Governor and everybody,

Your loving

J

18. *Agatha Milsom to Olive Farebrother*

15, WHITTINGTON TERRACE, BAYSWATER
8.11.28

DEAREST OLIVE,

Ever so many thanks for sending the order from Mrs Pottersby; I will get on with it as quickly as I can. I have two more scarves in hand, and Mr Perry wants two dozen calenders for people in the parish, so you see I am quite busy just at present. I am glad Tom's rheumatism is no worse, and that Joan's little illness turned out to be such a trifling matter after all. It must have given you a lot of anxiety.

I am feeling very much better, I am glad to say – in fact, we are all brighter and happier for our period of peace and quietness. The Bear came back in quite a good mood, for him! – and dear Mrs Harrison seems quite a different person. She reads a lot, and I am encouraging her to live in her books, and abstract herself altogether from the wearing and irritating realities of life. It is easy, because she has a wonderfully vivid and romantic imagination, which makes the world of literature very real to her. Of course, that is

47

what Mr Harrison would never be able to understand. It is hopeless to try to discuss anything with him. I tried to get him to talk about Gilbert Frankau's new book the other day. He said he hadn't read it and didn't want to. I gave him an outline of the plot, but I don't think he was listening. At any rate, he only said, 'Oh!' and went on to talk interminably about his eternal fungi and hedgehogs. Still, provided he keeps his temper, it doesn't much matter what he talks about, and Mrs Harrison listens to it all most patiently. I wonder how she can do it, but she is in a wonderfully serene and happy frame of mind. I am rather proud of my work, for I am sure it was our little talk in my bedroom the other day that showed her the way out of her troubles.

I am sorry for what you say about Ronnie. It is most trying for you that he should have got mixed up with that sort of girl, but no doubt it will all blow over. Dr Trevor says that that kind of adolescent love-affair should always be dealt with sympathetically, and will work itself out naturally if not thwarted. I'm sure it would be *most unwise* of Tom to exert his authority in any way. I cannot forget how our poor dear Mother *ruined* my life – of course, with the best intentions – by her old-fashioned ideas of what was 'nice'. Nobody will ever know what I suffered as a girl, and I am sure it is all due to that early unhappiness that I am in the doctor's hands now. It was not the same thing for you, of course – you never had that complicated and delicately-balanced temperament, and would probably always have been happy enough, whether you had married or not. People of your kind are much the most fortunate, but then one cannot help one's temperament, can one? If you take my advice, and treat Ronnie with sympathy and indulgence, you will avoid making the mess of his life that our parents made of mine. I feel that Ronnie and I are very much akin – perhaps a few words from me would help to explain him to himself. I am writing to him tonight.

Your loving sister,
AGGIE

19. *The Same to the Same*

DEAR OLIVE,

I have been much surprised and deeply hurt by Ronnie's letter to me, which I enclose for you to see. I cannot believe that he would have written in that spirit of his own accord. I can only suppose that you and Tom have been prejudicing him against me. Of course, he is your child and not mine, but it is quite a mistake to imagine that, merely because of the physical accident of parenthood, you are, for that reason, divinely qualified to deal with a sensitive temperament like Ronnie's. I (not having my eyes blinded) can see quite clearly through what he writes, that you have succeeded in *apparently* bringing him into agreement with your point of view; but, if you did but know it, you are merely encouraging him to repress his natural feelings, with consequences which may be *terrible to contemplate*. I can imagine nothing worse for him than what you call change of scene and companionship, when I know perfectly well that you mean that unimaginative and completely insensitive Potts person. I cannot imagine a more dangerous influence for a boy in Ronnie's state of mind than a footballing parson. The harm done by men of that class is quite incalculable, and their minds are, as a rule, perfect sinks of dangerous and sublimated libidos (I don't know whether that is the right way to spell the plural). However, it is your own affair, and I am powerless to interfere, but I do think you ought not to set the boy against me, merely because I am, unhappily, in a position to know more than you do about certain facts of life.

Thank you, I am glad to say we are all very well. Mrs Harrison's portrait is finished. It is a very striking piece of colour. Of course, Mr H. thinks it does not do her justice, but then, as you would expect, he is quite out of sympathy with modern art.

We are relieved from the presence of Mr Munting, who

has gone to Oxford, on a visit to some friends, or so he says. I think it is much more likely that he is leading a double life somewhere. He unblushingly confesses to having innumerable disreputable entanglements, and I am very sorry indeed for the girl he is engaged to.

Your affectionate sister,
AGGIE

20. *George Harrison to Paul Harrison*

15, WHITTINGTON TERRACE
20.11.28

MY DEAR BOY,

I was very glad to get your letter – the one dated 7th October – and to know that all goes on so well with you and the bridge. You took exactly the course I should have advised myself in the matter of the man Matthews. In such a case, consideration is out of place. Your duty to the firm (to say nothing of the thousands who will use the bridge) must come before any sympathy for the man and his special circumstances. Far too much laxity is shown nowadays to outbreaks of so-called 'temperament', with most disastrous consequences, and there is far too much talk about 'not being able to help one's self'. I should not let the matter prey on your mind in the least. I quite understand that the man has brilliant powers and an attractive personality, and that you are sorry to lose him, but it is fatally easy for a man like that to imagine that the ordinary rules of morality do not apply to him, and to indulge him in such ideas is bad for him, and may easily be ruinous to other people and to his work. I entirely approve your decision, and so, I am sure, must Sir Maurice, if the matter comes to his notice.

I am feeling greatly benefited by my little holiday, and am glad to be back to work again. I found all well at home on my return. Margaret was in very good spirits over a little surprise that she and Lathom had prepared for me.

She has been sitting to him for her portrait, and he has made a very striking piece of work of it. While I cannot say I think it does her justice, there is no doubt that it is a handsome piece of *coloratura*, and the kind of thing to attract attention at the present time. Lathom belongs, of course, to the modern school. He paints, I feel, in too much of a hurry, and his pictures have not the beautiful smooth finish of a Millais, or, among living artists, of a Lavery – but no doubt he will grow out of this slapdash method when he is older. It is a kind of affection which besets the young painters of today, and, while I cannot help but see the defects of the method, I am not blind to the merits of the work and to the kind thought which prompted the execution. He is anxious to show it at the Academy next year, and Margaret is (naturally, I suppose) delighted with the idea. I was obliged, however, to say that I did not care about the project. It is the kind of picture to attract a good deal of comment of one sort and another, and these young people do not quite see the amount of undesirable publicity it might involve. I fear they are both rather disappointed, but later on, when I was able to speak quietly about it to Lathom alone, he saw the matter in the right light, and was very nice about it. We are hanging it in a good light in the drawing-room, where it will look very well.

There has been a very amusing sequel to this. Your old friend (or should I say enemy?) Miss Milsom has taken it into her head that *her* fair features ought to be immortalised, too! Lathom, with his usual extraordinary good nature, has actually consented to make a picture of her – but only on the understanding that this time, if it turns out well, he shall have the right to do as he likes with it! Miss Milsom is only too enchanted at the idea of being hung at Burlington House. I did not feel called upon to interefere, since he is obviously only 'pulling her leg', and there is not the remotest chance of the portrait's being exhibited; for, as you know, the lady is scarcely the Venus of Milo! She is very much excited about it, and has produced the most incredible garment to be painted in – very tight as to the bust and voluminous as to the skirt. I understand that a quattrocento effect is aimed at.

I am very hard at work of an evening now – with a number of sketches to work up and my little *opus* to prepare, I am illustrating it with water-colours of various plants and fungi in their natural habitat, and it should turn out a very pretty and useful volume.

I enclose the formulae you asked for, and remain

Your affectionate

DAD

21. *Agatha Milsom to Olive Farebrother*

15, WHITTINGTON TERRACE
22.11.28

DEAR OLIVE,

I have received your letter about Ronnie. No doubt you think you know best. I will not allude further to the matter.

I am feeling *much* too upset to discuss such things just now. Mr Harrison has been behaving abominably, undoing all the good his absence has done, and creating his usual atmosphere of unpleasantness.

Mr Lathom painted a most *beautiful* picture of Mrs Harrison. They both worked like galley-slaves to get it finished in time for his return (H.'s, I mean). I say both, for sitting is most exhausting work, as you would know if you had ever sat to anybody for a portrait, and she would end up sometimes so cramped she could scarcely move. As for Mr Lathom, he seemed quite inspired over it, and painted and painted away without food or rest, till I got quite worried about him, and had to bring him up cups of hot Bovril and Ovaltine, for fear he should over-tax his strength. He is an extraordinarily generous young man, because, though he cannot be well off, he actually painted the portrait to *give* to Mr Harrison, when I feel sure he could have sold it for a big price, it is such a splendid piece of work, and he says himself it is one of the best things he has ever done.

Well, they got it finished in time for the Bear's return, and Mrs Harrison was ever so delighted with it, and thought the creature would be pleased. It was quite pathetic to see how eagerly she looked forward to surprising him, poor woman. Well, he was pleased, in his grudging kind of way, though he had the impertinence to criticise the painting – as if Mr Lathom didn't know more about Art with his eyes shut than Mr Harrison could learn in a month of Sundays. And then it was all spoilt by the Bear's horrible selfishness. Mr Lathom said – very nicely and courteously – he hoped Mr Harrison would see no objection to its being sent to the Academy. Of course, as it was the best thing he'd done, you'd think anybody would see he had a right to exhibit it, and you'd think, too, that when anybody had received a valuable present like that, he'd be only too willing to be obliging. But the PIG just said, 'Well, Lathom, I don't quite think we can go as far as that. My wife would hardly like to be put on show, you know.'

I could see that Mrs Harrison felt the discourtesy to Mr Lathom *dreadfully*, and she said at once she would be quite pleased to let the portrait be shown, and then he laughed – just laughed, as if it was of no importance to anybody, and said, 'Oh, Lathom won't insist on making an exhibition of you, my dear.' I could see how vexed Mr Lathom was, and so could Mrs Harrison, and she begged and prayed him not to be so selfish and unkind, and Mr Lathom spoke up and said, if Mrs Harrison would like her portrait shown, surely he was not going to be a Victorian husband. Of course, that was unwise (as I could have warned him if I could have got the chance), and we had one of the worst rows even I can remember. Mr Lathom couldn't stand it and went out of the room in disgust, and Mrs Harrison cried, and her husband said the most insulting and unjustifiable things, ending up with: 'Of course, if you want to make a public exhibition of yourself you can. Do exactly as you like' – as though anybody *could*, when they had been spoken to like that about it. So that was the end of trying to do something to please one's husband! It was a most miserable ending to the day we had all looked forward to with so much hope and pleasure.

For once Mrs Harrison has taken a firm line with him and refuses to speak to him. It is a very uncomfortable situation for me, and I am feeling very unwell. All my insomnia has come back, and so has the uncontrollable longing for shrimps. It is very tiresome and disappointing.

Mr Lathom has been perfectly sweet about it all. He went in to see Mr Harrison when the uproar had calmed down a little, and finding it impossible to move him, gave way gracefully. I was determined to do my best to make it up to him, so I went up and said how sorry I was, and added that I *insisted* that he should do exactly as he liked with my own portrait. He could show it anywhere he chose, I said, even if he liked to call it *Portrait of a Middle-aged Spinster*. He laughed, and said he wouldn't think of calling it anything of the sort, and he certainly wouldn't show it if I would rather he didn't, and I said I was determined he *should* show it, whatever it turned out like. So he said, very well, that was a bargain, then. So we have begun the sittings. I am rather nervous about the result, because as you know, I always photograph very badly. But then a photograph cannot show the animation of the face as a portrait can, and people have so often told me that my animation is what gives character and interest to my looks. I hope it will be a good likeness – perhaps you will say that if it is it won't be an attractive picture, but Mr Lathom seems very keen on it, so perhaps it will turn out better than you, with your sisterly prejudice, might expect.

I am very tired with keeping the pose – I sat for two hours this morning and again in the afternoon – so I hope I may get some rest tonight.

The scarf will be finished tomorrow, if I can get the right shade of silk for the fringe.

Your affectionate sister,
AGGIE

15A, WHITTINGTON TERRACE
1.12.28

BELOVED BUNGIE,

Here we are again! Back home and full of beans and fit to face anything, even Lathoms and Milsoms.

By the way, I've got to take back what I said about Lathom. I'll forgive him anything for being such a bloody fine painter. My God, he has made a fine thing of Mrs Harrison – old Halkett would grunt in his funny gruff way and say, 'It's a masterpiece.' He wants to send it to the Academy (where it would probably be the picture of the year, if the Committee didn't hang themselves in their own wires under the shock of seeing a decent bit of painting for once) – only, of course, those imbecile women have made a hash of it and put Harrison's back up. Blether, blether blether – rushing at the poor man with chatter about newspaper sensations and standing under my portrait on opening day, blah! blah! blah! before the poor man had finished reeling under the impact. Row, of course. I told Lathom not to be a silly ass, and to go and apologise quietly to Harrison afterwards and tell him there wasn't any slightest intention of showing it against his wishes. If he uses a little tact, the old boy will take it for granted three months hence that the thing *is* going to be shown and imagine he suggested it himself. I've got Harrison fairly well sized up, but his wife is a silly egoist, and Lathom has no practical sense at all as regards human relationships. Anyway, I hope the thing will be there, because I'd like you to see it. It's really first-rate. And revealing, my God! only Mrs H. doesn't see that, and I don't think Lathom realises it either.

I've had a letter from Merritt – he 'has read the book with much interest and it would be glad if I could find time to call and discuss it with him at my convenience.' First time anybody's even offered to discuss it. I suppose that if I will consent to cut out all the 'advanced' passages, and 'brighten' the style and give it a more 'satisfactory' ending, he will consider doing something with it. Well, he won't get the chance, that's all.

Thank heaven, the *Life* is practically finished with. I'm thankful to get rid of it. It has led me into reading a lot of scientific and metaphysical tripe which is of no use to anybody, and least of all to a creative writer (a fact I have taken delight in rubbing in, in the course of the work!) And the further you go with it, the worse it gets. Lucretius could make great poetry out of science, and Bacon got some good work in on it – and even Tennyson could screw some fine lines out of an unsound theory of evolution and perfectibility and all the rest of it. But now, oh, heavens! after the bio-chemist, the mathematician. What can you make out of the action of the glands of internal secretion upon metabolism, or Pi and the square root of minus one? Despair and a kind of gloomy grubbiness, that's all. I'd rather have a Miltonian theology to make poetry of than all this business of liver and gonads and the velocity of light. Perry the parson gets out of it by pretending that the Catholic Church knew all about it from the beginning, and that inaccurate theological metaphors can be interpreted as pseudo-scientific formulae, which is a lie. The origin of life is our great stamping-ground for discussion. You can't make life synthetically in a laboratory – therefore he deduces that it came by divine interference! Rather an assumption! But, after all, he is little worse than the man of science. 'In some way or other, life came,' they say. 'Sometime, somehow, we may learn how to make it.' But even if one could learn to make it, that doesn't account for its having arrived spontaneously in the first place. The biologist can push it back to the original protist, and the chemist can push it back to the crystal, but none of them touch the real question of why or how the thing began at all. The astronomer goes back untold million of years and ends in gas and emptiness, and then the mathematician sweeps the whole cosmos into unreality and leaves one with mind as the only thing of which we have any immediate apprehension. *Cogito, ergo sum, ergo omnia esse videntur.* All this bother, and we are no further than Descartes. Have you noticed that the astronomers and mathematicians are much the most cheerful people of the lot? I suppose that perpetually contemplating things on so vast a scale makes them feel either that it doesn't matter a hoot anyway, or that anything so large and elaborate must have some sense in it somewhere.

I wish I had Lathom's robust contempt for all this kind of thing. His attitude is that bio-chemistry cannot affect his life or his art, so let them get on with it. I am tossed about with every wind of doctrine, and if I'm not damn careful I shall end by writing a *Point Counterpoint*, without the wit. You can't really make a novel hold together if you don't believe in causation.

> Said a rising young author, 'What, what?
> If I think that causation is not,
> No word of my text
> Will bear on the next
> And what will become of the plot?'

Perhaps this accounts for my never having been able to produce a book with a plot – except, of course, the one Merritt wants to see me about. And that was a sort of freak book.

Well, never mind. Only a fortnight now and I shall be seeing you. Praise God (or whatever it is) from (if direction exists) whom (if personality exists) all blessings (if that word corresponds to any percept of objective reality) flow (if Heraclitus and Bergson and Einstein are correct in stating that everything is more or less flowing about).

Your ever faithful

JACK

23. *The Same to the Same*

4.12.28

BUNGIE DEAREST,
    Just a line to say that the unexpected has happened! Mer-

ritt is all over the book!!! Thinks it's the biggest thing that ever happened, and has offered me a first-class contract (£100 advance, 10% to 500, 15% to 1,000 and 20% thereafter, with a firm offer for the next two beginning at top previous rate), on condition he can get it into print instanter to publish before the end of Jan. The man's as mad as a hatter!

I nearly sent round to get him certified, but instead found myself accepting the terms. When you consider the frightful flop *Deadlock* was, you realise that the thing is sheer stark raving madness, but who cares?

Damn it, I always believed there was something in the book, but I thought I was a fool to think so. But how can he ever imagine that it will *sell*! . . . But that's *his* funeral.

He says it must have a new title. Try and think of something that will look well on a jacket, there's an ingenious cherub. It's fearfully urgent, because he's got to get his travellers out with it at the beginning of next month.

Lathom's portrait of Miss Milsom is the wickedest piece of satire you ever saw. She, fortunately, does not see it at all. In fact, she lugged up the parson to have a look at it yesterday. Perry, though a parson, is no fool. He looked grave, said that it was a striking picture, and added that Mr Lathom had a great gift which should be put to great uses. Lathom grinned, and Miss Milsom began to babble about the Academy and Mrs Harrison's portrait, at which Perry looked graver still. I suppose he thinks that idiots should be charitably protected from themselves. Lathom is in wild spirits and is working like something inspired. *O si sic omnes*, meaning me!

Jim reports that he is toiling away like stink and really sticking to it. I hope so. He will be at home when term ends, so you will meet the white-headed boy of the family. I trust you will be able to bear with us all. His is inflicting on us a friend of his who went down from Caius this year – man called Leader – one of those infernally high-spirited youths who bounce all over the shop like Airedale puppies – he rouses all my worst instincts, but is perfectly harmless. He is now in London, at St Anthony's College of Medicine, and I suppose one of these days he will muddle through his hospital work and be turned out as a genial G.P. – 'Dr Leader is *such* a nice, cheerful man; he makes you feel better the minute he comes into the room.' I hate cheerful people. Still, he and Jimmy will amuse one another, and we shall have a chance to get off on our own a bit.

Bless you, Bungie! I am counting the days till we meet.

Your own

JACK

24. *George Harrison to Paul Harrison*

15, WHITTINGTON TERRACE, BAYSWATER
20th December, 1928

MY DEAR BOY,

A line at Christmas-time to send our best love, and to say that all our thoughts are with you. Next Christmas, if all goes well, we shall have you back, and things will seem more like themselves. Here, of course, a sad shadow is cast on our festivities by the illness of the King. There are distressing rumours, but I feel a great confidence that he will pull through in the end.

In spite of this feeling of depression and anxiety, we have decided to make a little jaunt over to Paris. Margaret has seemed rather restless lately, and I think this small excitement will do her good. I am such a quiet sort of old fellow, that I fear she finds her life a trifle dull at times. A visit to the 'gay city' will set her up again, and it will be beneficial to me, too, to be shaken out of my rut. We shall be staying at the Hotel Victoria-Palace in the Rue – ; it is a pleasant, respectable place, and not dear, as Paris hotels go. We shall do a theatre or two and perhaps go up to Montmartre to see the 'night-life' one hears so much about. Young Lathom says he may be running over to Paris for a few days, and, if so, will look us up and show us round the town. It is kind and attentive of him, and we shall appreciate having an up-to-date cicerone, for my own memories of Paris are very antiquated, and I expect everything is very much changed.

I was very glad to hear that your work was progressing so well and that your action in the matter of the man you dismissed was approved of. Leniency in such a case is always a mistake, as I have found out from bitter experience.

We are doing better over here than we had really any right to expect under the present depressed conditions. I think we shall secure the contract for the Middleshire High-Power Station. If so, that will mean a big job, which will probably take me away from London in the spring.

I am really wondering whether, before this happens, I ought not to take some steps about replacing Miss Milsom by somebody who would be a more suitable companion for Margaret. Miss Milsom has always seemed to me a very tiresome woman, and lately she has been getting altogether above herself. She consults these psycho-analytical quacks, who encourage her to attach an absurd importance to her whims and feelings, and to talk openly at the dinner-table about things which, in my (doubtless old-fashioned) opinion, ought only to be mentioned to doctors. Besides, she is very lazy and untidy, and, instead of putting her mind to the housework, she litters the place with wool and bits of paper which she calls 'art materials' and she borrows my paints and forgets to return them. There is no harm, of course, in her doing needlework and making calendars, if it does not interfere with her duties, but she has frequently been very impertinent when I have had occasion to speak about the unsatisfactory cooking. Lathom has been painting a picture of her – a very clever thing, certainly, but it seems to have turned her head completely. However, Margaret wishes to be kind to the woman, and says, truly, that she would find it hard to get another post, so perhaps it will be better to put up with her a little longer and see if the situation improves. She is certainly most loyal and devoted to Margaret, and that outweighs a great many drawbacks.

Well, I must not worry you with these small domestic matters. I hope that you will be enjoying a very happy Christmas in your exile, and that our little offerings have arrived quite safely. By the way, your Plum-pudding was not, I can assure you, an example of Miss Milson's culinary genius. I attended to that important matter myself – otherwise you might have found many strange things in it – such as glass beads or stencil-brushes! The calendar, however, was all the lady's own work. She wonders regularly every day whether you will like it, and whether your colleagues will think it was painted for you by your fiancée. She means kindly, poor woman, so, if you have not already expressed your hearty delight, pray do so, and assure her that the masterpiece has an honoured place on your walls.

With much love,

Your affectionate

DAD

25. *Note by Paul Harrison*

I can find only one letter for the next few weeks with any important bearing on the subject of this inquiry. My father and stepmother were in Paris from the 15th of December to the 7th of January. I received a few picture postcards with accounts of places visited, but they contained nothing of any moment, and I did not preserve them.

Lathom joined them on or about the 28th of December, and spent the Jour de l'An in their company. I believe that Mrs Harrison wrote several letters to Miss Milsom from Paris, but these I have been unable to secure; in fact, I am informed that they have been destroyed. I visited Miss Milsom (see my statement No. 49), and questioned her as tactfully as possible on the subject, but could only get from her a rambling diatribe, full of the same demented prejudice she has always displayed against my father, and, in the absence of any direct evidence (such as the original letters would have afforded), I feel bound to ignore her remarks. Indeed, it is obvious that nothing which Miss Milsom says *later* than April, 1929, is of any evidential value whatsoever, and that *all* her statements, without exception, must be received with extreme caution, except in so far as they tend to prove the influence exerted, consciously or unconsciously, by her upon my stepmother.

Mr Munting, who spent the Christmas season with his family and in the company of his fiancée, not returning to town till the 15th of January, has handed to me the only letter which he received from his friend during this period.

26. *Harwood Lathom to John Munting*

POLPERRO
4th Jan., '29

DEAR MUNTING,

How are you? And how did the season of over-feeding and Christian heartiness leave your soul? Did honourable love survive the domesticities? If so, I swear that you and your intelligent young woman are either gods or beasts. Gods, probably – with that dreadful temperateness of the knowledge of good and evil, seeing two sides to every question. You will analyse your bridal raptures if you have any, and find the whole subject very interesting. You will have, Heaven help you! a sense of humour about the business, and your friends will say how beautiful it is to see such a fine sense of partnership between a man and woman. A copulation of politic tape-worms! But where is the use of being offensive to a man who will allow for my point of view? I hate being allowed for, as if I were an incalculable quantity in an astronomical equation.

Having (thank God!) no family, except my aunt at Colchester, I escaped good King Wenceslas and departed for Paris, where everything is jejune enough, and the weather just as snow-bound and bitter as our own happy island, but where at least the stranger is not sucked into the *vie familiale*. I found the Harrisons dismally vegetating in a highly respectable Anglophile hotel, and toted them round the usual stale shows, getting my pleasure from their naïve enjoyment. Or, at any rate, from *her* enjoyment; the old boy was as peevish as ever, and brought the blush of shame to my cosmopolitan cheek by walking out of a cabaret in the middle, trailing his wife and friend after him in the approved barn-door style. Being too wrathful for speech, I said nothing, and had the pleasure of sitting out a family row in the taxi afterwards. *La belle Marguerite* was actually quite as shocked as he was, poor child, but thrilled to an unregenerate ecstasy nevertheless. She has the makings of a decent pagan soul if one could teach her. However, I needed to do no teaching. His vulgar disgust (with which, if he had had the elementary tact to leave her alone, she would have agreed) drove her into an excited opposition, and she argued the point with an obstinacy and whole-heartedness which it was a pleasure to listen to. I wouldn't be appealed to – I didn't want a row, and besides she will learn nothing except by arguing it out for herself. In fact, I apologised and said, in effect, that an artist became rather blind to the properties, legs, as the bus-conductor said, being no treat to him. In fact, I controlled myself marvellously, and – went away and walked about in a fury all night!

After that we did picture-galleries, and I had to listen to Harrison's lectures on art. Never have I heard – not even in Chelsea – so much jargon applied over so grisly a substructure of ignorance and bad taste. The man ought to be crucified in the middle of all his own abominable daubs. You would have enjoyed it, I suppose, or made copy of it.

We saw the New Year in with dancing and the usual imbecile festivities. Mrs H. thanked me with tears of excitement in her eyes – it was pathetic – like giving sweets to a kid. Even H. was a little moved from his usual grimth. I procured him a partner – no! I didn't hire her, I knew her – a decent little soul who used to live with Mathieu Vigor and is now, I believe, Kropotzki's *petite amie* – and she trundled him round in the most amiable way. He emerged from the fray quite sparkling (for him!), and solemnly led Madame out for the next dance! That didn't go so well, because he found fault with her steps, so I pushed him back on to Fleurette, who could dance with a kangaroo, I think, clever little devil.

I crossed on the 2nd, and came down here for warmth and sunshine (what a hope!). The place has been ruined, of course, by 'artistic' tourists, and is lousy with Ye Olde Potterye Shoppes. The brave fishermen dangle around in clean blue jerseys and polish up the boats in the harbour, while they long for the film-season to start again.

I shall be back in Bayswater some time next week. I hope your sense of humour is feeling robust, for I am in a foul mood and nothing pleases me.

Yours ever,
LATHOM

27. *John Munting to Elizabeth Drake*

15A, WHITTINGTON TERRACE, BAYSWATER

[The opening sheets of this letter are lost, but the date is evidently some time in January.]

. . . proofs coming along at express speed, I am enjoying a magnificent illusion of importance and busy-ness. The novel will be out before the *Life,* which is being held up considerably by copyright bothers over the plates. All the better, as it is a mistake to bung two books out right on top of one another.

I am feeling a great deal more sympathetic with Lathom just now. The earnest Harrison has transferred his attentions, for the moment, to me, because, as a literary man, I can, of course, tell him exactly how best to prepare his fungus-book for the press. He comes teetering in at my busiest moments to discuss points of grammar. I tell him my opinion and he contradicts it at great length, pointing out subtleties in his phrasing which I have not grasped. At length I either tell him that his own original idea expresses his personality best, or fall back on *The King's English* if the error is really too monstrous to let pass. This works all right for a time, and he carries the book off with much gratitude – returning later, however, with the demurrer to Mr Fowler carefully written down on paper. I once made the foolish suggestion that he should write to Fowler and thrash it out with him direct; this was fatal, as I had to listen to (a) the letter; (b) the reply; (c) the rejoinder – so I now fall back as a rule on the phrase about expressing personality. There was also a dreadful day when a water-colour picture of fungi came out too green by three-colour process. Lathom and I suffered dreadfully over this abominable toadstool, and were at length forced to go out and drown the recollection in Guinness.

All the same, I try my best to be helpful, because I am the only person who can enter into Harrison's interests, and he has really written a very entertaining little piece of work, full of odd bits of out-of-the-way knowledge, scraps of country lore and queer old-fashioned recipes and things. He must have made extraordinary good use of his holidays, and there's not a plant or animal in the country fit for food that he doesn't know the last word about. He has made a wonderful collection of botanical diaries, which ought to be of considerable scientific value, and he brings a really scholarly mind to his rather unscholarly subject. His water-colours, though too prim considered as pictures, make really rather attractive book-illustrations, and his drawings of plants and fungi are beautifully accurate in line and colour – far better than the stuff you find in the usual textbooks. And, indeed, the vagaries of the three-colour process are enough to make Job irritable. I told him that he should take as his motto for the book the famous misprint in the Bible, 'Printers have persecuted me with a cause' – which pleased him.

Profiting by my position as literary guide and mentor, I have (with colossal tact) persuaded him to let the famous portrait be shown. We got around to it by way of cookery, oddly enough. I said that cookery was really a very important creative art, which was not properly understood in this country, being chiefly left in the hands of women, who were not (pardon me, Bungie) as a rule very creative.

That led on to a general discussion of Art, and the yearning that every creative artist feels to obtain a public response to his art. And so, by devious ways, to Lathom and his picture. I said that, while I entirely understood Mrs Harrison's quite natural feeling that to exhibit her portrait would be, to a great extent, exhibiting herself, to Lathom

5   65

it was, of course, quite a different matter. It was his work, his handling of line and colour, for which he wanted public recognition. But I admitted that a woman could not be expected to appreciate this point of view.

As I had foreseen, Harrison took this as an indirect criticism of his wife, and promptly reacted against it. She was not, he said, like the ordinary woman. She had a remarkable gift for artistic appreciation. He felt sure that if he put it to her in the right light, she would see that it was not a personal question at all. Indeed, she had made no objection herself – it was he who had been afraid of exposing her to unwelcome notoriety. But it should be made quite clear that the painting was the important matter, and that the subject had no personal bearings of any kind.

It was very odd, Bungie, to see him reassuring himself in this vicarious way. And it was still odder that I had a feeling all the time as if I was doing something unfair. His attitude about the thing was preposterous, of course, but I have a queer feeling about Mrs Harrison. She isn't so stupid that she can't see Lathom's point of view. It would matter less if she were. It is that she is clever enough to see it and adopt it when it is pointed out, and to make it into a weapon of some kind for something or other. Not knowing that it is a weapon, either; practising a sort of ju-jitsu, that overcomes by giving way – good God! what a filthy bit of obvious journalese metaphor!

Anyhow, Mr Harrison worked off my little lecture on the creative artist with great effect under my very nose the same evening, as though it was all his own work. Mrs H. started off with her usual lack of tact by saying: 'I thought you said,' and 'I don't want to discuss it,' but, catching my eye, resigned herself to listen graciously and give consent. So the Hanging Committee is, after all, to have the happiness of gazing upon the portraits of Mrs Harrison and Miss Milsom – blest pair of sirens – and I hope they will be duly appreciative. Lathom is pleased – and so damn well ought to be! I hope it will calm him down, for what with the portraits and the fungus-book and one thing and another, he and I are both getting into a state of nerves.

I want peace and quiet. Damn all these people! Thank

66

Heaven I've got the proofs to see to, because I'm in no fit state to write anything. My ideas are all upside down. I can't focus anything. I suppose it's just the usual 'between-books' feeling. I am going to take a few weeks' lucid interval and read astronomy or physics or something. Personally, I'm dead sick of the blasted creative instinct!

Yours all-of-a-dither, but still devotedly,

JACK

28. *The Same to the Same*

15A, WHITTINGTON TERRACE, BAYSWATER
1st February, 1929

BUNGIE, MY DARLING,

What, in God's name, are you going to do with me if I get jealous and suspicious? Or I with you, if it happens that way? I ask this in damn sober earnest, old girl. I've got the thing right under my eyes here, and I know perfectly well that no agreement and no promise made before marriage will stand up for a single moment if either of us gets that ugly bug into the blood.

You remember – months ago – I passed on a cheerful little matrimonial dialogue that took place by the umbrella-stand. Tonight we had the pleasure of hearing the thing carried on to the next stage.

Harrison had the brilliant idea of inviting Lathom and me to dinner to taste his special way of frying chicken. Well, there we all were – Miss Milsom frightfully kittenish in a garment she had embroidered herself with Persian arabesques. ('I don't know *what* they mean, you know, Mr Munting. Probably something frightfully improper! I copied them off a rug.') Harrison who allows nobody to penetrate into 'his' kitchen when he's working out a masterpiece, was frying away amid a powerful odour of garlic. No Mrs Harrison! We furiously make conversation – enter H. – gives a black look round, and disappears again. I count the things on the mantelpiece – two brass candlesticks, brass doorknocker representing the Lincoln imp – two imitation brass mulling-cones – ill-balanced pottery nude – quaint clock and pair of Liberty nondescripts. Front door goes. Kitchen door in the distance heard to burst open. 'Well, where have *you* been?' Awful realisation creeps over us all that the sitting-room door has been left open. I say hurriedly: 'Have you read the new Michael Arlen, Miss Milsom?' We are all aware that a prolonged cross-examination is proceeding. Lathom fidgets. Voice rises to appalling distinctness: 'Don't talk nonsense! How *long* were you at the hairdresser's? – Well, what *were* you doing? – Yes, but *what* kept you? – Yes, of course, you met somebody. You seem to be meeting a lot of people lately! – I don't care who it "only" was – one of the men from the office, I suppose – Carrie Mortimer? nonsense! – I shall *not* be quiet – I shall talk as loudly as I like – Did you or did you not remember – ?' Here I grow desperate and turn on the gramaphone. In comes Harrison, putting a good face on it. 'Here's the wife, late as usual!' We sit down to dinner in embarrassed silence. I murmur eulogies on the chicken. 'Over-cooked,' says Harrison, shovelling it all aside and savagely picking at the vegetables. After this, everybody is afraid to eat it, for fear of not seeming to know good food from bad. 'It seems delicious to me, Mr Harrison,' says Miss Milsom, profiting nothing from long experience. 'Oh,' says Harrison, sourly, 'you women don't care what you eat. It's overdone, isn't it, Lathom?' Lathom, quite helpless with rage, says in a strangulated voice, that he thinks it's just right. 'Well, you're not eating it,' says Harrison, gloomily triumphant. By this time everybody's appetite is taken thoroughly away. There is nothing on earth the matter with the chicken, but we all sit staring at it as though it was a Harpagus-feast of boiled baby.

Well, I'll spare you the rest of the nightmare. The point is that *this* time, Mrs Harrison didn't come in bubblingly eager to say where she had been and what she had been doing – and that *next* time the alibi will hold water – and then Harrison will start saying that you can't trust women, and will very likely be perfectly justified.

Bungie – I *see* how these things happen, but how does one insure against them? What security have we that we – you and I, with all our talk of freedom and frankness – shall not come to this?

Love makes no difference. Harrison would cheerfully die for his wife – but I can't imagine anything more offensive than dying for a person after you've been rude to them. It's taking a mean advantage. And what's the good of it all to him, if he loves her so much that everything she says gets on his nerves? I like Harrison – I think he's worth a hundred of her – and yet, every time there's a row, she ingeniously manages somehow to make him appear to be in the wrong. She is completely selfish, but she takes the centre of the stage so convincingly that the whole scene is engineered to give her the limelight for her attitudes.

This house is becoming a nightmare; I shall have to chuck it, but I must stay on till Easter, because the rent is paid up to the quarter and I can't afford to lead a double life and Lathom can't manage more than his own share. Hell!

I to Hercules comes out next month. I hope old Merritt won't be let down over it. He continues to be enthusiastic. Senile decay, I should think. Well, we'll hope for the best. If my Press is as good as yours I shan't complain, my child.

Your envious

JACK

29. *Note by Paul Harrison*

It is unfortunate that throughout this important and critical period, from the end of November to the end of February, we should have no help from the Milsom correspondence. It seems that Miss Milsom and Mrs Farebrother had a renewed quarrel during the Christmas period, on the subject of the youth Ronnie Farebrother, mentioned in former letters, and that as a result they remained for some time not on speaking or writing terms. Mr Munting's letters also contain no references to my father's domestic affairs during the month of February – no doubt because he was preoccupied with his own private concerns.

During the last week of January, the wretched young

Farebrother shot himself. This gratifying fulfilment of her prophecies of disaster seems to have driven Miss Milsom into a highly hysterical state of mind, which probably precipitated the mental collapse that followed. Her correspondence with her sister (which was then resumed) is therefore quite useless for evidential purposes. We can, therefore, only guess at the development of the situation between my stepmother and Lathom during February – the month in which my father's duties took him away from home for fourteen days, in connection with the electrical installation in Middleshire. In view of the extraordinary incident which finally broke up the two households, it is, however, not difficult to form a correct opinion.

30. *John Munting to Elizabeth Drake*

15A, WHITTINGTON TERRACE, BAYSWATER
17.2.29

DARLING BUNGIE,

You have seen the reviews, of course! Bless my heart and soul, what has happened to the people? Of course, it was all started by that tom-fool at the Guildhall (I don't know why Cabinet Ministers should be the only people who can sell one's books for one nowadays) – but oh, my lights and liver! Oh, goroo! goroo! The silly mutton-headed G.P. is walking into the blooming shops by thousands and *buying* the thing! *Paying* for the thing. Shoving down their hard-earned seven-and-sixpences for it! Lord help us – what have I done that I should be a best seller? Is thy servant a tripe-hound that he should do this thing? First edition sold out. Presses rolling out new printings day and night – Merritt nearly off his head and saying, 'I told you so.' Blushing author besieged in his charming Bayswater flat (! ! ! !) – Remarkable portrait of blushing author by that brilliant young artist Mr Harwood Lathom (done in a fit of boredom one afternoon when the model hadn't turned up) being scrambled for by four Press agencies, two literary hostesses and an American lion-tamer! Everything gas and gaiters! Worm-like appeals, from publishers who turned *Hercules* down, for the next contract but seven, and the *Wail* and the *Blues* and the *Depress* and all the Sunday Bloods yapping over the phone for my all-important, inspired and inspiring views on 'What does the Unconscious means to me?' – 'Is Monogamy Doomed?' – 'Can Women tell the truth?' – 'Should Wives Produce Books or Babies?' – 'What is wrong with the Modern Aunt?' – and 'Glands or God – Which?'

Bungie, old thing, it all seems absolutely ghastly and pre-posterous, but the blasted book is BOOMING – and – shall we get married, Bungie? Will you take the risk on the strength of one fluky Boomer (which may perfectly well be a Boomerang and prevent me from ever writing anything worth doing for the rest of my life), and a set of contracts which I may go mad with inability to fulfil? Because, if you will – say so, my courageous infant, and we will tell your Uncle Edward to put up the banns, and prance off hand in hand our own primrose way to the everlasting bonfire.

Pull yourself together, Jack Munting!

Bungie, I've never told you how jealous I was because your books sold and mine didn't. If I tell you so now, don't remember it against me. Parson Perry says confession is a good thing. Perhaps he's right. I confess it now – and now forget it, there's a good girl. Perhaps even now it only means that my wretched book is howlingly bad. I always comforted myself with thinking that I *must* write better than you to be so unsaleable – but I'm filthily pleased and cock-a-hoop all the same.

Pull yourself together, Jack Munting! You are becoming hysterical. Your glands are functioning madly in the wrong places, and your Unconscious has come unstuck!

Anyhow, I'm going to have quite enough to depress me tomorrow. That crashing nuisance, Leader, has suddenly dis-covered that he knows the fellow who's written the book of the season, and is coming along to 'Look me up, old boy, and celebrate!

> *There was a young student of Caius*
> *Who passed his exams with a squaius,*

71

> *Ere dissecting at St Bartholomews*
> *Inward St Partholomews, such as St*
> *Heartholomews,*
> *To discover the cure of disaius.*

Oh, well, I suppose one of the penalties of success is the way it brings you in touch with your friends. I had an invitation to dine from the Sheridans last week. 'Such a long time since we met, isn't it?' I will see to it that it shall be longer still.

Well, let me know about the matrimonial outlook, won't you? I have a great many important engagements, of course, but I daresay I might be able to fit this little matter in somewhere!

Yours *pomposo e majestuoso*,

JACK

P.S. You need not trouble to make it a quiet one. I can easily afford a top-hat – in fact, several.

31. *The Same to the Same*

15A, WHITTINGTON TERRACE
20.2.29

DARLING BUNGIE,

Glory, alleluia! Then we will be married at Easter. Curse Uncle Edward's scruples! I could make you just as good a husband in Lent – but, as you say, it's a shame to upset the old boy. Now that the remote prospect has really come so (comparatively) near, I feel all wobbly and inadequate. It's like bracing your muscles to pick up a heavy bag and finding there's nothing in it. One thought it was years off – and here it is – and there it is, and that's that.

Well!

Well, we are going to be married at Easter.

Well – it will be a good excuse for refusing silly invitations. No time. Frightfully sorry. Going to be married at

Easter, you know. A lot to do. Ring. Best man. Bridesmaids' presents and all that. Excuse me, old man, I've got to see my tailor. Cheer-frightfully-ho, don't you know.

I couldn't get rid of Leader that way, though. He was horribly hearty and stayed a very long time, and insisted on Lathom's and my going down to the College to see over the labs and 'meet a few of the men', who all hated me at sight, by the way, when they *did* see me. I thought the sooner we got it over the better, so we went this afternoon. Lathom is in one of his vagrom moods – doing no work, and catching at any excuse to waste time. I tried to get out of it, but no! I 'absolutely must come, old man'. I take it the idea was to impress Leader's friends with the idea that men of intellect are proud to know him. It had not occurred to me that best-selling had such idiotic accompaniments.

Leader was in his element, of course, showing off his half-baked knowledge, and exhibiting fragments of anatomy in bottles. I can see Leader one of these days as the principal witness at an inquest, frightfully slapdash and cocksure, professing that he can tell the time of the murder to within five minutes by taking half a glance at the corpse, and swearing somebody's life away with cheerful confidence in his own infallibility. He was highly impressive in the dissecting-room, but at his best, I think, displaying his knowledge of poisons (which, by the way, they seem to keep handy on the open shelves for any passing visitor to help himself to). He was very great on synthetic drugs – all made on the premises out of God knows what, and imitating nature so abominably – abominably well, that is – that chemical analysis can't tell them apart. Indeed, indeed, sirs (and apart from the wearisomeness of Leader), but this troubles me. Synthetic perfumes from coal-tar are bad enough, and synthetic dyes, and I can put up with synthetic camphor and synthetic poisons, but when it comes to synthetic gland-extracts like adrenalin and thyroxin, I begin to get worried. Synthetic vitamins next, I suppose, and synthetic beef and cabbages – and after that, synthetic babies. So far, however, they don't seem to have been able to make synthetic life – the nearest they have got is stimulating frog-spawn into life with needles. But what of the years to come? If, as the bio-chemists say, life is only a

very complicated chemical process, will the difference between life and death be first expressible in a formula and
then prisonable in a bottle?'

This is a jolly kind of letter to write to you, old girl, on
this auspicious occasion, but this everlasting question of life
and the making of life seems to haunt me – and it is, after
all, not so remote from the problem of marriage. We can
pass it on and re-continue it, but what is it? They say now
that the universe is finite, and that there is only so much
matter in it and no more. But does life obey the same rule,
or can it emerge indefinitely from the lifeless? Where was
it, when the world was only a dusty chaos of whirling gas
and cinders? What started it? What gave it the thrust, the
bias, to roll so ceaselessly and so eccentrically? To look forward is easy – the final inertia, when the last atom of energy
has been shaken out of the disintegrating atom – when the
clocks stand still and time's arrow has neither point nor
shaft – but the beginning!

One thing is certain. If I begin to think like this, I shall
never write another best-seller. Heaven preserve us from
random speculation! Our own immediate affairs are as
important as the loves of the electrons in this universe of
infinitestimal immensities, and as far as we are concerned . . .

[The remainder of this letter, being of a very intimate
nature, is not available.]

32. *The Same to the Same*

SMITH'S HOTEL, BLOOMSBURY
25.2.29

DEAREST,
Just a hasty line to say that I have had to leave Whittington Terrace on account of a very unfortunate incident,
which I will tell you about later on. I am here for a few
days till I can get my belongings moved out and ware-
housed somewhere *pro tem.*

It is all extremely tiresome. However, it only means that we shall have to do our house-hunting a little earlier than we expected. I think I had better run up to Kirkcudbright and have a yap with you about it, if I can get away from publishers and agents.

All my love,

JACK

33. *Agatha Milsom to Elizabeth Drake*

15, WHITTINGTON TERRACE, BAYSWATER
25.2.29

DEAR MADAM,

You will probably be very angry at what I am going to say, but I feel it is my duty to warn you against Mr John Munting. Girls do not always know how men go on behind their backs, and it is only right they should be told by those who have had *unfortunate experience* of these men's real character.

You may think that Mr Munting is honourable, but he has been turned out of this house on account of indecent behaviour, and your eyes ought to be opened to his goings-on. You may believe me because I have the best right to speak of what *I know*. I have no doubt he will tell you that this is all false and try to pull the wool over your eyes, but I have *proof* of what I say, and if you should want further evidence you can write to Mr Harrison at this address, and he will tell you that every word is true.

I am sending you this warning for your good, because you ought not to marry a man like that; he is not fit to marry a decent woman. You are young, and you do not know what the consequences may be of marrying a man of depraved habits. This is one incident I can tell you about of my own knowledge, but *there are others*, or why does he so often come in late at night?

Do not tell him I have written to you, as it is not a

pleasant thing to have to do, and naturally I do not care to write or talk about it in detail. But ask him why he was ordered out of the house, and do not believe the excuses he makes, because everybody here knows the truth and could tell it if necessary.

Now for your own sake pay attention to what I say and have no more to do with that disgusting man. I know I shall get no thanks for doing my duty, but in this world one must not expect gratitude. I have already been deprived of my livelihood and made to suffer mental and financial persecution on this man's account. However, I bear no malice, and remain

Your sincere well-wisher,
AGATHA MILSOM

34. *Elizabeth Drake to John Munting*

[Endorsed on the above.]

DEAR JACK,

What on earth is all this about? Is the woman mad?

Yours, in all confidence and love,

E

35. *Telegram from John Munting to Elizabeth Drake, dated* 26.2.29

A little mad and quite mistaken. Do not worry. Am starting North tonight.

JACK

36. *George Harrison to Paul Harrison*

27.2.29

MY DEAR PAUL,

I have to inform you of a most disagreeable incident which has caused a disturbance in our family life, and in consequence of which I have had to turn that man Munting out of the house. It occurred while I was unfortunately obliged to be absent over the Middleshire Electrical Installation, and, but for the accidental intervention of Miss Milsom, Margaret might have been exposed to an annoyance and risk that I shudder to think of.

I was summoned home by an urgent and rather incoherent letter from Miss Milsom, accusing Munting of an indecent assault upon herself. You will naturally understand that I found this rather difficult to believe, since the man (to do him justice) had shown no signs of being actually demented. By the same post I received a letter from Margaret written in great mental distress, and begging me to take no notice of Miss Milsom, on the ground that she was suffering from delusions. Obviously, whatever was the truth of the matter, it was necessary that I should intervene, and I hastened home at once (at a most inconvenient moment of my work, but, fortunately, the greater part of the contract was settled, and Freeman is quite competent to carry on).

On arriving, I immediately interrogated Miss Milsom closely. Her story was that, on the night of the 22nd, at about 12.30, she had felt a sudden craving for sardines (the woman is certainly unbalanced), and had gone downstairs to ransack the larder. She came up again in the dark – knowing the house well she did not trouble to turn on the light – and was just entering her bedroom, which, if you remember, is next to ours, when to her alarm she heard somebody breathing quite close to her. She gave some sort of exclamation and tried to get her hand on the landing switch but encountered the hand of a man. Thinking it was a burglar, she started to scream, but the man gripped at her arm and said in a whisper, 'It's all right, Miss Milsom.' She clutched at his arm, and felt she at once recognised as the

77

sleeve of Munting's quilted dressing-gown, which he frequently wears when doing his writing. She at once asked him what he was doing on her landing, and he mumbled something about fetching some article or other from his overcoat on the hall-stand and missing his way in the dark. She expostulated, and he pulled her away from the lighting-switch, saying, 'Don't make a disturbance – you'll alarm Mrs Harrison. It's quite all right.' She told him she did not believe him, and according to her account, he then made advances to her, which she repelled with indignation. He replied, 'Oh, very well!' and started off upstairs. She went back and turned the light on in time to see the tail of the dressing-gown disappearing upstairs. Thoroughly frightened, she rushed into my wife's bedroom and had an attack of hysterics. Margaret endeavoured to soothe her, and they spent the rest of the night together. The next night, Miss Milsom summoned up courage to remain in her own room, bolting the door. Margaret did the same, and they suffered no further disturbance.

I then questioned Margaret. She was, naturally, very much upset, but thought that Miss Milsom was completely mistaken, and making a mountain out of a mole-hill. She is too innocent to see – what I, of course, saw very plainly – that this shameless attack was directed against herself and not against Miss Milsom. I did not suggest this to her (not wishing to alarm her), and promised to hear Munting's version of the affair before taking any further steps.

I then interviewed Munting. He took the thing in the worst possible way – with a cool effrontery which roused me to the highest pitch of indignation – treated the whole matter as a triviality, and positively laughed in my face. 'The woman is demented,' he said. 'I assure you my tastes do not lie in *that* direction.' 'I never supposed they did,' I answered, and made quite clear to him what my suspicions were. He laughed again, and said I was mistaken. I said I knew very well that I was *not* mistaken, and asked him what other explanation he could offer of being found outside my wife's door in the middle of the night. 'You have heard the explanation,' said he, airily. 'And a very convincing one it is,' said I; 'at least you don't deny that you were there, I suppose?' He said, 'Would you believe me if I did deny it?' I said that his manner had convinced me that the story was true, and that nothing he said would persuade me to the contrary. 'Then it's not an atom of use my denying it, is it?' said he coolly. 'Not an atom,' I said. 'Will you leave the house straight away or wait to be kicked out?' 'If you put it that way,' said he, 'I think it would cause less excitement in the neighbourhood if I went of my own accord.' I gave him half an hour to be out of the house, and he said that would suit him very well, and had the impudence to request the use of our telephone to order a taxi. I told him I would not have him in our part of the house on any pretence whatever. 'Oh,' said he, 'then perhaps you would be good enough to order the taxi yourself.' I did so, in order to give him no excuse for hanging about the place, and he took himself off. On the way downstairs he said, in a more subdued tone, 'Look here, Harrison. Won't you believe that this is all a mistake?' I told him to get out of the house before I sent for the police, and he went without another word.

All this has upset us very much. I am only thankful that no further harm has come of it. Margaret says he had never previously offered her any rudeness, and I believe her; but, looking back on the matter, I can remember occasions when I have not altogether cared for the tone of his conversation. He is too experienced a man in this kind of thing, however, to have shown his hand while I was there. I am only sorry that our friendship with young Lathom whom we all like so much, should have led to this unpleasantness.

Lathom is extremely distressed, as you may imagine. I thought it well to warn him to show more discretion in future with regard to his choice of friends. He was too genuinely horrified and unhappy to wish to talk about the matter; still, I think he was grateful for the advice. Unhappily, this means we shall lose him as well, since his means do not permit of his keeping on the upper maisonette by himself. I suggested that he might stay till the end of the quarter, but he said he was engaged to visit some friends next month, and would be leaving anyway at the end of the week.

This incident has made it very clear to me that Miss Milsom must be got rid of. She is in a state of violent hysteria, and is obviously subject to delusions about herself, and in no way a fit companion for Margaret. I have given her a month's salary in lieu of notice, and sent her home. Out of all this hateful episode this one good thing has come: that I have now a valid reason for insisting on this woman's departure.

Other news has been rather over-shadowed by these anxieties, and must wait till my next letter. I hope all is well with you.

Your affectionate

DAD

37. *Statement of John Munting*

It was a mistake from the very beginning for Lathom and myself to set up housekeeping together. It happened purely by chance – one of those silly, unnecessary chances that set one spinning out cheap platitudes about fatality and the great issues that hang upon an accidental meeting. It used to be considered highly unphilosophical to indulge in speculations about coincidence, still more to base any work of art upon it – but that was in the days when we believed in causality. Now, thanks to the Quantum theory and the second law of thermo-dynamics, we know better. We know that the element of randomness is what makes the Universe go round, and that the writers of sensation novels are wiser in their generation than the children of sweetness and light.

All the same, there still remains an appearance of causation here and there, and I persist in attributing some of the blame to the imbecilities of the public-school system. If Lathom had not worn an old Wincastrian tie, I should never have spoken to him in the little restaurant Au Bon Bourgeois in Greek Street. Or, at the most, I should have asked him to pass the French mustard. As it was, my natural aversion to my fellow-creatures being broken down by Burgundy, I was fool enough to say: 'Hullo! you come from the old school, I see. Did I know you?' – and was instantly swamped and carried away in the flood of Lathom's expansiveness.

Lathom is an incorrigible extrovert. His thyroids and liver function with riotous vigour. He beams out enthusiastically upon the world and is refracted out from everything and everybody he meets in a rainbow of colour. That is his fatal charm. In the ordinary way, I am ill-adapted for prismatic function. That evening was an unfortunate exception. I couldn't keep it up afterwards; that was the trouble.

When Lathom mentioned his name I recognised it at once. He is six years younger than I am, and was an obnoxious brat in the Upper Third when I was preparing for Oxford in the Sixth, but he had penetrated to my Olympian seclusion in virtue of his reputation.

Lathom, of course – Burrage's celebrated fag, who scrounged toasting-forks. He was always in trouble with the other prefects for his apparent inability to distinguish other people's property from Burrage's. If anything was wanted, he took it; if anything had to be done, he did it, regardless of other people's convenience, or, indeed, of his own. He was attached to Burrage, who naturally stood up for him. In fact, I think we were all jealous of Burrage for having a fag so ruthlessly competent. Burrage patronised the kid in his large, appreciative way, and Lathom basked in the rays of Burrage's approval. I don't blame Burrage altogether, but he certainly spoilt Lathom. He protected him from the consequences of his actions. Perhaps Burrage had advanced ideas about the non-existence of causation and imparted them to Lathom. But Burrage was rather an ass, and his reactions were probably more human and immediate.

Lathom was saved from disaster, partly by Burrage and partly by Halliday. Halliday was a great man and captain of the First Eleven. He took things easily and when he said that the kid was just potty we all accepted the explanation. That was on the day of the picnic, when Lathom turned up at feeding-time without his overcoat, and said he had

6

thrown it away because it got in his way. The weather turned to soaking rain and Lathom got pneumonia and nearly died. We were all rather frightened and distressed, and when Lathom turned up next term we made allowances for him. I reminded Lathom that we had called him 'Potty', and he laughed and said we were perfectly right.

I remembered, too, that in those days Lathom had earned a reputation for himself by making caricatures of the masters. This fascinating gift had earned him still more toleration. I was not surprised to hear that he had become an artist. He said he was looking for a studio, and had seen just the thing in Bayswater, only he couldn't afford to take it.

I asked, why Bayswater, of all places? Why not Chelsea or Bloomsbury? But Lathom said no, the rents were too high, and besides, Chelsea and Bloomsbury were hopelessly arty and insincere. They lived at second-hand and had no beliefs. To see life lived in the raw, one ought really to go to Harringay or Tooting, but they were really not central enough. Bayswater was near enough to be convenient and far enough out to be a healthy suburban.

'The suburbs are the only places left,' said Lathom, 'where men and women will die and persecute for their beliefs. Artists believe in nothing – not even in art. They live in little cliques and draw the fashionable outlines in the fashionable colours. They can't love – they can only fornicate and talk. I've had some. And the aristocracy has lost the one belief that made it tolerable – its belief in itself It's fool enough to pretend to believe in the people, and what is the good of an aristocracy playing at being democratic? And the people . . . ' He made a violent gesture. 'Cheap scientific textbooks – cheap atheism – cheap sociology – cheap clothes – your blasted educationists have left them no beliefs at all. They marry, and then the woman comes howling to the magistrate for a separation order on any pretext, so as to get money for nothing and go to cheap dance-halls. And the man goes yelping away for a dole to shuffle all his responsibilities on to the State. But the blessed people of the suburbs – they do believe in something. They believe in Respectability. They'll lie, die, commit murder to keep up appearances. Look at Crippen. Look at Bywaters. Look at the man who hid his dead wife in a bath and ate his meals on the lid for fear somebody should suspect a scandal. My God! Those people are living, living with all their blood and their bones. That's reality – in the suburbs – life, guts – something to chew at, there!'

At the time I was rather struck by this.

It ended, of course, in my consenting to share the maisonette with Lathom. An hour earlier, the very word would have put me off, but under the spell of Lathom's enthusiasm, and stupefied with food and public-school spirit, I began to think there was really something raw, red and lifelike about living in a maisonette with an Old Wincastrian. And perhaps Lathom was right after all. The trouble is that raw, red life is possibly better seen at second-hand. A good still-life of a piece of rump-steak has none of the oozing clamminess of the real thing.

I wish, all the same, that I had tried to play up to Lathom better. It was irritating, of course, to find that he was still regardless of other people's convenience. I did not object to his bagging the best room for his studio – that was in the bond – but it was tiresome to have him overflowing into my room all day when I was at work. Lathom is one of those spasmodic workers who need constant applause and excitement. He would work like fury for several hours, snarling at me if I came in to retrieve a garment or lighter that he had borrowed; but, the fit over, he would wander in to where I was grimly struggling with a knotty piece of biography and talk. He talks well, but his interests are lopsided. He is a real creator – narrow, eager, headlong, and loathing introspection and compromise. He questions nothing; I question everything. I am only semi-creative, and that is why I cannot settle and dismiss questions, as he does, in one burst of inspired insight or equally inspired contempt. Lathom is all light and dark – a Rembrandt. I am flat, cold, tentative, uneasily questioning, a labourer in detail. I caught no fire from Lathom, and I quenched his. It is my disease to doubt and to modify – to be unable to cry at a tragedy or shout in a chorus. It was my fault that I did not help Lathom more, for, just because of my uneasy sensitiveness, I under-

83

stood him far better than he ever understood me. It would have suited him better if I had violently disagreed with him. But I had the fatal knack of seeing his point and cautiously advancing counter-arguments, and that satisfied neither of us. I see this now, and, indeed, I saw it then; it is characteristic of people like me to see a thing and do nothing about it.

This, of course, was where the Harrisons came in. I liked Harrison. If I had not liked him, I should not be making this statement, which is, I am afraid, entirely contrary to the public-school tradition. Harrison was a man of very great sincerity, no imagination and curiously cursed with nerves. It is all wrong for a man of his type to have nerves – nobody believes or understands it. In theory, he was extremely broad-minded, generous and admiringly devoted to his wife; in practice, he was narrow, jealous and nagging. To hear him speak of her, one would have thought him the ideal of chivalrous consideration; to hear him speak to her, one would have thought him a suspicious brute. Her enormous vitality, her inconsequence, her melodrama (that is the real point, I think), got on his nerves, and produced an uncontrollable reaction of irritability. He would have liked her to shine for him and for him only; yet a kind of interior shyness prompted him to repress her demonstrations and choke off her confidences. 'That will do, my dear'; 'Pull yourself together, my girl,' checked a caress or an enthusiasm; a grunt, a 'Can't you see I'm busy,' a 'Why have you suddenly got these ideas about' music or astronomy or whatever the latest interest might be. Into the muffling of his outer manner, her radiance sank and was quenched. Yet to others he spoke with earnest pride of his wife's brilliance and many-sided intelligence.

Harrison's instinct was to dominate, but by nature and training he was unfitted to dominate that particular woman. It could have been done in two ways – by capturing the limelight, or by sheer physical exuberance. But neither of these things was in his power; he was inexpressive and sexually unimaginative, as so many decent men are.

He had his means of self-expression: his water-colours and his cookery. It was his misfortune that in the former he should have been weak, conventional and sentimental, and bold and free only in the latter. I believe, indeed, that all the imagination he possessed ran to the composition of sauces and flavourings. It is surely a matter for investigation whether cookery is not one of the subtlest and most severely intellectual of the arts; else, why do its more refined manifestations appeal to women hardly at all and to men only in their later and more balanced age? Unlike music or poetry or painting, food rouses no response in passionate and emotional youth. Only when the surge of the blood is quieted does gastronomy come into its own with philosophy and theology and the sterner delights of the mind. If Harrison could have made a big public splash with anything, she could have understood that and preened herself happily as the wife of a notoriety. But she had no eyes for the half-lights.

At first it was amazing to me that Lathom showed so much patience with Harrison. Lathom is a barbarian about food and magnificently intolerant of bad painting. Twaddle about Art and Atmosphere got short shrift with him. Yet he let Harrison bore him to any extent with his prattle and his picturesque bits. Harrison did, indeed, treat him with a deference flattering in a man of his age, but under ordinary circumstances that would merely have infuriated Lathom, who, to do him justice, is no drawing-room lion. It was not that Harrison provided the response which I gave so awkwardly. In time I realised that, though I had my selfish reasons for refusing to see it. Mrs Harrison was the radiant prism for Lathom's brilliance, and Lathom used Harrison in that service as carelessly as in the old days he had used the prefects' toasting-forks. He saw the tool ready to his hand and took it, without shame and without remorse.

I have put all this down, as I saw it, without consideration for the feelings of anybody. It is useless to blame people for their peculiarities of temperament. At the time I did not interfere, because, to tell the truth, I was working hard and involved in my own concerns, and did not want to be bothered with Lathom's affairs. Besides, I rather prided myself on a cynical detachment in such matters. As it turns out, I should have done far better to preserve this cheerful selfishness throughout. That I did not was again due to sentimentality and public-school spirit, and I am heartily ashamed of it.

I suppose I must say something about Mrs Harrison. It is difficult, because I both understood and disliked her. Just because she had no use for me, I was detached enough to see through her. I have not the superb and centralised self-confidence that could strike the colours from her prism. I come back to that image, because it expresses her with more accuracy than any description. My diffusion left her dead glass. But in Lathom's concentration she shone. He gave her the colour and splendour her dramatic soul craved for. She saw herself robed with all the glowing radiance that dazzled her half-educated eyes in the passionate pages of Hichens and de Vere Stacpoole. I hardly think she was wicked – I do not think she had any moral standards of her own. She would adopt any attitude that was offered to her, provided it was exciting and colourful enough. I think she had enjoyed herself at her office; she had radiated there in the little warmth of popularity which always surrounds people of abundant physical and emotional vigour, but at home she had only the devotion of Miss Milsom, with her warped mind and perilous preoccupations. She visualised herself into the character of a wronged and slighted woman, because that was the easiest way to evoke clamorous response from Miss Milsom – and, of course, from Lathom when he came along.

It is rather surprising, I feel, that Harrison was never jealous of Lathom, as he was of every other man, including myself. I fancy it was because he looked on Lathom as his own friend, primarily. Now I come to think of it, it was of his wife's personal life that he was jealous – her office, her interests, the friends she had made for herself – everything that had not come to her through him. My position was different. He distrusted me because of my work and opinions. I had written an unpleasant book and I had no definite moral judgements. From such a man, nothing but impropriety could be expected. He was wary and uneasy in my presence. He could talk food with me, and did, but only, I think, in despair for want of other appreciation. He was fearfully lonely, poor soul, and I failed him miserably. And he was jockeyed by me into letting his wife's picture be shown at the Academy – but only because he thought I was belittling his wife's character. His change of mind was a chivalrous rush to her defence. I was pleased with myself at the time, I remember; I suppose my light-hearted diplomacy was about as disastrous as diplomacy usually is. What devilish things we do when we try to be clever. After all, Harrison probably understood his wife only too well, but he could not bear that anyone should suspect the clay of his idol. He destroyed himself rather than let her down. I rather think that Harrison had something heroic behind his primness and his gold spectacles.

There was one thing which I ought most certainly to have left severely alone, and that was the final disaster, in which Miss Milsom was concerned. For once I was seized with the idiotic whim to play the martyr and the noble-spirited friend. At the very moment when my reasonable and deliberate policy of detachment should have come to my aid, I must choose to take the centre of the stage and indulge in high-mindedness.

Lathom woke me up. He came and sat on my bed, and I noticed with irritation that he had been borrowing my dressing-gown again. He always took things.

'I'm in a mess,' he said.

'Oh?' said I.

He told me what had happened. I have seen Miss Milsom's account. It is accurate in all points but one. Far from repulsing Lathom, she had encouraged him. He had broken from her at the foot of the staircase with considerable difficulty. He was filled with a righteous disgust, which struck me as funny under the circumstances.

'Disgusting old woman,' said he.

'True,' said I. 'None should have passions but the young and the beautiful. What are you going to do? Serve with Leah seven years in the hope of getting Rachael in the end?'

'Don't be filthy,' said he. 'There will be a row about this, I'm afraid.'

'Very likely,' said I. 'But that is your affair.'

'Not altogether,' said Lathom. 'You see, she thinks it was you.'

'Me?' I was considerably taken aback.

'Yes. You see, I had your dressing-gown – '

'So I observe.'

'She recognised the feel – the quilting, you know – damn it all, she rubbed her ugly face in it – '

'Really.' I said, 'the kittenish old creature.'

All the same, I was not pleased. Gestures which delight in the right person are so indecent when performed by the wrong. In fact, it is only when we contemplate the loves of unpleasant people that we see the indecency of passion. It is disgusting to think of the amorous transports of, let us say, Mr Pecksniff. Grotesque characters only exist for us from the waist upwards.

'I suppose,' I went on, 'it didn't occur to you to mention that you were not me?'

'I didn't say anything. I got away. I didn't want to make a noise. In fact...'

In fact, he had made use of me cheerfully enough, and was now wondering whether I should put up with it.

'Look here,' I said, 'what do you intend to do? If you want to carry on an intrigue with Mrs Harrison, I tell you, frankly, I'm going to get out and leave you to it. It bores me and I don't care about these alarms and excursions. Anyhow, why didn't you leave the woman alone? You're doing her no good.'

Then he exploded and started to tramp about. She was the greatest miracle God had ever made. They were meant for one another. They had got into each other's blood and all the rest of it. That, of course. Equally, of course, if Harrison had been a decent sort of man he would have sacrificed his own feelings. (As if Lathom had ever thought of sacrificing anything.) But Harrison was a brute, who did not appreciate the wonderful woman who had been entrusted to him. Lathom could suffer himself, but he could not bear to see her suffer. It was all so damned unjust. The man was not fit to live. He deserved to be murdered for his rotten paintings, let alone for his cruelty to his wife. And to think that his revolting hands should have the right . . .

And so on.

It is so very odd that in moments of excitement we should all talk like characters in a penny novelette. However long one lives, I suppose it always strikes one with the same shock of surprise.

'That'll do,' I said at last. 'We can take that as read. If Mrs Harrison feels as you do about it – '

He interrupted me to assure me at unnecessary length that she did.

'Very well,' I said, 'why not do the decent and sensible thing and take her away? You won't find this kind of back-stairs intrigue permanently inspiring, you know. Besides, it seems to be the kind of thing you do very badly.'

'I wish to God,' replied Lathom, 'that I could take her away. Heaven and earth, man, do you think I wouldn't do it like a shot if I had half a chance? But she won't hear of it. She's got some poisonous idea about not making a scandal. It's this damned awful suburban respectability that's crush-ing the beautiful life out of her. When you see what she was meant to be – free and splendid and ready to proclaim her splendid passion to the world – and then see what this foul blighter has made of her – '

'Well, there you are,' said I. 'That's the raw, red life of the suburbs, as per specification. That's what you came here for, isn't it? Look here, Lathom, buzz off and let me get to sleep, there's a good chap. You can blow your feelings off in the morning.'

'Oh, all right.' He got up from the bed and hesitated at the door. 'I only thought I'd warn you,' he added, a little awkwardly, 'in case the old woman says anything to you.'

'Dashed good of you,' I said dryly. 'What am I to do? Make love to the confidante while you make love to the mis-tress, and go stark mad in white linen?'

'Oh, you needn't bother to do that,' said he. 'I should just treat the whole thing as a joke. Or, if she makes a fuss, apologise and say you were a bit screwed. I'll back you up.'

I was so infuriated with him for shoving the responsibility on to me in this light-hearted way that I told him to clear out, which he did.

As a matter of fact, I rather under-estimated the seriousness of the thing. I mean, I did not realise the lengths to which Miss Milsom's resentment might go. I determined merely to avoid the woman in future, and, in fact, treat the whole episode as if it hadn't occurred. I thought Lathom had received a salutary shock and useful lesson on the difficulties attending suburban love affairs, and that he might bethink himself and stop the whole thing before it had gone too far. A good thing, too. I was clearing out and getting married at Easter, and there, so far as I was concerned, was an end of it. Lathom could fish it out for himself after that. My book had made a sudden success, and I was feeling rather cock-a-hoop with myself.

Consequently, I was quite unprepared for the arrival of Harrison with his accusation. He was dead-white with fury and intensely quiet. He did not offer me a single opening by scattering his usual fiery particles of rage. He put the accusation before me. Such and such things had been stated – what had I to reply? I tried to dismiss the thing with airy persiflage. He was not abashed by my assumption of ridicule. He simply asked whether I denied being on the landing at that time, and, if not, what I was doing there. When I refused to answer so absurd an accusation, he told me, without further argument, to leave the house. His wife must not be subjected to any kind of disagreeable contact. The mere fact that I could take such an attitude to the matter (and, indeed, my attitude had nothing dignified about it) showed that I was an entirely unsuitable person to come into any sort of contact with Mrs Harrison. He was there to protect her from persons of my sort. Would I go quietly or wait to be removed by force?

The deceived husband is usually considered to be a ridiculous figure, but Harrison was not ridiculous. Sometimes I wonder whether he was deceived. I thought at the time that he was, but perhaps the light of faith in his eyes was really the torch of martyrdom. It is fine to die for a faith, but perhaps it is still finer to die for a thing you do not believe in. I do not know. He baffled me. If the garrison was disarmed and beaten behind that impenetrable façade, I was never to know. Nobody would ever know it.

It is ironical that Lathom, coming to Surburbia to find

raw, red life, should have failed to recognise it when he saw it. It was there, all right, in this dry little man, with no imagination beyond beef-steak and mushrooms, but it did not wear bright colours, and Lathom liked colours. The thing was farcical. And I believe I was the most farcical fool in the whole outfit. Even then, the mocking censor which views one's personality from the outside sat sniggering in a corner of my brain. Here was I, a successful novelist, presented with this monstrous situation – one which was quite in my own line of work, too – and I hadn't even had the wits to see it coming. The thing was a gift.

I could see myself tackling it, too, in quite the right modern, cynical way. No nonsense. No foolish shibboleths about honour and self-sacrifice. A lucid exposure of the situation – an epigram or so – a confrontation of Harrison (as representing the old morality) with the unsentimental frankness of the new.

And the damnable thing was that I didn't do it. When it came to saying, 'My good man, you are mistaken. My friend Lathom is the man you ought to be after. He and your wife are carrying on a love affair, for which you are largely to blame, if, indeed, any blame attaches to these unsophisticated manifestations of natural selection' – when it came to the point, I didn't say it. Looking at Harrison, I couldn't say it. I behaved like a perfect little gentleman, and said nothing whatever.

After that, I can only suppose that I became quite intoxicated by this new and heroic view of myself. I went straight off to Lathom and told him about it. I oozed priggishness. I said:

'I have stood by you. I have kept silence. I have agreed to leave the house at once. But I will only do it if you will promise me to chuck the whole business – clear out at the same time that I do. Leave these people alone. You have no right to ruin the life of this decent man and his wife, who were getting along quite well in their way till you came along.'

I grew solemn and portentous about it. I enlarged on Harrison's sufferings. I painted a vivid picture of the miseries the woman must needs undergo in the course of a secret love-affair. I called it vulgar. I called it wicked and selfish. I used expressions which I thought had perished from the vocabulary since the eighties. And I ended by saying:

'If you do not promise me to do the decent thing, you cannot expect me to stand by you.' Which was mere blackmail.

There must be more of the old inhibitions alive in even the most modern of us than one would readily credit. Lathom was actually abashed by my eloquence. He protested at first; then he grew sulky; finally, he was touched.

'You're quite right, old man,' he said, 'damn it. I've been behaving like a cad. I couldn't make her happy. I ought to go away. I will go away. You've been damned decent to me.' He wrung my hand. I clapped him sentimentally on the shoulder. We wallowed in our own high-mindedness. It must have been a touching sight.

The first disagreeable consequence of this foolish interference with the course of events arrived in the shape of a letter from my fiancée. Miss Milsom had felt it her duty to send one of those warnings. I dashed up to Scotland to put matters right. The greatest compliment I can pay to the open mind and generous common sense of Elizabeth is to say plainly that I had no difficulty about doing this. But I was reminded with a slight shock that Victorian quixotry has a way of landing one in complications. However, no harm appeared to be done, and later I received a letter from Lathom, dated from Paris, in which he informed me that he was playing the game (the words were proof in themselves of the conditions to which I must have reduced him), and that, after a highly emotional scene, Mrs Harrison and he had agreed to part.

I got married soon after that, and forgot all about Lathom and the Harrisons – the more so as Elizabeth did not encourage me to dwell on the subject. A natural jealousy, I thought, particularly as she had not seemed altogether impressed by my quixotic gesture. But women are unconquerable realists, and nowadays they are not taught to flatter male delusions as they once were. It is uncomfortable to think that perhaps our repressed Victorian ancestresses were as clear-sighted as their franker granddaughters. If so, how they must have laughed, as they made their meek responses. In this century we do know, more or less, what they are thinking, and meet them on equal terms – at least, I hope we do.

I was reminded of Lathom by receiving my ticket for the Private View at the Academy on May 3rd. We had had our honeymoon, and were ready to return to our place in the world. Almost the first thing I saw, as we surged through the crowd, was the painted face of Mrs Harrison, blazing out from a wall full of civic worthies and fagged society beauties, with the loud insistence of a begonia in a bed of cherry-pie. There was a little knot of people in front of it, and I recognised Marlowe, the man who paints those knotty nudes, and created a sensation two years ago with 'The Wrestlers'. He was enjoying his usual pastime of being rude to Garvice, the portrait-painter. His voice bellowed out over the din, and his black cloak flapped gustily from a flung-out arm. 'Of course you don't like it,' he boomed lustily, 'it kills everything in the place dead. That's none of your damned art – that's painting – a *painting*, I tell you.' Several pained people, who had been discussing values in low tones, shrank at the unseemly noise, and dodged waveringly from the sweep of his hairy fist. 'None of you poor pimples,' went on Marlowe, threateningly 'can *see* colour – or thickness – you're only fit to colour Christmas cards at twopence a hundred. There isn't a painter in the whole beastly boarding-house crowd of you except this chap.' I will do Marlowe the justice to say that, except where nudes are concerned, he is singularly generous to the younger men. He glowered round through his bush of beard and spectacles, and caught sight of me. 'Hullo, Munting!' he bawled. 'Come here. Somebody said you knew this fellow Lathom. Who is he? Why haven't you brought him round to see me?'

I explained that I had only just returned from my honeymoon, and introduced Marlowe to my wife. Marlowe roared approval in his characteristic way, and added:

'Come along on Friday – same old crowd, you know, and

93

bring this man Lathom. I want to know him. He can *paint*.'

He spun round to face the picture again, and the crowd retired precipitately to avoid him.

'Well,' said a man's voice, almost in my ear, 'and how do you think it looks, now it's hung?'

I spun round and saw Lathom, and with him, before I could adopt any suitable attitude to the situation, Mr and Mrs Harrison, flung up from the waves of sightseers like the ball from a Rugby scrum.

Retreat was hopeless, because Marlowe now had me tightly by the shoulder, while with his other hand he sketched large, thumby gestures towards the portrait to indicate the modelling and brushwork.

'Hullo, Munting!' said Lathom.

'Hullo, Lathom!' I said, and added nervously, 'Hullo-ullo-ullo!' like something by P. G. Wodehouse.

'Good God!' exploded Marlowe, 'is this the man? The man and the model, by all that's lucky,' he bellowed on, without waiting for my embarrassed answer. 'I'm Marlowe; and I say you've done a good piece of work.'

Lathom came to my rescue by making a suitable acknowledgement of the great man's condescension, and I was sliding away with a vague bow and a muttered remark about an engagement, when I felt a tap on the shoulder. It was Harrison.

'Excuse me one moment, Mr Munting,' said he.

A row in the Academy would have its points from the point of view of my Press agent, but I was not anxious for it. However, I asked Elizabeth to wait a moment for me, and stepped aside with Harrison.

'I think,' said he, 'I am afraid – that is, I feel I owe you an apology, Mr Munting.'

'Oh!' I said. 'That's all right. I mean, it doesn't matter at all.' Then I pulled myself together. 'I'm sorry,' I said, 'it's my fault, really. I ought not to have come. I might have known you would be here.'

'It's not that,' he said, determined to face it. 'The fact is – I fear I did you an injustice that – er – that last time we met. Er – the unfortunate woman who made all the trouble –'

'Miss Milsom?' I asked; not because I didn't know, but to help him on with his sentence.

'Yes. She has had to take a rest – in fact, to undergo a course of treatment – in fact, she is in a kind of nursing-home.'

'Indeed?'

'Yes. There can really be no doubt that the poor creature is – well, demented is perhaps an unkind way of putting it. Perhaps we had better say, unbalanced.'

I expressed sympathy.

'Yes. From what my wife tells me – and Mr Lathom – and from what I hear from the poor creature's relatives, I now feel no doubt at all that the – the accusation, you know – was entirely unfounded. A nervous delusion, of course.'

'Yes, yes,' said I.

'I quite understand, of course, your very chivalrous motives for not putting the blame on her at the time. The position was most awkward for you. You might perhaps have given me a hint – but I perfectly understand. And my wife, you will realise, was so very much upset – '

'Please,' I broke in, 'do not blame her or yourself for a single moment.'

'Thank you. It is very kind of you to take it in this reasonable spirit: I cannot say how much I regret the mis-understanding. I hope you are very well and prosperous. You are quite a famous man now, of course. And married. Will you do me the honour to present me to your wife? I hope you will come and see us some day.'

I was not keen to make the introduction, but it could scarcely be avoided. The preposterous situation was there, and had to be imagined away. Mrs Harrison glowed. For the first time I saw her in full prismatic loveliness, soaked and vibrating with colour and light. I asked her what she thought of the show.

'We haven't seen much of it yet,' she said, laughing, 'we came straight to see *the* picture. Is it going to be the picture of the year as they call it, do you think, Mr Munting?'

'It looks rather like it,' said I.

'Fancy that! It does make me feel important – though, of

course, I don't count for anything, really. The painting is the thing, isn't it!'

'The subject of the portrait counts for something, too,' said Elizabeth. 'I don't see how anybody can make a picture of one of those cow-faced people. Except a satirical one, of course. It's the painter's job to get the personality on the canvas, but what is he to do if there is no personality? Mr Lathom . . . '

She looked at the portrait, and then at Mrs Harrison, and something seemed to strike her. It was the thing that had struck me, months before, when I first saw what Lathom had made of it. She grew a little confused, and Lathom struck in.

'Mrs Harrison and you would agree about the importance of subject-matter,' he said. 'I can't persuade her to admire Laura Knight.'

Mrs Harrison blushed a little.

'I think they are very clever pictures,' she said, a trifle defiantly, and with a side-glance at her husband, 'but they are rather peculiar for a woman to have painted, aren't they? Not very refined. And I mean, they are so unnatural. I'm sure people don't walk about, even in their bedrooms, like that, with nothing on. And I think pictures ought to make one feel – uplifted, somehow.'

'Come, come, Margaret,' said Harrison, 'you don't know what you are talking about.'

'But you said the same thing yourself,' she came back at him.

'Yes, but I don't care about your discussing them here.'

'Oh!' said Marlowe, loudly, 'you are afraid of the flesh. That is our trouble – we are all afraid of it, and that is why we insist and exaggerate. *"Hoc est corpus,"* said God – but we turn it into hocus-pocus. There's no hope for this generation till we can see clean flesh and "sweet blood" – Meredith's phrase – without being shocked at its fine trouble-someness. If one were to strip all these people now' – he waved a hand at a fat man in a top-hat and an emaciated girl, who caught his eye and stood paralysed – 'you would think it indecent. But it's not as indecent as the portrait-painter who strips their souls for you. Some men's work would be publicly censored, if the powers knew how to distinguish between flesh and spirit – which, thank God, they don't.' He clapped Lathom on the shoulder. 'How about that other thing of yours, my boy?'

Lathom laughed a little awkwardly.

'Is that the portrait of Miss Milsom?' I interrupted, hastily – for I saw trouble coming up like a thunder-cloud over Harrison's horizon. 'We must go and have a look at it. You're doing pretty well to have two pictures in such a crowded year. We mustn't keep you too long. Which room is it in, Lathom?'

He told us, and when we had said our farewells, pursued us into the next room.

'I say, old man,' he whispered breathlessly, 'I couldn't really help this. Couldn't in decency get out of it, could I?'

'No,' said I, 'I suppose you couldn't. It's not my funeral, anyhow.'

'It's the first time we've met,' he went on, 'and it will end here.'

'But for my damned interference it wouldn't have begun here,' I answered. 'I'm not blaming you, Lathom. And I've really no right to make conditions. I don't think it's wise – but I can't set up to be a dictator.'

'Oh, you admit that, do you?' said Lathom. 'I'm rather glad to know it.' He hesitated, and added abruptly, 'Well, so long.'

I was thankful to see the end of the episode. From every point of view it seemed advisable to drop all connection with Lathom and the Harrisons, and I saw none of them again until the 19th of October.

38. *Margaret Harrison to Harwood Lathom*

May 4th, 1929

PETRA DARLING,

Oh, how wonderful it was, darling, to see you again, even

under the Gorgon's eye – such a cold stony eye, darling, and
with all those people around. I had been dead all through
those dreadful months. When you went away, I felt as if the
big frost had got right into my heart. Do you know, it made
me laugh when the pipes froze up in the bathroom and we
couldn't get any water and He was so angry. I thought if
he only knew I was just like that inside, and when the terrible numb feeling had passed off, something would snap in
me, too. Was that a foolish thing to think, Petra? Not a
very poetical idea, I am afraid, but I wished I could have
told it to you and heard your big, lovely laugh at your
Darling Donkey!

Oh, Petra, we can't go on like this, can we? I couldn't
go through those long, long weeks again without seeing or
hearing you, not so much as your dear untidy writing on an
envelope. And, darling, it was so dreadful to hear you say
you couldn't work without your Inspiration, because your
work is so wonderful and so important. Why should He
stand between you and what God meant you to do? The life
we live here is so cramped and useless; the only way I can
fulfil any great purpose is in being a little help in your
devine work of creation. It is so wonderful to know that one
can really be of use – part of the beauty you make and
spread all about you. It isn't even as if I counted for anything in *His* work. A woman can't be an inspiration for an
electrical profit and loss account, or a set of estimates, can
she? He doesn't think so, anyway. He just wants to have
me in a cage to look at, darling – not even to love. He
doesn't care or know about love – thank God! I say now,
because I can keep myself all for my own marvellous Man.
Oh, I have so much to give, so much, all myself, such as I
am – not clever, darling, you know I am not that, though
I love to hear about clever, interesting things – but loving
and real, and *alive* for you, only you, darling, darling Petra.
I never knew how much beauty there was in the world till
you showed it to me, and that's why I feel so sure that our
love must be a *right* thing, because one could not feel so
much beauty in anything that was wrong, could one? Fancy
going on living for years and years, starved of beauty and
love, when there is all that great treasure of happiness wait-

ing to be taken. Oh, darling, he was going on at dinner last night about how his grandfather lived to be a hundred, and his father about ninety-four, and what a strong family they were, and I could see them, going on year after year, grinding all the happiness out of their wives and families and making a desert all round them, just as He does. I looked up Gorgons in a book, darling, and it said they were immortal, all except the one Perseus killed, and I'm sure they are, darling, the stony horrors. Sometimes I wish I could die. Do you think they would let me come and be near you after I was dead? But I know you think we don't live after we are dead, but just turn into flowers and earth again. It does seem much more likely, doesn't it, whatever the clergymen say – so I suppose it would be no good me dying, would it? Just think – only one life, and to be able to do nothing with it – nothing at all, and then just die and be finished. It makes me shudder. It's all so cold and dreary. What right have people to make life such a wasted, frozen thing? Why are they allowed to live at all if they don't *live* in the true sense of the word? And life can be such a great thing if it is really *lived*. Oh, Pet darling, thank you for having taught me to live, even if it was only for a few short, wonderful weeks! When I'm all alone (and I'm always alone, nowadays, not even poor Aggie Milsom to talk to now), I sit and try to read some of the books you told me about. But I stop reading, and my mind wanders away, and I'm just living over again the hours we had together, and the feel of your dear arms round me. Sometimes he comes in and finds me like that, and scolds me for letting the fire out and not putting the light on. 'You're always mooning about,' he says, 'I don't know what you think you're doing.' Oh, darling, if he only did know, how angry he would be and how wicked he would think me in his ugly little mind!

Dear one, you won't leave me all alone again, will you? We said we would try to forget one another, but I think you knew as well as I did how impossible it was. Well, we have tried, haven't we, and we've found it is no good. You thought it would be better for me, but it isn't. I feel far, far more miserable than I did, even in the days when we were seeing each other and trying to keep down all the things we were thinking and feeling together. I would rather suffer the awful pain of seeing and wanting you, than feel so dead and empty, as if my heart had been all drained out of me, beloved. And I know now that it is just as bad for you, because you can't do your work without me, and your work ought to come first, darling, even if you have to mix your paints with my heart's blood.

Darling, if you think it's better we shouldn't be real lovers don't leave me altogether. Let us see each other sometimes. It doesn't matter even if the Gorgon is there and we have to talk the silly meaningless tea-party talk. Our real selves will be saying the real things to one another all the time, and we can look at one another and be a little bit happy. I can *feel* with my eyes, can't you, darling? When you met us yesterday and stood there with that absurd top-hat in your hand – it was so funny to see you in that stiff, formal morning dress, but you looked very splendid and it made me so proud to think you were really all mine and no one knew it – well, when I saw you, I could feel in all my fingers, darling, the queer lovely feel of your hair that first day – do you remember – when you put your head on my knees and broke down and said you loved me. Such a dear head, darling, all rough and crisp, and strong, splendid bones under it, full of wonderful thoughts. If I shut my eyes I can feel it – I'm doing it now darling. Shut yours – now, this minute – and see if you can't feel my hands. Did you, Petra darling – did you feel all the love and life in them? Tell me when you write if you can feel me as I feel you!

You will write, darling, won't you? You will spare me that little ray at least from the great fire of your life and love. Don't leave me all in the dark, Petra, and I'll be content with whatever you give me. Everything has been so ghastly that I haven't got it in me to be exacting, dear.

Always your own, only, for ever,

LOLO

39. *The Same to the Same*

June 6th, 1929

PETRA, MY DARLING, MY DEAR, DEAR MAN DARLING,

Oh, my dearest, isn't it terrible to see the summer coming, and to feel so wintry and lonely. Your letters have been a help, but what wouldn't I give for you yourself, the real you!

You will tell me again that I'm not telling the truth. That I don't really love you because I won't give up being conventional and respectable and go away with you, but it isn't that, Petra darling. You think in your dear, impetuous way that it would all be so easy, but it wouldn't really, darling. You think that because you are a man, and you don't consider how awful it would be, day after day, all the sordidness and trouble. It wouldn't really be fair to make you go through all that. Even if He would let me go – which, of course, he wouldn't, because he is so selfish – it would be a long, drawn-out misery. I know how horrid it is because I know a woman who got her divorce. Of course, her husband took all the blame, but it was a miserable time for everybody, and she and her man friend had to go right away, and he gave up his post, a very good post, and they are living in quite a slummy little place in rooms, and don't even get enough to eat sometimes.

Anyway, the Gorgon would *never* consent to me divorcing him, because he prides himself on being very virtuous and proper, and he would probably have to leave his firm or something. He would never do that. He thinks more of his firm than of anything in the world – far more than he does of me or my happiness, which he has never considered at all from the day he married me.

Doesn't it seem too awful that one has to pay so heavily for making a mistake? I keep on thinking, if only I hadn't married him. If only I were free to come to you, Petra darling – what a wonderful time we could have together! But then I think again that if I hadn't married him, I should never have lived here, never met you, and oh, darling, what could make up for that? So I suppose, as they say in the nature-books, that He has 'fulfilled his function' in bringing us together. I looked at him last night as he sat glooming over the mutton, which wasn't quite done as he likes it (you would never let a stupid thing like mutton poison the whole beautiful day for you, but he does), and I thought of Mr Munting saying once, 'All God's creatures have their uses,' when Miss Milsom had made me one of her lovely scarves – and I said to myself, 'If only you could know, my dear Gorgon, what is the one thing in our lives I thank you for!' That would really have given him something to gloom about, wouldn't it?

It is so funny – he is always asking when you are coming to see us again. His Cookery Book is going to be published in a few weeks' time, and he is ridiculously excited about it. He thinks it is a great work of art, and is going to send you a copy as from one artist to another. Wouldn't that make a good reason for you to call on us, if you could get over to England? It is clever of you to be able to find so many things to say about his silly little water-colours – you who are a really great painter (I have learnt not to say artist now. Do you remember how impatient you were with me when I called you 'artistic'? We nearly had a quarrel that day. Fancy us quarrelling about anything – now!).

It makes me sad, Petra darling, to think of my poor lonely Man so far away, wanting his Lolo. And I'm a little frightened, too, when I think of all the beautiful ladies in Paris. I expect they think a lot of you, don't they? Do you go to a great many fashionable parties? Or do you live the student-life I used to read about and think how gay and jolly it must be? You don't tell me very much about the people you see and the places you go to. I wish you weren't a portrait-painter – you must have so many opportunities to find someone more beautiful than your poor Lolo and so much cleverer. Don't say they aren't more beautiful than I am, because I shall know you aren't telling the truth. I'm not really beautiful at all – only when I had been with you I sometimes used to look in the glass and think that happiness made me *almost* beautiful, sometimes. I have been reading in a book about the real Laura and Petrarch – did you know, she was really only a little girl and that he hardly saw her at all? Perhaps she was only beautiful in his imagination, too. But that didn't prevent her from being his inspiration, did it? I wonder if you are the same. Perhaps I inspire you better from a distance. I don't think a woman *could* feel like that. She wants her Man always, close to her. Darling, do say you want me to like that, too.

I must stop now. The Gorgon will be wanting its tea. I am living just like a hermit now. I never go anywhere and I try to do all I can to keep him in good temper, for fear he should get the idea that there is Somebody Else in my life. How dreadful it would be if he suspected anything. He is fairly reasonable now, except when his food isn't quite right. But oh! I am so lonely.

Darling, I love you so much I don't know what to do with myself. I have kissed the paper twenty times where your dear, darling name is. You must kiss it, too, and think you are kissing your own, your absolutely ownest own.

LOLO

40. *The Same to the Same*

14th June, 1929

DARLING,

Your letter hurt me so dreadfully, I cried and cried. Oh, Petra, you can't love me at all, or you wouldn't say such awful things. You can't really think that if I love you I ought to let *him* divorce *me*. Darling, do think how horrible it would be! How could I go through all that terrible shame in public, and all my friends looking on and thinking hateful things about our beautiful love! At least, I suppose I could go through with it – one can go through all kinds of agonies and still live – but that you should *want* me to do it – that you could think of your Lolo in such a sordid way – that's what hurts me, darling. You used to say you wanted to stand between me and trouble, and couldn't bear to think of anything ugly touching our pure and lovely passion. And yet now you want to smirch me with the stain of the divorce courts and see my name in the papers for people to snigger at. Oh Petra, it's absolutely clear you don't really love me one bit.

You couldn't feel the same to me, Petra, I know that, if I came to you all dirtied and draggled from an ordeal like that. Just think of having to stand up in the witness-box and tell the judge all about our love. It would all sound so different to their worldly, coarse, horrible minds, and our love would seem just a vulgar, nasty – I don't like to write the word they would call it, even to you – instead of the pure, clean, divine thing it really is.

Darling, I'm not thinking of myself – I'm thinking of you and our love. I don't want a single spot to touch it. It would be better to suffer all our lives as we are suffering now – as *I* am suffering, for sometimes, Petra, I don't think you suffer at all – rather than to look at each other with the shadow of an ugly scandal between us. You don't understand. You don't realise what a difference these things make to a woman. It does not make any difference to a man, but even you would see the stain on me for ever afterwards, and would turn against me.

Tell me you don't really mean it, darling. There must be some other way out. Let us think very hard and find out. Or if you really think so little of me, tell me so, and we will say good-bye again – for always, this time. I expect I was wrong to stick to our agreement before. You wanted to be released then, and you wouldn't have asked it if you hadn't been tired of me already in your heart. Let's end it all, Petra. Perhaps I shall die, and then you will be free. I feel unhappy enough to die – and if I'm too strong for wretchedness to kill me, there are always easy ways out of it all.

Your heart-broken

LOLO

15, WHITTINGTON TERRACE
30th June, 1929

DARLING, DEAR PETRA, MY DEAREST,

Of course I do forgive you. It's you really that must forgive me for saying such awful things. I didn't mean them. I knew really, deep down in my heart, that you loved me all the time. Of course I couldn't say good-bye – it would kill me – Yes, I meant that part of it.

But you do see now, don't you, that we can't take that way out. For my sake, you say, darling, but, indeed, I could bear anything for myself – only I don't want to spoil the lovely thing we have made. We will do just as you say, wait for a year and see if anything happens. It may, if we only want it enough. God might make a miracle to help us. Such things have happened before now. He might even die – 'in him Nature's copy's not eterne' – doesn't somebody say that in a play somewhere? We used to go and see Shakespeare sometimes when I was at school, and do the plays in class, though I didn't pay much attention to them then. I didn't understand what a difference art and poetry make to one's life. I was waiting for you to come and teach me, my dear.

I am going to do some really solid reading now, to try and be more worthy of my darling when the happy time comes. (I must believe there will be a happy time, or I should go mad.) This year of waiting shall be a year of self-development. That will make the desolate days pass more quickly. Goodness knows I shall have time enough, for He never lets me go out anywhere or have any of my own friends to see me. The only people I ever have to talk to are his friends from the office. They talk about bridges and electrical plant interminably. I don't know how people can live with such petty, dull things taking up all their minds. Sometimes one or two of them have the graciousness to ask me if I have seen the latest play or film, but I never have, and I just have to sit and smile while He says, 'We're quiet, domestic people, my wife and I; we don't care about this night life.' And if I ever suggest going out, he pretends that I want to be 'gadding round' in night-clubs at all hours. I am ashamed of being so ignorant of the things everybody is talking about. Other husbands take their wives out. But no – if I want to stir out of doors, I'm a bad woman – 'one of these modern wives who don't care for their homes'. What kind of place is my home, that I should care about it?

I have got that book you were talking about, *Women in Love*. It is very queer and coarse in parts, don't you think, and rather bewildering, but some of the descriptions are very beautiful. I don't understand it at all, but it is thrilling, like music. That bit about the horse, for instance. I can't quite make out what he means, but it is terribly exciting. What funny people Lawrence's characters are! They don't seem to have any ordinary lives, or have to make money or run households or anything. That woman who is a schoolmistress – she never seems to have to bother about her work, one would think it was all holidays at her school. I suppose the author means that the humdrum things don't really count in one's life at all, and I expect that is true, only in actual life they do seem to make a lot of difference.

Oh, I do hate this cramping life – always telling lies and smothering up one's feelings. But tyrants make liars. It is what somebody I read about in the papers calls 'slave-psychology'. I feel myself turning into a cringing slave, lying and crawling to get one little scrap of precious freedom – a book, a letter, a thought even – and carrying it off into a corner to gloat over it in secret. That is the way in which I am learning to build up an inner life for myself, a lovely, secret freedom, so that the things He says and does can't really hurt me any longer. The real Me is free and happy, worshipping in my hidden temple with my darling Idol, my own dear Petra darling.

How I do love you! My starved life is full when I think of you – brimmed with joy and inward laughter. And one day, perhaps, we shall come out of the dark catacombs and build our temple of Love in the glorious sunlight, with the golden gates wide open for all the world to see and marvel at our happiness.

Yours, beloved, yours utterly and completely,

LOLO

I love to write the name you call me by – the name that is only yours. Such a silly name it would sound to people who didn't know what it mean. *He* uses the name other people use – just like an uncle or something. That's all he is – a sort of Wicked Uncle in a fairy-tale. I can bear him better if I think of him just as that.

42. *The Same to the Same*

15, WHITTINGTON TERRACE
18th July, 1929

DARLING, DARLING,

I hardly know how to breathe for joy! To know that I shall see you, hear your dear voice, hold your hand again! He heard me singing in the kitchen this morning and asked what I was yowling about. I should have liked to tell him. Think of his face if I had said: 'My lover is coming home and I am singing for joy!' I said meekly that I was sorry if it disturbed him, and he said in his courteous way that it didn't matter to him if I liked to hear the sound of my own voice, but the girl would probably think I was mad. I said I didn't care what the girl thought of me, and he answered: 'That's just the trouble with you. You don't care. You're right up in the air.' So I am – so I am! Right above the clouds, Petra darling, up in the golden sunlight, where nothing can touch me. He's quite right for once, if he did but know it.

Darling, we must be very careful when you come. I don't know how I shall manage to keep the happiness out of my eyes and voice. But he won't notice – he never notices how I'm feeling. Besides, he will monopolise you with his precious book. It's really out at last, and he's clucking over it like a hen that's laid an egg. People say to me: 'So your husband has written a book, Mrs Harrison. So clever of him. Fancy a man knowing such a lot about cooking! What exciting meals you must have. Aren't you afraid he'll poison himself sometimes with those queer toadstools and things?' And I smile and say, 'Oh, but my husband would never make a

107

stupid mistake. He knows so much about them, you see.'
That's quite true, too. He doesn't make mistakes about
things – only about people. He never gets anything right
about me – not one single thing. But then he really *cares*
about mushrooms and takes trouble to study them.

I wonder how his first wife put up with him. She was a
homely sort of person, from all accounts – the sort that are
good housekeepers and mothers and all that. I think, if I'd
ever had a child I could have been happier, but he has
never given me one, and doesn't seem to want to. I'm glad
of that now – since I met you. It would be terrible to have
his child now – it would seem like a sort of treason to you,
beloved. Don't be afraid, dearest. He never touches me – you
know what I mean – and I wouldn't let him. I don't let
him even give me his usual morning peck if I can help it.
I don't refuse, of course – that would make him suspicious
at once. I just happen to be busy and keep out of his way.
He's glad, I think, because he always used to grumble at any
demonstration and say, 'That'll do, that'll do' – though he'll
let the cat swarm all over him and knead bread on his
chest for hours together. I suppose he thinks a woman's
feelings don't matter as much as a cat's!

But I don't know why I bother about him at all, when
you, you, you are the one thing filling my heart. Oh, my
darling, my Petra, my heart's heart! You are coming back.
Nothing else is of importance in the whole world. The sun's
shining and everything is happy. I went out to do some shopping today – silly, trivial things for the house – and I could
have kissed the bread and the potatoes as I put them into
my basket, just for joy that you and I and they exist in the
same world together! Petra, beloved, you and I, you and
I – oh, darling, isn't it wonderful!

Your happy

LOLO

15, WHITTINGTON TERRACE
August 2nd, 1929

PETRA, OH, MY DEAR!

Oh, darling, never say now that the luck isn't on our side sometimes. Something even bigger than luck, perhaps. That we should save that last, wonderful evening out of the wreck – so perfect, so unspeakably wonderful – our evening of marvellous love. Just think – that it should be your last night, and that he should be called out suddenly like that, and ask you, himself, not to go before he got back. And even then, if it hadn't been the girl's night out, we shouldn't have been safe. But it was, by such incredible luck, Petra mine.

Do you know, there was a moment when I was frightened. I thought, for a horrible minute, that he had suspected something after all, and had only pretended to go out, and would come slinking back on purpose to catch us. Did that occur to you? And were *you* afraid to say anything, lest *I* should be frightened? I was. And then, quite suddenly, I felt certain, absolutely *certain* that it was all right. We were being watched over, Petra. We had been given that great hour – a little bit of eternity, just for you and me. God must be sorry for us. I can't believe it was sin – no one could commit a sin and be so happy. Sin doesn't exist, the conventional kind of sin, I mean – only lovingness and unlovingness – people like you and me, and people like him. I wonder what Mr Perry would say to that. He is just crossing the road now to Benediction, as he calls it. He thinks he knows all about what is right and what is wrong, but lots of people think his candles and incense wicked, and call him a papist and idolater and things like that. And yet, out of his little, cold, parish experience, he would set himself up to make silly laws for you, darling, who are big and free and splendid. How absurd it all is! He preached such a funny sermon the other day, about the Law and the Gospel. He said, if we wouldn't do as the Gospel said, and keep good for the love of God, then we should be punished by the Law.

And he said that didn't mean that God was vindictive, only that the Laws of Nature had their way, and worked out the punishment quite impartially, just as fire burns you if you touch it, not to punish you, but because that is the natural law of fire.

I am wandering on, darling, am I not? I only wondered what kind of natural revenge Mr Perry thought God would take for what he would call our sin. It does seem so ridiculous, doesn't it? As if God or Nature would trouble about us, with all those millions and millions of worlds to see to. Besides, our love is the natural thing – it's the Gorgon who is unnatural and abnormal. Probably that's *his* punishment. He denies me love, and our love is Nature's revenge on him. But, of course, he wouldn't see it that way.

Oh, darling, what a wonderful time these last weeks have been. I enjoyed every minute. I have been so happy, I didn't know how to keep from shouting my happiness out loud in the streets. I wanted to run and tell the people who passed by, and the birds and the flowers and the stray cats how happy I was. Even the Gorgon being there couldn't spoil it altogether. Do you remember how angry he was about *The Sacred Flame*? And you were holding my hand, and your hand was telling mine how true and right it was that the useless husband should be got out of the way of the living, the splendid wife and her lover and child. Darling, I think that play is the most wonderful and courageous thing that's ever been written. What right have the useless people to get in the way of love and youth? Of course, in the play, it wasn't the husband's fault, because he was injured and couldn't help himself – but that's Nature's law again, isn't it? Get rid of the ugly and sick and weak and worn-out things, and let youth and love and happiness have their chance. It was a brave thing to write that, because it's what we all know in our hearts, and yet we are afraid to say it.

Petra, darling, my lover, my dearest one, how can we wait and do nothing, while life slips by? The time of love is so short – what can we do? Think of a way, Petra. Even – yes, I'm almost coming to that – even if the way leads through shame and disgrace – I believe I could face it, if there is no other. I know so certainly that I was made for you and that you are all my life, as I am yours.

Kiss me, kiss me, Petra. I kiss my own arms and hands and try to think it's you. Ever, my darling, your own

LOLO

44. *The Same to the Same*

15, WHITTINGTON TERRACE
5th Oct., 1929

'Oh, Petra, I am so frightened. Darling, something dreadful has happened. I'm sure – I'm almost quite sure. Do you remember when I said Nature couldn't revenge herself? Oh, but she can and *has*, Petra. What shall I do? I've tried things, but it's no good. Petra, you've *got* to help me. I never thought of this – we were so careful – but something must have gone wrong. Petra, darling, I can't face it. I shall kill myself. He'll find out – he must find out, and he'll be so cruel, and it will all be too terrible.

Petra, I was so desperate I tried to make him – don't be angry, Petra – I mean, I tried to be nice to him and make him love me, but it wasn't any good. I don't know what he will do to me when he discovers the truth. Darling, darling, do *something* – anything! I can't think of any way, but there must be one, somehow. Everybody will know, and there will be a frightful fuss and scandal. And even if we got a divorce, it wouldn't be in time – they are so slow in those dreadful courts. But I don't expect he would divorce me. He would just smother it all up and be cruel to me. I don't know. I feel so ill, and I can't sleep. He asked me what was the matter with me today. I'd been crying and I look simply awful. Petra, my dearest, what *can* we do? How cruel God is! He must be on the conventional people's side after all. Do write quickly and tell me what to do. And don't, don't be angry with me, darling, for getting you into this trouble. I couldn't help it. Write to me or come to me – I shall go mad with worry. If you love me at all, Petra, you must help me now.

LOLO

45. *Statement of John Munting*
[Continued.]

The next news I had about the Harrisons was about the middle of October, 1929, when I got a note from Lathom, written, rather unexpectedly, from 'The Shack, Manaton, Devon'. He said that he was staying with Harrison, who was having his annual 'camp' among the water-colour 'bits' and the natural food-stuffs. Harrison, it appeared, had been so pressing that he really had not known how to refuse, especially as he was really feeling rather played-out after several months' strenuous work in Paris. After the unbearable hot and prolonged summer, the prospect of pottering about a bit among the lush grass and deep lanes of Devon had seemed attractive, even when coupled with the boredom of Harrison's company. 'As a matter of fact,' he added, 'the old boy is not so bad when you get him in the country by himself. This is the kind of life that really suits him. As a family man he is a failure, but he quite comes out and blossoms doing the odd bits of work about the shack. And he certainly is a first-class cook, though up to the present I have successfully avoided his nettle-broth and stewed toadstools, not wishing to be cut off in my youth. This is a pretty place – miles away from everywhere, of course, stuck down on a circumbendible lane which runs down from Manaton (half a dozen houses and a pub) to the deep valley which separates the Manaton Ridge and Becky Falls from Lustleigh Cleave. The only neighbours are the sheep and cows – an old ram walked into the kitchen the other day. Harrison was grunting over the stove and didn't see him at first. "Be-hey-hey," says the ram; "Eh-heh-heh," bleats Harrison, looking up; and damn it, he was so exactly like the old fellow that he wanted nothing but a pair of horns to complete the resemblance! We wash the crockery, and then Harrison takes his newest superfine painting-box, with the collapsible legs and all the rest of it, and trundles away into the valley, where he sits all day in a gorse-bush, trying to put the tumbling of the stream on paper. The drought has dried it up a good bit, but never was anything so desiccated as the arid little plan of it he produces with pride for me to see, painted with a brush with three hairs in it – peck, peck, scratch and dab – like a canary scrabbling for seed. Why don't I take the opportunity to do some work in this glorious place? No, thanks; I'm a figure and portrait wallah – besides, I've come here for a rest. It is not mine to sing the stately grace – I smoke my pipe in the doorway, drive the cattle out of the back garden, and see that the stewpot doesn't boil too fast.

'So here I am, in comfortable exile with Menelaus, while Helen sits at home and sews shirts. And it's a better way, too. One mustn't take these things too seriously. Damned if Harrison hasn't got the right idea after all. Look after the grub and leave women to their own fool devices. They give a man no peace. You, being married, have perhaps got your house in order. Do you find it as easy to do your work, now that you're hooked up to a whirlwind? But, of course, your whirlwind works too, and helps to turn the mill-wheel, which no doubt makes all the difference.'

Lathom went on in this strain for a page or so. Cynicism from him was something new, and I took it to spell restless-ness of some sort or other. Either, I thought, he was getting fed up with the lady's exactions, or the trio had arrived at a *modus vivendi*. It was no affair of mine.

He ended up by saying that he would be running up to town in a day or two and would look me up. I was then living in Bloomsbury – in fact, in my present house – and my wife was away with her people. I had arranged to go with her, but at the last moment an urgent matter turned up – an Introduction to an anthology, which had to be rushed out in a great hurry before some other publisher got hold of the idea, and I had to stay behind to get the thing fairly going, as it meant a good deal of work at the British Museum.

When Lathom turned up at about one o'clock on the 19th, I explained this to him and apologised for having no lunch to offer him. Like most men, and women, too, when left to themselves, I found solitary meals uninspiring. So, appar-ently, did 'the girl', whom, till my wife left me, I had imagined to be a good cook. Not that I had ever expected Elizabeth to leave her writing to see after my meals, so I can only suppose that her moral influence was enough to make the difference between roast mutton and raw.

Lathom commiserated me, and we went and had some grub at the 'Bon Bourgeois'. He seemed to be in high spirits, when he thought about it, but had a way of going off into fits of abstraction which suggested nerves or preoccupation of some kind. He asked about the anthology and my work generally with apparent interest, and then, to my surprise, broke suddenly into my description of the plot of my new novel by saying:

'Look here, if the wife's away, why don't you come down to the Shack with me for the weekend? It'll do you good, freshen you up and all that.'

'Good heavens,' I said, 'it's Harrison's place. He won't want me.'

'Oh yes, he'd love to have you. Oh, rather. In fact, he only said to me yesterday, when I was starting off, he wished I could bring you back with me. He's quite forgotten all that misunderstanding. He's rather distressed about it, really. Thinks he did you an injustice. Would like to make it up. He says you must be harbouring resentment, because you've been in town all this time and haven't been to see them.'

'That's nonsense,' I said. '*You* know why I've thought it best to keep out of it.'

'Yes, but he doesn't. Naturally he thinks you're offended.'

'Didn't you tell him I was busy?'

'Of course. Oh, yes. Played up the popular literary man for all it was worth. So he said, of course you were too important nowadays to remember your old friends.'

'Damn it,' I said, 'what a tactless devil you are, Lathom. You needn't have hurt his feelings.'

'No, but look here. Why not come down? It'll please the old boy no end, and as neither of the women will be there, there won't be any awkwardness. It's a damned good opportunity for being civil to him without involving your wife.'

'Civil is a good word for it,' I objected. 'I don't know that it's particularly civil to plant myself on the man like that, and make him feed me and so on, without notice, when

114

he probably doesn't want me. Just at the weekend, too, when it's difficult to get extra supplies.'

'Oh, that doesn't matter,' said Lathom, 'we'll take some grub down with us. I was going to in any case. Everything has to be brought out there by a carrier twice a week. Frightful desolate hole. We'll take a bit of beef and a couple of pounds of sausages. That'll see us through all right.'

I considered it.

'I say,' said Lathom, suddenly. 'Do come, old man. I wish you would. It's all right there, you know, but I do get a bit bored at times. I'd like to have a yap with somebody who talks my language.'

'If you're fed up,' I said reasonably, 'why do you stay?'

'Oh, well – I promised I would, don't you see. It's not bad really, but it would do us both good to have a bit of a change.'

'Now, look here, Lathom,' said I, 'I don't like the idea particularly. I'm not particularly puritan' (I don't know why one uses that phrase – I suppose it is easier to disown one's decencies when one represents them as something grotesque in a black suit and steeple-hat), 'but considering the way you behaved to Harrison, I think it's rather thick to go and push your friends on to him. What you do is your own business' (looking back on it, I seem to have extracted a great deal of satisfaction from this original thought), 'but it's rather different for me.'

'Punk!' said Lathom. 'That's all absolutely over. Finished. Washed out. It's you who keep on digging it up again. Can't you forget it and come down and help me out with old Harrison?'

'Why so keen?'

'Oh, I'm not particularly keen. I thought you'd like it, that's all. It doesn't matter. What are you doing this afternoon? B.M. again?'

I said, no; I avoided the Reading Room on Saturday afternoons, because it was so crowded, and asked him about his work.

He talked about it a little, in the same vague way as before, saying how difficult it was to settle to anything, and displaying some irritability with his sitters of the moment. His triumph at the Academy had made him fashionable, and fashionable women were all alike, it seemed; small-minded and featureless. One might as well paint masks. All of which I had heard so often from other painters that I put Lathom down as already spoilt.

I suggested that he should stay up in town and do a show with me, but he said he was fed up with shows. He had only come up to see his agent, and was catching the 4.30. Why didn't I change my mind and come with him?

It ended in my changing my mind, and going. I hardly know why, except that I was only six months married and my wife was away, which, to the well-balanced mind, is no good reason for idle behaviour.

The express ran us down in smooth, stuffy comfort, and reached Newton Abbot dead on time at 9.15. I cannot say – though I have tried – that I remembered any particular incident on the way down. I hate talking on railway journeys, anyway, and Lathom did not seem very conversational. I read – it was Hughes's *High Wind in Jamaica* – an overrated book, I think, considered as a whole, but memorable for that strange and convincing description of the earthquake. The thick heat and silence, and then the quick, noiseless shift of sea and shore, like the tilting of a saucer. Good, that. And the ghastly wind afterwards. And the child, not realising that anything out of the way had happened, because nobody gave the thing its proper terrifying name. That is very natural. I do not care for the part about the pirates. It is an anti-climax.

I know we dined on the train, but railway meals are seldom memorable. Lathom grumbled, and left his portion half-eaten, and I said something about his acquiring a taste for hedgehog-broth and stewed toadstools – some silly remark which he took as a deadly insult.

At Newton Abbot we changed into the local, and dawdled through Teigngrace, Heathfield and Brimley Halt, taking over half an hour about it, till we were turned out, twenty minutes late, on the platform at Bovey Tracey. It was a quarter-past ten and dark, but the smell of the earth came up pleasantly, with a welcome suggestion of rain in the air. I stood on the platform, clutching an attaché case in one hand and the bag with the beef and sausages in the other, while Lathom transacted some occult business with a man outside. Then he came back, saying briefly, 'I've got a man to take us,' and we stumbled out to where an aged taxi thrummed mournfully in the gloom. Lathom bundled in, and I parked my bags at his feet.

'What the devil's that?' he said crossly.

'The grub, fathead,' said I, following him in.

'Oh, yes, of course, I'd forgotten,' he said. 'Come on, let's get going, for God's sake!'

Being used to Lathom, I ignored his irritability. We jolted off.

The taxi had a churchyard smell about it, and I mentioned the fact. Lathom slammed the window down with an impatient grunt. I remarked, foolishly, that he didn't seem very enthusiastic about the trip. He said:

'Oh, don't talk so much.'

It seemed to me that the prospect of seeing Harrison again had rather got on his nerves, and I looked forward to an exasperating week-end.

'*Vous l'avez voulu*, Georges Dandin,' I reflected, and lit a cigarette resignedly. The narrow road heaved and sank between dark hedges, but climbed on the whole, wriggling determinedly up and round to the ridge. A dim light or so and a cluster of black roofs announced civilisation, and Lathom roused himself to say: 'Manaton – there's a good view from here by daylight.'

'We shan't be long now, then, I suppose,' said I.

He did not reply, and I suddenly became aware that I could hear him breathing. Once I had noticed it, I couldn't seem to shut my eyes to the sound. It was like hearing your own heartbeats in the night – when they seem to grow louder and louder, till they fill the silence and keep you from going to sleep. The breaths seemed quite to rasp my ear, they were so heavy and so close.

'Eh!' said Lathom, unexpectedly. 'What did you say?'

What had I said? It must have been ages ago, for Manaton was well behind us now, and the car was nosing her broken-winded way steadily down and down, with deep cart-ruts wringing her aged bones. I recollected that I had said

I supposed we shouldn't be long now.

'Oh, no,' said Lathom. 'We're nearly there.'

We bounced on in silence for ten minutes more; then creaked to a standstill. I put my head out. Dim fields, trees and the tinkling of a distant stream coming remotely up on a puff of south-west wind. No light. No building.

'Is this it?' I asked, 'or has the engine conked?'

'What?' said Lathom, irritably. 'Yes, of course this is it. What's the matter? Push along – we don't want to stay here all night.'

I wrestled with the door and edged out. Lathom close at my heels. He paid the driver, and the car began to move off, lurching on down the slope to find a place to turn.

'Here!' said I; 'have you got the beef?'

'Oh, hell,' said Lathom, 'I thought you had it.'

I plunged after the taxi, reclaiming the food, and came back to where Lathom was standing. His hurry seemed to have left him. He was striking a match and having a little trouble with it. The car, a hundred yards off, choked, crashed its gears, burbled, choked again, burbled, choked, and came thudding up on bottom gear. It passed us, labouring and bumping, moved up into second, hesitated into top, and its red rear light vanished, showed, jerking, vanished and span slowly skywards.

'Ready?' said Lathom.

I did not point out that I had been patiently waiting for him to make a move, but grasped the bags and followed.

'We've got a field to cross,' he explained, holding a gate open for me.

We staggered along for a little. Then he stopped and I bumped up against him.

'Over there;' he said.

I looked, and saw a patch of extra darkness, between the darkness of some tree-stems.

'There's no light,' I said. 'Is he expecting you? I hope he won't be annoyed with me for coming.'

'Oh, he won't be annoyed,' said Lathom, shortly. 'He's gone to bed, I expect. Early bird. Up with the lark and down with the sun and all that. It doesn't matter. We can forage round for ourselves.'

A few more minutes, and we stood at the door of the shack. You know what it's like – indeed, all England knows by now – a low, two-roomed cottage, ugly, built of stone, with a slate roof. Only one story – what in Scotland they call a but and ben. The windows were unshuttered, but not a spark of light showed through them – no candle, not so much as the embers of a fire.

Lathom gave an ejaculation.

'He must have gone to sleep,' he muttered. I was fumbling for the handle of the door, but he pushed me aside, and I heard the latch click open. He paused, staring into the dark interior.

'I wonder if he's gone wandering off and got lost somewhere,' he said, hesitating on the threshold.

'Why not go in and see?' I countered.

'I'm going to.' He stepped in and the unmistakable rattle of matches in the box told me that he was getting a light. He was clumsy about it, and only after several futile scratches and curses did the small flame flare up; he held it high, and for a moment I saw the living-room – a kitchen-table cluttered with crockery, a sink, an empty hearth, and a jumble of painting gear, clumped in a corner. Then the match flickered and burnt his fingers, and he dropped it, but made no effort to strike another.

'Juggins!' said I, defiantly, for this cheerless welcome was getting on my nerves. 'Here – isn't there a candle or anything?'

I hunted through my pockets for a petrol lighter. This gave a steadier light, by which I found and lit a bedroom candle on a bracket just behind the door. The untidy room leaped into existence again. I set the candle down on the table, beside the sordid remnants of a meal. A chair lay overturned on the floor. I righted it mechanically and looked round. Lathom was still standing just inside the door, with his head cocked sideways, as though he were listening.

'Well, I'm damned,' said I, 'this is very cheerful. If Harrison – '

'Listen a minute,' he said, 'I thought I heard him snoring.'

I listened, but could hear nothing except a tap dripping into the sink.

'Looks to me as if he'd gone out,' I said. 'How about starting the fire up? I'm chilly. Where's the wood?'

'In the basket,' said Lathom, vaguely.

I investigated the basket, but it was empty.

'Oh, well,' I said, 'let's have a drink and get to bed. If Harrison comes in later, you'll have to do the explaining.'

'Yes,' said Lathom, eagerly, 'Good idea. Let's have a drink.' He wandered about. 'Where the devil's he put the whisky?' He flung open a cupboard door, and groped about, muttering.

At this point a thought occurred to me.

'Would Harrison go out and leave the door unlocked?' I said. 'He's a careful sort of fellow as a rule.'

'What?' Lathom's head emerged for a moment from the cupboard. 'No – no – I should think he would lock up.'

'Then he must be about somewhere,' I said. We had been talking almost in whispers – I suppose with the idea of not disturbing the sleeper, but now I lost patience.

'Harrison!' I shouted.

'Shut up!' said Lathom. 'He must have left the whisky in the bedroom.' He picked up the candle and plunged into the inner room.

The shadows parted and flowed in after him as he went, leaving me in darkness again. His footsteps shuffled to a halt and there was a long pause. Then he spoke, in a curious, thick voice with a catch in it, like a gramophone needle going over a crack.

'I say, Munting. Come here a minute. Something's up.'

The inner room was in a sordid confusion. My hurrying footsteps tripped over some bedclothes. There were two beds in the room, and Lathom was standing by the farther of the two. He stepped aside, and his hand shook so that the candle-flame danced. I thought at first that the man on the bed had moved, but it was only the dancing candle.

The bed was broken and tilted grotesquely sideways. Harrison was sprawled over it in a huddle of soiled blankets. His face was twisted and white and his eyeballs rolled up so that only the whites showed. I stooped over him and felt for

120

his wrist. It was cold and heavy, and when I released it it fell back on the bed like dead-weight. I did not like the look of the nostrils – black caverns, scooped in wax – not flesh, anyway – and the mouth, twisted unpleasantly upwards from the teeth, with the pale tongue sticking through.

'My God!' I cried, but softly – and turned to look at Lathom, 'the man's dead!'

'Dead?' He was looking at me, not at Harrison. 'Are you sure?'

'Sure?' I put a finger beneath the fallen jaw, which woodenly resisted me. 'Why, he must have been dead for hours. He's stiff, man, stiff!'

'So he is, poor old b—' said Lathom.

He began to laugh.

'Stop that,' I said, snatching the candle away from him, and dumping him roughly down on to the other bed. 'Pull yourself together. You want a drink.'

I found the whisky with some trouble. It was on the floor, under Harrison's bed. He must have grasped at it in his struggles and let it roll away from him. Fortunately, the cork was in place. There was a tumbler, too, but I did not touch that. I fetched another from the living-room (Lathom cried out not to be left in the dark, but I paid no attention), and poured him out a stiff peg, and made him swallow it neat. Then I stood over him as he sat and shuddered,

'Sorry, old man,' he said at last. 'Silly of me to make an ass of myself. Bit of a startler, isn't it? But your face – oh, Lord! – if you could have seen yourself! It was priceless.'

He began to giggle again.

'Don't be a fool,' said I. 'We've got no time for hysterics. Something's got to be done.'

'Yes, of course,' he said. 'Yes – something must be done. A doctor, or something. All right, old man. Give me another drink and I'll be as right as rain.'

I gave him another small one and took some myself. That seemed to clear my mind a little.

'How far are we from Manaton?'

'About three miles, I think – or a little over.'

'Well,' I said, 'I suppose somebody there will have a telephone, or can send a messenger. One of us had better get along there as fast as possible and get on to the police.'

'Police?'

'Yes, of course, you ass. They've got to know.'

'But you don't suppose there's anything wrong about it?'

'Wrong? Well, there's a dead man – that's pretty wrong, I should think. He must have died of something. Did he have a heart, or fits, or anything?'

'Not that I know of.'

I surveyed the distasteful bed again.

'It looks more as though – he'd eaten something – '

I stopped, struck by an idea.

'Let's look at the things in the other room,' I said. Lathom jumped to his feet.

'When I left him he said something about fungi – he was going to get some special kind – '

We went out. In a saucepan on the table was a black, pulpy mess. I sniffed it cautiously. It had a sourish, faintly fungoid odour, like a cellar.

'Oh, Lord,' whimpered Lathom, 'I knew it would happen some day. I told him over and over again. He laughed at me. Said he couldn't possibly make a mistake.'

'Well, I don't know,' I said, 'but it looks rather as if he had. Poor devil. Of course, it would happen the very day there was nobody here to help him. I suppose he was absolutely on his own. Didn't any tradesmen call, or anything?'

'The carrier comes over on Mondays and Thursdays with supplies,' said Lathom, 'and takes the orders for the next visit.'

'No milkman? No baker?'

'No. Condensed milk, and the carrier brings the bread. If there's nobody in he just puts the things on the window-sill.'

'I see.' It seemed to me pretty ghastly. 'Well,' I went on, 'will you go or shall I?'

'We'd better both go, hadn't we?'

'Nonsense.' I was positive about this. I don't know why, except that it seemed damnable, somehow, to leave Harrison's body alone, when leaving it could do no possible harm. 'If you don't feel fit to go, I will.'

'Yes – no!' He looked about him uneasily. 'All right, you go. It's straight up the hill, you can't miss it.'

I took up my hat, and was going, when he called me back.

'I say – do you mind – I think I'd rather go after all. I feel rather rotten. I'll be better in the fresh air.'

'Now look here,' I said firmly. 'We can't stay shilly-shallying all night. If you don't like staying in the house, you'd better go yourself. But make up your mind, because the quicker we get on to somebody the better. Get the police and they'll probably be able to find a doctor. And you'll have to give them Mrs Harrison's address.'

'I hadn't thought of that. Yes – I suppose – I suppose – they'd better break it to her.'

'Somebody's got to. It's a beastly business, but you don't know any relations you could get hold of, do you?'

'No. Very well. I'll see to it. Sure you won't come with me? You don't mind staying?'

'The sooner you go, the shorter time I'll have to stay,' I reminded him.

'Right-ho!' He paused, appeared about to say something, then repeated 'right-oh!' and went out, shutting the door behind him.

Three miles uphill in the dark – it would take him close on the hour, certainly. Then he had to knock somebody up, find a telephone, if there was one, get on to the police – say half an hour for that. Then, it all depended whether there was an available car in the village – whether he came straight back, or waited for the officials, who would come, presumably from Bovey Tracey. I need not, I thought, expect anything to happen under a hour and three-quarters or so. I suddenly remembered that I was cold, and started to hunt for kindling. I found some, after a little search, in an outhouse. The fire consented to light without much persuasion, and after that, and when I had found and lighted two extra candles, I began to feel in better condition to take stock of things.

A bottle of Bovril on the mantelpiece presented itself to me with helpful suggestiveness. I took up the kettle to fill it at the tap. A glance at the sink nearly turned me from my intention, but I conquered the sudden nausea and drew my water with care. Impulse would have flooded the repulsive evidences of sickness away, but as the phrase flashed through my mind the word 'evidence' asserted itself. 'I must preserve the evidence,' I said to myself, and found myself subconsciously taking note that this trifling episode went to prove – as I had always believed – that Anatole France was right in supposing that we always, or at any rate usually, think in actual words.

The Bovril and the psychology together restored my self-confidence. I began to reconstruct Harrison's manner of death in my mind. He was quite stiff. I tried to remember what I had read about *rigor mortis*. One thinks one knows these things till it comes to the point. My impression was that rigidity usually set in about six or seven hours after death, and that it began in the neck and jaw and extended to the limbs and trunk, going away in the same order, after an interval which I could not remember. I braced myself up to go back to Harrison and feel him again. The jaw was rigid, the limbs still fairly flexible. It seemed to me, then, that he must have died some time that morning. I could not quite recollect by what train Lathom had said he had come to town, but, presumably, whenever it was, he had left Harrison fit and well. It was now getting on for midnight on Saturday. Say Harrison had been dead six hours – what then? I had no idea how long fungus-poisoning – if it was fungus-poisoning – took to act. Presumably, it would depend on the amount taken and the state of the victim's heart.

What meal was it whose remains lay on the table? I looked into the cupboard. In it there was a large cottage-loaf, uncut. On the table was another from which a couple of slices or so seemed to have been taken. Thursday, Friday, Saturday, Sunday. If two loaves represented four days' allowance before the carrier called again, the suggestion was that the last meal had been taken some time on the Thursday Say Harrison had finished up the old loaf on Thursday morning, the remains probably represented Thursday's midday or evening meal. The cupboard also contained about a pound of shin of beef, still in the paper in which the butcher had wrapped it, and smelling and looking rather on the stale side, a dried haddock, and a large quantity of tinned food. The meat was not 'off', but the blood had dried and darkened. It looked as though the carrier had left it on his Thursday's visit. Evidently, therefore, Harrison had been alive then to take it in. But since he had not cooked it, I concluded that he must have been taken ill some time on the Thursday night or Friday morning.

Pleased with these deductions, I reasoned a little further. How soon after the meal had the trouble started? He had not cleared the table. Was he the kind of tidy man who clears as he goes? Yes, I thought he was. Then the illness had come on fairly soon after the meal. The chair which had stood before the used plate was now lying on its side, as though he had sprung up in a hurry and knocked it over. Searching about on the floor, I came upon a pipe, filled, and scarcely smoked. There was a cup, half-filled with coffee. I began to see Harrison, his supper finished, his chair pushed back against the edge of the rug, his pipe lit up, lingering over his after-dinner coffee. Suddenly he is gripped with a spasm of pain or nausea. He jumps up, dropping his pipe. The chair catches the edge of the carpet and falls over as he makes a dash for the sink. He clings to the edge of it and is horribly sick. What next?

I took up the candle and went out into the little yard at the back of the house, where there was the usual primitive country convenience. It occurred to me, as I pursued my sordid investigations, that the lot of coroners' officers, policemen, doctors and detectives was much more disagreeable than sensational fiction would lead one to suppose. I soon had enough of the yard and came in again.

After that – the bedroom, I supposed. And whisky, of course. Pain and exhaustion would call for spirits. Well, I knew where I had found the whisky and the tumbler. Then more sickness – by that time he had been too bad to move. Then – I did not like the look of the broken bedstead. How did one die of fungus-poisoning? Not peacefully, I supposed. There was no peace in that twisted body and face. How long had the agony of delirium and convulsion lasted. It must be a damnable thing to die in so much pain, absolutely alone.

I did not like these ideas. I took a sheet from the other bed, and laid it gently over Harrison's body, being careful to disturb nothing. Then I went back and sat by the fire.

At about half-past two, I heard voices outside, and opened the door to Lathom, a police-sergeant, and a man who was introduced as Dr Hughes of Bovey Tracey. He was a brisk and confident middle-aged man, and brought an atmosphere of reassurance along with him.

'Oh dear, yes,' he said, 'I'm afraid he's quite dead. Been dead for seven or eight hours, if not more. How very unfortunate!' He drew a pair of forceps from his pocket and rolled up the dead eyelids delicately. 'Mmm! The pupils are slightly contracted – looks as if your diagnosis might be correct, Mr Lathom. Poisoning of some kind seems indicated. No tablets? Glasses? Anything of that sort?'

I produced the tumbler from under the bedclothes, and explained about the whisky-bottle.

'Oh, yes. Here, Sergeant – you'd better take charge of these.'

'The whisky is all right,' I volunteered. 'At least, we both had some about three or four hours ago, without any ill effects.'

'That was rash of you,' said Dr Hughes, with a sort of grim smile. 'We'll have to impound it, all the same.'

'The mushrooms are in here, doctor,' said Lathom, anxiously.

'Just a moment. I'll finish here first.' He felt and flexed the body, and looked it over carefully. 'Was this bed like this when you left him? No. Broken in a convulsion, probably. Yes. All right, Sergeant, you can carry on here. I shall want the body and these bedclothes taken down to the mortuary, just as they are. And any other utensils – '

Lathom pulled my arm. 'Let's clear out of this,' he urged. I stood my ground. Something – either inquisitiveness or the novelist's greed for copy – impelled me to hang about and get in the way.

The doctor finished his investigations and covered the body up again.

126

'Now then,' he said, 'that's about all I can do for the moment. Where's this saucepan you were telling me about? Oh, yes. Fungus of some sort, obviously, but I can't say what by looking at it. That will all have to go to London, Sergeant. When the Superintendent comes he'll see the things packed up. I'll give you the address they're to go to. Sir James Lubbock, the Home Office Analyst – here you are, and you'll see they telephone him to expect them, won't you?'

'Yes, sir.'

'What will you do, Sergeant? Hold the fort here till they send down to relieve you?'

'Yes, sir. The Superintendent will be here very soon, sir, I expect. They've called him up.'

'Very well. Now I'd better be off. I'm wanted for a baby case. You'll find me at Forbes's place if you want me. Lucky I hadn't started. I don't for a moment suppose anything will happen for hours, but it's her first, and they're naturally fidgety. If I don't get there pronto, it'll be B.B.A., out of pure cussedness, and I shall never hear the last of it. Well, good-night. Sorry I can't give anybody a lift, but I'm going out in the opposite direction.'

He hastened out, and we heard his car chug away down the lane. The sergeant observed that it was a bad business all round, and suggested that he should take down notes of what Lathom and I could tell him. I found some logs in an outhouse and piled them on the fire till it roared up the chimney. More and more I began to feel this was a scene from a book; it was like nothing in life at all. It was – hang it – it was almost cosy. I should have ended, I think, by almost enjoying it – the policeman's voice cooing like the note of a fat wood-pigeon, the ruddy blaze on his round face, the thick thumb that turned the pages of his notebook, the pink tongue licking the stubby pencil, and Lathom, talking, answering, explaining so lucidly (he had got over his nervousness and was childishly eager to tell his story) – I could have enjoyed it, if it had not been for a fear in the back of my mind.

The sun . . .

You do not want a description of that stiff, cold sunrise.

127

I was facing the window, and saw it – first a whiteness, then a hardening of the skyline – then a bluish reflection on the ceiling – then an uncertain gleam under the blanket of cloud. The weather was going to change.

I got up and wandered out across the fields. The stream, far off, was the only voice in the silence, and that was impersonal. It had no blood nor life behind its chatter.

I wandered to the edge of the slope, where the valley plunged down, gorse and heath and bracken all jumbled among the grey boulders, and looked across to where the huge tors humped their granite shoulders over the heights of Lustleigh Cleave. They looked grim enough.

What I was wondering was just this: Had Harison ever guessed about his wife and Lathom? What had Lathom said to him in those long, solitary days? Had Harrison decided that his best way out was to clear out from the place where he was not wanted? I knew that, for all his irritating mannerisms, the man had a sterling unselfishness in him – and it would have been so easy for him – with his knowledge – to make a mistake on purpose when he was gathering fungi.

Would anyone choose a death so painful? Well – a man only the other day had committed suicide by pouring petrol over his clothes and setting himself on fire. And nothing could be made to appear more natural than this poison-death of Harrison's. Why had Lathom been so anxious for me to come down with him? Had he had doubts about his reception? Had he expected something? Had Harrison – possibly – agreed, promised, even hinted that Lathom might return to find the way clear? Or had Lathom spoken some shattering word – shown irrefutable evidence – and left the facts to do their bitter work?

A cock crew in the valley. A sheep said 'Baa!' just behind me, so that I started and laughed. This kind of thing was morbid, and Harrison was the very last man to lay violent hands on himself. *He* clear meekly out to make way for a rival? Not likely!

I hurried back to the shack. The sergeant was dozing, his belt off and his tunic unbuttoned. Lathom was staring into the fire with his chin on his hands.

'Hullo, you two!' I said with unnecessary heartiness. The

policeman jerked awake. 'Lor' bless me,' he muttered apologetically. 'I must 'a' dropped off.'

'Why not?' said I. 'Best way to pass the time. Look here, there's a pound of sausages in our kit that we brought down last night. How about a bit of grub?'

We did not care about using any of the pots and pans in that place, so whittled a stick to a point, and toasted the sausages on that. They tasted none the worse.

SECTION TWO

Analysis

46. *Margaret Harrison to Harwood Lathom*

15, WHITTINGTON TERRACE, BAYSWATER
20.10.29

OH, PETRA, MY DEAR, MY OWN DEAR AT LAST!

When I heard your voice on the phone this morning, telling me what had happened, I didn't know how to believe
it. It all seemed so strange. And when I hung the receiver
up, I had to pinch myself to be sure it wasn't a dream. I went
upstairs, and there was the girl in her dressing-gown on the
landing. She must have been hanging over the stairs, for she
said, 'Oh, ma'am. Whatever's happened? I heard the telephone a-ringing and looked out and heard you talking. Has
there been an accident ma'am?' I said, 'Yes; a dreadful
accident. Mr Harrison's dead.' She stared at me, and I said,
'He's poisoned himself with eating some of those nasty
toadstools.' She began to cry. 'I knew he would! Oh, ma'am,
what an awful thing. Such a nice gentleman as he was.' That
seemed to make it real, somehow. 'A nice gentleman' –
well, she wasn't married to him. She couldn't know how I
was feeling. That was just as well, wasn't it, Petra? She
hung about and brought me some tea, sniffing and sobbing
over it. I couldn't say anything, but that was all right. She
thought I was stunned with grief, I suppose. I did feel
stunned. I can't realise, even now – though I've just seen it
in the paper. Fancy that! People keep on calling, but I've

said I can't see them. I want to be alone with my freedom.

Oh, Petra – didn't I tell you that God was on our side? Our love is so beautiful, so *right* – He had to make a miracle happen to save it. Isn't it wonderful – without our doing anything at all! That shows how right it was. I am so glad, now, that we didn't do anything of the terrible things we thought about. It would have been so dangerous – and we might – I don't know – we might have wondered afterwards. It would have been like living over a volcano. And now, Heaven has stepped in and made everything all right for ever and ever.

How glad I am you weren't there when it happened. That seems like a special providence, too, doesn't it? Because you would have had to go for a doctor, and then he might have recovered. And besides people might have thought you had something to do with it – if they ever found out about you and me, I mean. Doesn't it seem like a judgement on him, Petra? And I used to be so angry about his cooking and his toadstool book and everything – and all the while he was digging a pit for himself to fall into, like the wicked man in the Bible! It was all planned out from the beginning, to set us free for our beautiful life together. What was that thing people used to say – something in Latin about when God wishes to destroy anybody He first makes him mad. He *was* mad about the toadstools and things, you know. Sometimes, when he had those dreadful fits of temper, I used to think he was really and truly mad. I was afraid of him then, but I see now there was nothing to be afraid of. It was all meant to help us in the end.

And Petra – that other thing I was afraid of – you know – it's all right! Nothing is going to happen! It was just a mistake. Isn't that splendid? Because now we shan't have to get married in such a hurry. That might have made people talk, you know. We only have to wait a little bit now – just a little patience, my sweetheart, and then – oh, Petra! Think of the happiness! Everything has come right at once, hasn't it, my darling? All the clouds cleared away and the sun is shining.

Well, now, darling – you won't mind if I talk just a little bit of business? It seems horrid to think of it, when our love ought to be the one thing in our minds, but we must be a little bit practical. Of course, I had to send for the lawyer this morning and he showed me the will. There will be about £15,000 when it is all cleared up. Half of this goes to his son, Paul, straight away, and I get the other half for my lifetime, after which it would all go to my children – his and mine – that is, if there were any, and failing them, it goes to Paul when I die. So you see, I shall only be bringing you a small income, dear, but you are making money now, so we shan't be so badly off, shall we? It's funny – I suppose if you and I had really had a child, the law would have presumed it was *his* (think of that!), and then it would have inherited the money! But I think perhaps it is better as it is. It might not have seemed quite honourable to profit by anything that wasn't quite true, and I should like to feel that everything about our love was absolutely clear and honourable, and that we had nothing to reproach ourselves about. Of course, narrow-minded people might think our love itself was wicked – but one can't help loving, can one, darling? One might as well tell the sun not to rise. Because you and I belong to one another, and nothing in all the world can alter that. So you won't mind about the money, will you, Petra? I was afraid he might have made some mean condition about my not marrying again, but I suppose he didn't think of that.

You will have to stay for the inquest, of course. Shall I have to go? I don't like the idea of standing up with everybody looking at me. Besides, I can't tell them anything, can I? Do you think he ought to be buried down there or brought back to London? I want to do whatever you think would look right. I have cabled Paul, but he is so far away in the wilds, I don't know whether I shall get an answer in time. All these things are so absurd and hateful. We surround death with such a lot of hypocrisy and formality. It ought to be made just simple and beautiful, like the leaves falling. I shall have to order mourning and a widow's veil – think of wearing black clothes when one is happy. I should like a robe made of the rainbow – I'm wearing it in my heart, darling – all for you!

Write quickly, dearest, and tell me what to do. And tell

me that you are as glad as I am and that you love me, love me, love me, love me as I love you!

LOLO

47. *Extract from the 'Morning Express' of Tuesday, October 21 st, 1929*

MUSHROOM DEATH MYSTERY INQUEST

POISONED MAN'S LONE AGONY

WELL-KNOWN ARTIST GIVES EVIDENCE

The little schoolroom in the remote village of Manaton in Devon was crowded today, when Dr Pringle, the coroner for the district, opened the inquest on the body of George Harrison, aged 56, Head of the Accounts Department of Messrs. Frobisher, Wiley & Teddington, Electrical Engineers, who was found dead under extraordinary circumstances in his little cottage, 'The Shack', on Saturday night.

Evidence of the deceased's curious hobbies was given by his friend, Mr Harwood Lathom, the brilliant young artist who had been staying with him in 'The Shack', and who discovered the body.

The deceased, who is the author of *Neglected Edible Treasures*, an interesting and highly original volume, dealing with the foodstuffs to be obtained from our native woods and hedgerows, was stated to have been fond of experiments in unconventional cookery, and it was suggested that he had fallen a victim to accidental poisoning, by consuming a dish of venomous toadstools, a portion of which, it is alleged, was discovered on the table in 'The Shack' at the time of his death.

The inquest was adjourned for a fortnight, to enable a chemical analysis to be made of certain organs.

After formal evidence of identification, the first witness called was Mr Harwood Lathom. Dressed in a suit of heather-mixture plus-four tweeds and with an expression of anxiety and distress on his face, Mr Lathom gave his evidence in a subdued tone.

SWEALED HEDGEHOG

Mr Lathom said that he had known Mr Harrison and his family for a period of rather over twelve months. He had occupied the adjoining maisonette to theirs in Bayswater, and had there formed an acquaintance with them, which had resulted in a considerable degree of intimacy. He had painted a portrait of Mrs Harrison, which had been exhibited in the spring of 1929 at the Royal Academy. Financial and other considerations had resulted in his giving up the lease of the maisonette in February, and going to live in Paris, but the friendship with the Harrisons had been kept up by correspondence and occasional visits.

Mr Harrison had been accustomed to take an annual holiday 'on his own' at 'The Shack', living a bachelor existence, and making the experiments in natural cookery in which he was interested. He also painted in water-colours. On Mr Lathom's return to England, in October, Mr Harrison had suggested that he should join him in his residence at 'The Shack'. They had gone down there together on Saturday, the 11th of October, and had passed a very enjoyable holiday.

The Coroner: Will you explain the arrangements made about obtaining supplies of food and so on? – Bread, meat and vegetables were brought, when required, by the carrier, who called on Monday and Thursday, and took the orders for his next visit. A supply of tinned food, including condensed milk, was kept in 'The Shack'. There was no delivery of newspapers. Letters were fetched from the post office at Manaton by anybody who happened to be walking that way, or brought by the carrier on his visits.

Who did the cooking and housework? – We shared the work of washing up, carrying wood and so on. Mr Harrison did all the cooking. He was a first-class cook.

Did he supplement the fresh and tinned meat and so on, with what may be called experiments in natural diet? – Oh

135

yes. One evening we had swealed hedgehog, for example. (Laughter.)

Was it good? – It was delicious. (Laughter.)

'I NEVER ATE ANY TOADSTOOLS'

The Coroner: Hedgehog – was that the only unconventional dish you saw prepared? – No. On two or three occasions Mr Harrison gathered fungi of various kinds and had them for breakfast or supper.

Did these fungi include the ordinary mushroom of commerce? – On one occasion, yes.

Did you eat any of that dish? – I ate a small quantity. I do not care very much for mushrooms.

And on the other occasions? – On, I think, two occasions, Mr Harrison brought in other fungi, which, he explained, were good to eat. A great number of fungi are to be found in the valleys and damp, low-lying spots in the neighbourhood. One variety was called, I believe, Chantarelles, or some such name, and there was also a purple one, called 'Amethyst' something-or-other.

These were fungi of a kind not usually eaten by the ordinary person? The sort commonly called toadstools. – Yes; common, wild fungi.

Was the flavour of them agreeable? – I do not know. They smelt very savoury, but I did not eat any of them.

How was that? – I did not think it was safe. I was afraid of eating something poisonous.

You knew that a great many edible varieties of fungi exist in addition to the common mushroom? There is a Government publication dealing with them, I believe? – I believe there is.

And Mr Harrison was considered an authority on the subject? – I do not know if he was generally so considered. He had devoted much attention to the subject and had written a book on our natural food resources.

Had you read the book? – I had read parts of it.

But you did not feel sufficient confidence in the deceased's judgement to partake of the toadstools yourself? – I suppose

I did not. These things are largely a matter of prejudice. I did not care about the idea of eating toadstools.

The Coroner: But Mr Harrison ate them and was none the worse. – Oh, certainly. He appeared to enjoy them very much and there was no ill-effects.

Did you ever remonstrate with the deceased about his habit of eating these dangerous fungi? – I told him I was afraid there would be an accident some day. The subject had frequently been mentioned previously, when he was preparing his book. Mrs Harrison and his friends often said, more or less jokingly, that there would be a coroner's inquest on him one of these days.

And how did the deceased receive these warnings? – He laughed, and said it was all ignorance and prejudice. He said there was no danger at all for anybody who had thoroughly studied the subject.

Can you tell us how these dishes of fungi were prepared? – He had several methods. Sometimes he would grill them with butter and garlic, and other times he would stew them with condensed milk or in beef stock. He was fond of inventing new methods of cooking things.

'I AM GOING TO HUNT FOR FUNGI'

The Coroner: Now let us come to the time of the death. You had gone up to London, I think? – Yes. I had occasion to consult my agents and to transact a few matters of business in town. I went up by the 8.13 from Bovey Tracey on the Thursday morning. I had ordered a taxi the day before.

Was Mr Harrison quite well when you left him? – Perfectly. He was in particularly good spirits. He had risen early, with the intention of gathering a certain kind of fungus for his supper. It was one particular sort which he said he knew where to get.

Do you recollect its name? – I am not sure. I think he

137

called it 'Warty Hat'. (Laughter.) He said he knew of a wood where it was very plentiful.

I have here a copy of Mr Harrison's book. I see there is a fungus mentioned as being of an edible nature, called 'Warty Caps'. Would that be the one? Its Latin name is *Amanita rubescens*. – I should think that would be the one.

Had Mr Harrison started out before you left? – No. He saw me off at the gate into the lane.

POISONED DEATH AGONY

Mr Lathom then stated that he had returned to 'The Shack' late on Saturday night, bringing with him Mr John Munting, a mutual friend of himself and the Harrisons, and the author of a successful novel.

Arriving at 'The Shack' at about eleven o'clock, they found the place in darkness and the fire out. The remains of a dish of mushrooms was on the table in the outer room, together with the shells of some boiled eggs, a loaf of bread and a cup one-quarter filled with coffee.

On penetrating into the inner room, they discovered the body of Harrison, lying half-dressed on the bed. It was cold when found, and the features much distorted. Various articles in the room were flung about in a disorderly fashion, and the trestle-bedstead was broken. Both in this and in the outer room there were signs that the dead man had vomited persistently. A bottle of whisky and a tumbler were found beneath the bed.

As there is no telephone communication between 'The Shack' and Manaton, Mr Lathom was obliged to go on foot to summon assistance. The landlord of the inn at Manaton telephoned to the police-station at Bovey Tracey. Sergeant Warbeck, who deceived the message, communicated at once with Dr Hughes, and proceeded in the doctor's car to the scene of the tragedy.

The Coroner: Was Mr Harrison a man of cheerful disposition? – He was a reserved man of quiet tastes and behaviour on the whole, though subject to occasional fits of annoyance about trifles.

During the time you were with him at 'The Shack', did he appear to have anything on his mind? – Certainly not: he was in excellent spirits.

In your opinion, he was not a man likely to lay violent hands on himself? – Far from it. I was convinced at the time, and still am, that his death was a pure accident, due to some fungi he had eaten.

It came as a great surprise to you? – Well, of course, I was very much shocked and upset, but when I came to think it over – no, I cannot say I was greatly surprised.

Dr Hughes gave evidence that he had examined the body of Harrison and formed the opinion that when seen by him at about 1.30 a.m. deceased had been dead seven or eight hours. He had had the body removed to Bovey Tracey for the purpose of an autopsy. Acting in collaboration with the police, he had sent certain organs, portions of bed-linen, and remains of food to be chemically analysed.

The Coroner: At this point of the inquiry, can you form any conclusion as to the cause of the death? – The appearances suggest that deceased was poisoned by some substance which produced violent sickness and diarrhoea, followed by prolonged delirium and convulsions, ending in coma and death. The pupils of the eyes were slightly contracted, suggesting also the action of a poison.

Would fungus-poisoning have this effect? – Yes, and so would certain other vegetable poisons; opium, for example. It is, however, unusual for the appearance to persist so long after death. I do not place much reliance upon this symptom.

Do the general symptoms, as noted by you, appear to point to poisoning by a deadly fungus? – They are consistent with that possibility.

Dr Hughes added that there were no exterior signs of the application of physical violence.

WIDOW SHEDS TEARS

Mr John Munting confirmed Mr Lathom's evidence in every particular.

A rustle of sympathy went round the little court when the

widow, Mrs Margaret Harrison, appeared in the box. Fashionably but quietly dressed in a black face-cloth costume and closely-fitting cloche hat, Mrs Harrison gave her evidence in a voice so subdued as to be scarcely audible.

She declared that her husband had greatly looked forward to this country holiday. On such occasions he was accustomed to go to 'The Shack' by himself, or with a male friend. She never accompanied him to 'The Shack'. On previous holidays he had frequently taken as his companion his son by an earlier marriage, Mr Paul Harrison, a civil engineer, now absent in Central Africa. She had always understood that the deceased cooked for himself at 'The Shack', and made experiments with unconventional foodstuffs.

She had warned him again and again of the danger attending such experiments, but deceased had great confidence in his ability to distinguish edible varieties of plants from poisonous kinds, and always laughed at any remonstrance.

On being asked whether the deceased was a man who might be considered likely to take his own life, the widow replied indignantly:

'He had no reason to do such a dreadful thing, and I am sure he was the last person to think of it.'

The witness here broke down and sobbed violently, and had to be assisted to her seat.

The coroner then adjourned the inquest for a fortnight to permit of an analysis of the contents of the viscera and the various articles found in the house.

48. *Extract from the 'Morning Express' of Wednesday, November 5th,* 1929

SIR JAMES LUBBOCK ON SHACK POISON DRAMA

'ACCIDENTAL DEATH' VERDICT

CORONER'S WARNING WORDS TO PARENTS

Startling evidence was given today at the resumed inquest at Manaton on the body of George Harrison, 56 years old, of 15, Whittington Terrace, Bayswater, who was found dead under mysterious circumstances in the lonely cottage known as 'The Shack', on Saturday, October 19th.

At the previous sitting of the coroner's jury, evidence was given by the well-known artist, Mr Harwood Lathom, of his finding of the body on returning with Mr John Munting, author of *I to Hercules*, from a brief visit to London. Mr Lathom, who had been spending his holiday alone in 'The Shack' with Mr Harrison, described the curious bachelor life led by the deceased at 'The Shack', and his habit of cooking and eating unconventional dishes of hedgehogs, mushrooms and other natural objects.

HOME OFFICE EXPERT AND 'DEADLY FUNGUS'

Sir James Lubbock, the Home Office Analyst, was the first witness to be called at the resumed inquest. He stated that he had made an analysis of the contents of the stomach and other organs of the deceased, together with vomited matter obtained from the bedclothes and elsewhere. He had also analysed the remains of a dish of mushrooms and other articles of diet found on the table.

'From the stomach, the vomited matter, and from the unconsumed portion of the dish of fungus,' said Sir James, 'I obtained by analysis a considerable quantity of a substance known as *muscarine*, which is the poisonous principle of a fungus, *Amanita muscaria*, or the Fly Agaric.'

Sir James added that, estimating the amount of the poison which had been rejected from the body in the course of the sickness, he came to the conclusion that deceased must have consumed a very large quantity of the poison.

Sufficient to cause death? – Certainly. Muscarine is an exceedingly deadly poison.

What would be the symptoms of poisoning by muscarine? – They vary in different cases. Generally speaking, a sensation of acute sickness would be experienced almost immediately after the meal, followed by violent vomiting and diarrhoea. There might also be a feeling of suffocation and dizziness, sometimes accompanied by blindness. The victim would suffer acute distress and intense depression and fear of death. Unconsciousness might supervene, or there might be violent convulsions and prolonged delirium. Death would probably ensue as a result of respiratory paralysis.

Will you explain that more simply to the jury? – The poison would paralyse the muscles of the throat and chest, and the victim would be unable to breathe and would die of suffocation.

You have seen that Dr Hughes mentioned in his evidence that the pupils of the eyes were slightly contracted when he first saw the body. What conclusion do you draw from that? – I cannot definitely say. Myosis (that is, contraction of the pupils) is characteristic of the effects of certain poisons, including muscarine, but the contraction usually disappears at death, though, curiously enough, in the case of eserine, a pronounced myosis has been found five hours after death. I should regard a slight degree of contraction as consistent with muscarine poisoning, but not, in itself, conclusive evidence one way or another.

Have you ever seen a case of muscarine poisoning? – I have seen perhaps half a dozen cases in my own experience, mostly among children who had eaten the Fly Agaric in mistake for an edible mushroom. One case, I remember, was brought to the hospital too late for anything to be done, and the patient expired in convulsions after a period of unconsciousness. Three or four were treated by the injection of atropin and recovered completely. Another case was not brought to my notice till after the symptoms had cleared up of their own accord; in this case the amount eaten was very small.

Such cases are not always fatal? – By no means. If the proper treatment can be given immediately, the prognosis is favourable. Without such treatment, however, and where a large quantity of the poison is consumed, recovery would be less likely.

The Coroner: In your opinion, what was the cause of death in the case of Mr Harrison?'

Sir James Lubbock: I have not the slightest doubt that he died of poisoning from muscarine, taken in the dish of fungus submitted to me for analysis.

Sir James further added that the Fly Agaric, *Amanita muscaria*, was frequently found in woods and sheltered places, and was liable to be eaten in mistake for another member of the same family, *Amanita rubescens*, or Warty Caps, an edible fungus which it very closely resembled.

Reference was made to the Government publications, *Edible and Poisonous Fungi*, and to the book *Neglected Edible Treasures*, written by the deceased, and pictures of the fungi in question were passed round among the jury.

Questioned with regard to the eggs, bread, coffee, whisky and other articles of diet found in 'The Shack', Sir James said he had subjected them all to careful analysis, without discovering anything of a deleterious character.

DECEASED SEEN GATHERING FUNGI

Dr Hughes of Bovey Tracey, who performed the autopsy, said that he had found the heart of the deceased very greatly dilated, a symptom characteristic of poisoning by *Amanita muscaria*.

Harold Coffin, a labourer, gave evidence that he had met with deceased on the morning of October 17th. He had a satchel slung over his shoulder, and appeared to be searching for something on the ground. The time would be about 8 a.m. Deceased was then entering a small wood situated in the valley below Manaton. The witness had frequently seen deceased wandering about the country, sometimes with a sketching-easel and sometimes gathering plants and roots. Deceased had sometimes conversed with the witness about making a meal of unnatural things, such as nettles and toadstools, and witness had always supposed him to be a little peculiar in his head.

Henry Trefusis, a carrier, stated that he had delivered a loaf of bread, a pound of shin of beef and other provisions to 'The Shack', at 10.30 a.m., on Thursday, October 17th. Deceased had called out to him from the outhouse to put the goods on the window-sill. As far as he could see and hear, deceased was then in his usual health and spirits.

Mr Lathom, recalled, confirmed his previous statement that Mr Harrison had spoken to him on the Wednesday evening about his intention of gathering fungi the next day, and had mentioned a name resembling 'Warty Hats' or 'Warty Caps'.

The coroner, in summing up the evidence to the jury, laid stress on the danger of experimenting in unusual articles of diet. It was notorious, he said, that other nations, such as the French, were accustomed to eat many natural products, such as frogs, snails, dandelions and various kinds of fungi, which in this country were considered unfit for human food. Such experiments, when conducted by highly expert persons, might sometimes turn out well, but, on the other hand, nobody was infallible, and undoubtedly a wise caution was in most cases to be preferred. Sir James Lubbock had cited some very sad instances of unfortunate children who had succumbed to the effects of accidentally eating those dangerous toadstools which unhappily grew in such great profusion in many parts of the country, and he would like to urge on all parents the advisability of strictly forbidding their boys and girls to tamper with anything which they might pick up on their rambles. The present case would serve as a terrible warning, which he hoped would not soon be forgotten. It was most unfortunate that, owing to the remote situation of 'The Shack' and the unlucky absence of Mr Lathom in London, there should have been no help at hand when the deceased was overtaken by this terrible accident. The circumstances of his lonely and agonising death were such as to arouse the deepest compassion for the widow and son of the deceased.

The jury, after a few minutes' consultation, brought in a verdict of Accidental Death, due to poisoning by *Amanita muscaria*. The foreman said that the jury desired to express their deep sympathy with the bereaved family. They would also like to add a rider to the effect that teachers in the schools of the surrounding districts should be encouraged to warn their pupils against the eating of toadstools, and that charts displaying the various kinds of poisonous fungi should be hung in the classrooms.

[An article on Fungi, by Professor Brookes, the distinguished naturalist, will be found on p. 8.]

49. *Statement by Paul Harrison*

I was in Africa when the news of my father's death reached me. The work on which I was engaged was nearly completed, and I at once made arrangements for handing over the concluding portions of the job and returning to England. It took a little time to settle all this and to arrange for my journey to the coast, and it was not till the 6th of January, 1930, that I arrived in London.

From the moment that I heard the cause of death assigned, I was positively convinced that there was no accident about it. My father's expert knowledge of fungi was very great; and he was a man of almost exaggerated precision in matters of this kind. It was entirely incredible to me that he could ever have mistaken a stool of *Amanita muscaria* for *Amanita rubescens*, even in the gathering of it; far more so that he could have peeled and prepared the fungus for eating without noticing the difference. To the average coroner's jury, accustomed to dealing with schoolchildren and trippers, such a mistake would no doubt seem perfectly natural; but my father was no more likely to take *Muscaria* for *Rubescens* than to take a piece of cast-iron for a piece of chilled steel. I immediately scouted the whole idea of accident. Two possibilities remained for me to investigate. Either my father, in his unselfish devotion to the worthless woman he had married, had destroyed himself by a painful method which would look like accident and so disarm suspicion; or else he had been murdered. In either case, I was determined that the woman should not benefit by the crime which she had caused.

Feeling as I did towards Margaret Harrison, I could not bring myself to take up my residence in my father's house. I therefore took a room at an hotel in the Bloomsbury district, which has the advantage of being central, and set myself to examine the problem under all its aspects.

I read and re-read carefully all the newspaper reports of the inquest, and also all the letters which my father had written to me during the last two years. The most important of these latter I have included among the documents submitted to you. There was another, the essentials of which are covered by Mr Munting's statement, which mentioned that Miss Agatha Milsom had had to be 'put away', and that the character of Mr Munting was accordingly considered to have been cleared from suspicion.

I fastened at once upon this incident. I had naturally never believed that Miss Milsom's version of this episode was the true one. I believed my father to have been quite correct in his original suspicions. Miss Milsom's illness had, I decided, enabled Munting to pull the wool over his victim's eyes very nicely. Margaret Harrison and Munting had been corresponding all along, until the convenient decease of my father set them free to come together again after a decent interval.

This suggestion led me directly to the idea of suicide. In some way my father's eyes had been opened to what was going on; and the agent must undoubtedly have been Lathom. He was Munting's friend and, deliberately or unconsciously, he must have let fall some words during his stay at 'The Shack' which made the situation plain. I thought it probable that this young man had played a double-faced part, and forwarded Munting's interests under pretence of being friendly with my father. As regards the idea of murder, Munting appeared to have an alibi. His arrival with Lathom on the Saturday night had been witnessed, and I did not think it likely that he could have made any earlier appearance in that sparsely-populated district without being seen. It seemed possible that he and Lathom had been confederates, and committed the murder in collusion; but at the moment I was inclined to think that my father had been hounded into self-destruction by this precious pair, or rather trio.

It seemed to me that any first step must be to see Margaret Harrison. She would learn before long that I was in London, from my father's solicitors, with whom I necessarily had business. It was better, therefore, to call on her at once, both to prevent her from suspecting my suspicions and to keep up appearances in the eyes of the neighbourhood.

Accordingly, I went round to Whittington Terrace on the day after my arrival. I sent up my name by the maid (a new girl since my time), and, after a short interval, Margaret Harrison came down to me. She was dressed in deep mourning, very fashionably cut, and came up to me with the gushing manner which I had always so greatly disliked.

'Oh, Paul!' she said, 'isn't this terrible? How dreadful it has been for you, poor dear, all that long way away! I am so glad you have managed to get home!'

'If you are,' I said, 'it must be for the first time on record.'

Her face took on the sulky look I knew so well.

'I knew you never liked me, Paul,' she said, 'but surely this is hardly the time to bear a grudge.'

'Perhaps not,' said I, 'but it hardly seems worth while to pretend that you are delighted to see me.'

'As you like,' she replied. 'We may as well sit down, anyway.'

She sat down, and I went over and stood by the window.

'You are staying here, of course?' she inquired, after a short silence.

I replied that I preferred to live at an hotel for the present, because it was more convenient for business.

'Of course,' she said, 'you will have a lot of things to see about. I quite understand. I kept the house on, because I didn't know what your plans would be. But perhaps you think it would be better to give it up?'

'Do just as you like,' I answered. 'The furniture is yours, I believe?'

'Yes; but this place is really more than I want when I am by myself. Besides' – here she gave an affected shudder – 'it seems, well, haunted, rather. If you are not coming here, I think I shall give it up and take a couple of rooms somewhere. I can look after your things till you get settled.'

I thanked her, and asked if she had made any plans for the future.

'None at all,' she said. 'I feel rather stunned, just at the moment. It has been such a shock. I shall wait for a little time, anyhow, and see how things turn out. I shall be rather lost at first. We saw so few people – I have rather lost touch.'

'You have all my father's friends,' I said.

'Oh, but they are not *my* friends. They only used to come to tea and dinner and so on. They wouldn't want me. I should only be an intruder. And, of course, they are all much older than I am. We should have really nothing in common.'

'Yes,' I said, 'you are a young woman, Margaret. You will probably marry again before very long.'

She made a great display of indignation.

'Paul! How can you say such a heartless thing, and your poor father only just passed away! Anybody would think you don't care for him at all. But I suppose a father isn't the same thing as a husband.'

I was nauseated.

'You need not trouble to display all this feeling on my account,' I said. 'It was quite enough to make him as un-happy as you did while he was alive, without playing the broken-hearted widow.'

'You are very like him, you know,' she observed. 'You have just his way of snubbing and repressing people. You don't seem to understand that everybody can't keep their feelings bottled up as you do. It was not my fault that he was unhappy. I think he had an unhappy nature.'

'That is nonsense,' I said, 'and you know it. My father was a most simple, friendly, companionable man – only you never would be a real wife to him.'

'He wouldn't let me,' she said. 'I know we didn't hit it off very well, at the end, but I did try, Paul. I did indeed. In the beginning I was ready to give him all the love and affec-tion that was in me. But he didn't like it. He dried me up. He broke my spirit, Paul.'

'My father was not a demonstrative man,' I said, 'but you know quite well that he was proud of you and devoted to you. If you had heard him speak of you as I have heard him – '

'Ah!' she said, quickly, 'but I never did. That was the trouble. What is the good of being praised behind one's back if one is always being scolded and snubbed to one's face? It only makes it worse. Everyone thinks one has such a good husband, and that one ought to be so happy and grateful – and all the time they never know what one is suffering from unkind words and cold looks at home.'

'Many women would envy you,' I said. 'Would you rather have had a husband who was all charming manners at home and unfaithful the minute your back was turned?'

'Yes,' she said, 'I would.'

'I can't understand you,' I said. 'You ought to be ashamed to speak like this.'

'No,' she said, 'you can't understand. That's it. Neither could he.'

'All I understand is that you ruined his life, and drove him to a dreadful death,' I burst out. I had not meant to go so far, but I was too angry to think what I was saying.

'What do you mean?' she said. 'Oh, no – you can't think that he – But why should he?'

I had gone too far now to retreat, and I told her what I thought.

'You are quite wrong,' she said. 'He wouldn't have done that.'

'He would have done anything for you,' I cried angrily, 'anything. Even to laying down his life to set you free – '

'Even to sacrificing his reputation as a connoisseur of fungi?' she interrupted, with an unpleasant smile.

'Even that,' I answered. 'It's all very well for you to sneer – you never cared for his interests – you didn't understand them – you understand nothing at all, and you care for nothing except your twopenny ha'penny emotions.'

'I do know this,' she said steadily, 'that if your father had thought that I wanted to be free of him - which he didn't, because he had too good an opinion of himself – but if he had, he would have taken care I didn't get rid of him without a row. He loved making rows. He wouldn't have made things easy for me. He wouldn't have missed the opportunity of rubbing it in.'

Her expression was as ugly and common as her words. I felt that I could not control myself much longer and had much better go.

'I repeat,' said I, 'that you never understood my father, and you never will. It isn't in you. I don't think it's any good prolonging this discussion. I had better be going. Can you give me Mr Munting's address?'

I hoped to have frightened her by the sudden question, but she only looked mildly astonished.

'Mr Munting? I'm sure I don't know. I've only seen him once since he was married, and that was at the Royal Academy. And at the – the inquest, of course. I think he lives in Bloomsbury somewhere. I expect he's in the tele-pone-book.'

I thanked her, and took my leave. Married! My father had never thought to mention that. It upset all my ideas. Because, if Munting was married, then what object could there have been in my father's suicide – or murder, which-ever it was? His death would have left Margaret no nearer to marrying Munting. And any other relation could have been carried on perfectly well, whether my father was alive or not. Certainly, he might simply have destroyed himself in sheer despair and misery, unable to bear the dishonour. But it did not seem so likely.

This news made me alter my plans. I determined not to go and see Munting at once. It would be better, I thought, to get hold of Lathom, and see if I could obtain any light on the question from him.

A little inquiry among the dealers produced Lathom's address. He was living in a studio in Chelsea. I presented myself at the place the next morning, and was received by a vinegary-looking elderly woman in a man's cap, who in-formed me that Mr Lathom was still in bed.

As it was already eleven o'clock, I handed her my card and said I would wait. She ushered me into an extremely untidy studio, full of oil-paint tubes and half-finished can-vases, and waddled away with the card towards an inner door.

Before reaching it, however, she turned back, sidled up to me and said in a glutinous whisper:

'Begging your pardon, Mr 'Arrison, but was you any relation to the pore gentleman wot died so mysterious?'

'What business is that of yours?' I snapped. She nodded with ghoulish enjoyment.

'Oh, no offence, sir, no offence. There ain't no need to

take a person up so sharp. That was a funny thing, sir, wasn't it? You'd be 'is son, per'aps?'

'Never you mind who I am,' I said. 'Take my card to Mr Lathom and say I should be glad if he could spare me a few minutes.'

'Oh, 'e'll spare you a few minutes, sir, I shouldn't wonder. Look funny if 'e didn't, sir, wouldn't it? There's lots of things as 'ud look funny, I daresay, if we knew the rights on 'em.'

'What are you getting at?' I said, uneasily.

'Ho, nothink, sir! Nothink! If you ain't a relation it ain't nothink to you, is it, sir? People do go off sudden-like, sometimes, and nobody to blame. There's lots of things 'appen every day more than ever gets into the papers. But there! That ain't nothink to you, sir.'

She sidled away again, grinning unpleasantly. I heard her talking and a man's voice replying, and presently she shuffled back again.

'Mr Lathom says 'e'll be with you in five minutes, sir, if you will be so good as to wait. 'E'll come fast enough, sir, don't you be afraid. A very agreeable gentleman is Mr Lathom, sir. I been doin' 'im over three months, now, ever since 'e come over from France. Some time in October that would be, sir, before this 'ere sad accident 'appened. Mr Lathom was very much upset about it, sir. You'd 'ardly 'ave known 'im for the same gentleman w'en 'e came back after the inquest. Looked as if 'e'd been seein' a ghost – that white and strange 'e was. A terrible sight the pore gentleman must 'a' been. A crool way to die. But there! We must all die once, sir, mustn't we? And if it ain't one way it's another, and if it ain't sooner it's later. Only some folks is misfortunit more than others. Would you care for a cup of tea, sir, while you're waitin'?'

I accepted the tea, to get rid of her. The stove, however, turned out to be in a corner of the studio, and having lit the gas and put the kettle on, she returned. All the time she was speaking, she rubbed one skinny hand over the other with a curious, greedy action.

'Very strange 'ow things turns out, ain't it, sir? There was a gentleman lived down our street, a cats'-meat man 'e was, and the best cats'-meat in the neighbourhood – thought very 'ighly of by all, 'e was. 'E married a girl out of one of them shops w'ere they sells costooms on 'ire purchase. They ain't no good to nobody, them places, if you asks me. Well, 'e died sudden.'

'Did he?'

'Ho, yes! very sudden, 'e died. A very 'ot summer it was, and they brought it in 'e'd got the dissenter, with eatin' somethink as didn't agree with 'im. So it may 'a' bin, far be it from me to say otherwise. But afore the year was up *she'd* gone and married the young man wot was manager of the clothes-shop. A good marriage it was for 'er, too. Ho, yes! *She* didn't lost nothink by 'er 'usband dyin' w'en 'e died, if you understand me, sir.'

I made no answer. She took the kettle off and filled the teapot.

'Now, that's a nice cup o' tea, sir. You won't find nothink wrong with *that*. That's 'olesome, that is. I knows 'ow to make the sort of tea that gentlemen like. Cutts is my name, Mrs Cutts. They all knows me about 'ere. I been doin' for the artists this thirty year, and I'm up to all their goin's-on. I knows 'ow to cook their breakfisses and look after their bits of paintings and sich, an' w'en to speak an' w'en to 'old my tongue, sir. That's wot they pays me for.'

'Thank you,' I said, 'it's an excellent cup of tea.'

'Yes, sir, thank you, sir. My name is Cutts, if you should ever be a-wantin' me. Anybody in these studios will tell you w'ere to find Mrs Cutts. 'Ere's Mr Lathom a'comin', sir.'

She lurched away as Lathom emerged from his bedroom.

I will admit that the first impression he made upon me was a good one. His appearance was clean, and his manners were pleasant.

'I see Mrs Cutts has given you a cup of tea,' he said, when he had shaken hands. 'Won't you have a spot of break-fast with me?'

I thanked him, and said I had already breakfasted.

'Oh, I suppose you have,' he answered, smiling. 'We're rather a late crowd in these parts, you know. You won't mind if I carry on with my eggs and bacon?'

I begged him to use no ceremony, and he produced some eatables from a cupboard.

'It's all right, Mrs Cutts,' he shouted. 'I'll do the cooking. This gentleman wants to talk business.'

The noise of a broom in the passage was the only answer.

'Well now, Mr Harrison,' said Lathom, dropping his breezy manner, 'I expect you have come to hear anything I can tell you about your father. I can't say, of course, how damned sorry I am about it. As you know, I wasn't there at the time – '

'No,' I said, 'and I don't want to distress you by going into details and all that. It must have been a great shock to you.'

'It certainly was.'

'I can see that,' I added, noticing how white and strained his face looked. 'I only wanted to ask you – after all, you were the last person to see him – '

'Not the last,' he interrupted, rather hastily. 'That man Coffin saw him, you know, gathering the – wretched fungi – and the carrier saw him later still, after I had left the place.'

'Oh, yes – I didn't mean quite that. I mean, you were the last friend to see and talk to him intimately.'

'Quite, quite – just so.'

'I wanted to hear from you whether you were, yourself, quite satisfied about it – satisfied that it really was an accident, that is?'

He put the bacon into the pan, where it sputtered a good deal.

'What's that? I didn't quite catch.'

'Were you satisfied it was an accident?'

'Why, of course. What else could it have been? You know, Mr Harrison, I hate to say anything about your father that might seem – to blame him in any way, that is – but, of course, I mean it is a very dangerous thing to experiment with wild fungi. Anybody would tell you the same thing. Unless you are a very great expert – and even then one is liable to make mistakes.'

'That is what is troubling me,' I said. 'My father *was* a

153

very great expert, and he was not at all a man to make mistakes.'

'None of us are infallible.'

'Quite so. But still. And it was odd that it should have happened just at the very time you were away.'

'It was very unfortunate, certainly.' He kept his eyes on the bacon, while he prodded it about with a fork. 'Damnably unfortunate.'

'So odd and so unfortunate that I cannot help thinking there may have been a reason for it!'

Lathom took two eggs and cracked them carefully. 'How so?'

'You are aware, perhaps, that my father was – not altogether happy in his married life.'

He gave an exclamation under his breath.

'Did you speak?'

'No – I have broken the yolk, that's all. I beg your pardon. You are asking me rather a delicate question.'

'You may speak frankly to me, Mr Lathom. If you saw much of my father's family life, you must have noticed that there were – misfits.'

'Well, of course – one sees and hears little things occasionally. But many happily-married people spar at times, don't they? And – well – there was a difference of age and all that.'

'That is the point, Mr Lathom. Without necessarily saying anything harsh about my father's wife, it is a fact that a young woman, married to an older man, may, not unnaturally, tend to turn to someone more of her own age.'

He muttered something.

'In such a case my father, who was the most unselfregarding man who ever breathed, might have thought it his duty to give her back her liberty.'

He turned round swiftly.

'Oh, no!' he said, 'surely not! That's a dreadful idea, Mr Harrison. It never occurred to me. I am sure you can put it out of your mind.' He hesitated. 'I think – ' he went on, with a troubled look, 'oh, yes, I am sure you need not think that.'

'Are you quite sure? Did he never say anything?'

'He never spoke of his wife except in terms of the deepest

154

affection. He thought very highly of her.'

'I know. More highly than she – more highly than any woman perhaps could deserve.'

'Perhaps.'

'But,' I said, 'that very affection would have been all the more reason for him to – to take himself out of her life in the most complete and unanswerable way.'

'I suppose so – from that point of view.'

'And, if it was so, I should like to know it. Will you tell me, Mr Lathom, on your honour and without concealment, whether there was anything between my father's wife and your friend Mr Munting?'

'Good Lord, no!' he said, taking the pan off the fire and shovelling the eggs and bacon out into a plate. 'Nothing of the sort.'

'Just a minute,' said I. 'Mr Munting is your friend, and you want to be loyal to him. That's obvious. And I'm aware I'm asking you to do one of those things which people with public-school education don't do. I am not a public-school man myself, and you must excuse me if I suggest that just for once you should come down to brass tacks and cut out the Eton-and-Harrow business. My father has died, and I want your personal assurance that he did not kill himself on your friend Munting's account. Can you give it to me?'

'On my word of honour, there was not the very slightest attachment or understanding of any kind between Mrs Harrison and Jack Munting. They rather disliked each other, if anything. Jack was married last Easter to a very charming woman, with whom he is much in love. He never gave a thought to Mrs Harrison, or she to him.'

I felt sure he believed what he said.

'Wasn't there a disturbance of some kind?' I asked.

'Oh, yes.' A cloud passed over his face. 'There was. That wretched potty woman, Miss Milsom, invented some sort of story. But it was the most absolute rubbish. And Mr Harrison came to see what utter nonsense it all was. My dear man, the woman's in an asylum.'

'There was no foundation for it then?'

'None whatever.'

'Then why did your friend Munting take it lying down,

and let himself be kicked out of the house?'

'I wish you wouldn't keep on calling him "my friend Munting," as if you took us for a pair of undesirables,' he retorted, irritably. He picked at his eggs and bacon, and pushed the plate away again.

'What else could he do but go? Your father was perfectly unreasonable – wouldn't have listened to the Archangel Gabriel. Anyway, the more you protest about these matters, the less you're believed. Munting did the right thing – cleared out and married somebody else. Couldn't have a row with a man twice his age, you know.'

I got up.

'Thank you very much, Mr Lathom. I'm sorry to have troubled you. I am very glad to have your assurance. Mr Munting is in town, I suppose?'

'You're not going to rake it all up with him?'

'I should feel more satisfied if I had a word with him,' I answered.

'I wouldn't. You can take my word for it. I mean to say, there's Mrs Munting to be considered.'

'I shouldn't say anything to her. After all, it's surely natural enough that I should wish to have Mr Munting's account of the business.'

'Yes – oh yes, I suppose it is.' He still looked worried and dissatisfied. 'Well, goodbye. If you really must see Munting, here's his address.'

As I opened the door of the studio, I nearly tripped over Mrs Cutts, who was washing the linoleum. She came and let me out at the house-door.

'Puttin' yer money on the wrong horse, young man, ain't you?' she whispered.

'Look here,' I said, 'you know something about this.'

'That's as may be,' said she, slyly. 'Mrs Cutts knows 'ow to govern 'er tongue. An unruly member, ain't it, sir? That's wot the Bible says.'

'I've no time to waste,' I answered; 'if you have anything to say to me, you will find me at my hotel.' I mentioned the name, and then, with a certain disgust at the business, slipped half a crown into her hand.

She curtseyed, and I left her bobbing and dipping on the doorstep.

I cursed myself for a fool as I set off to find Munting. Undoubtedly Lathom would have warned him by telephone of what to expect. I was sure of it when I saw him. He struck me as conceited and pretentious – the usual type of modern literary man.

He was perfectly polite however; assured me in a tone of the utmost sincerity that the story about himself and Margaret Harrison was entirely unfounded, and referred me back to Lathom for evidence as to my father's state of mind in the week preceding his death.

Finding myself quite unable to penetrate this polished surface of propriety, I took my leave. The manner of both men left me in no doubt that there was something to conceal, but I could get no farther than a moral certainty.

Mrs Cutts seemed to offer the best hope of information, but I could not as yet reconcile myself to handling so dirty a tool. It occurred to me that it might possibly be worth while to get hold of Miss Milsom. I was not at all clear in my mind that her madness might not have some method in it.

At first I could not think how to trace her. I could have asked Margaret Harrison, of course, but I did not want to do that. Finally, I decided to call on the local padre, the Rev. Theodore Perry, and see if he knew where his lost sheep had strayed to.

I knew him well, of course, and it did not seem unnatural that I should ask after the welfare of a woman who had been for some time in my father's employment. I sandwiched the question in, in the course of a casual conversation, and he told me at once what he knew.

'Poor woman, I'm afraid she is not altogether normal. One hopes it is only a passing phase. I don't quite know where she is – one of these nursing-homes of the modern sort, I think. Her sister, Mrs Farebrother, would be able to tell you. No, I don't suppose they are very well off. The fees in these places are high. In the days of faith – or superstition, if you like – a convent or a béguinage would have provided the proper asylum for such a case, with some honest work to do and a harmless emotional outlet – but nowadays they make you pay for everything, not only your pleasures.'

He gave me Mrs Farebrother's address, and I said I would see what could be done. He smiled at me in a futile, clerical way, and said it would be a work of charity.

I left him, feeling anything but charitable, and went to see Mrs Farebrother. She seemed to be a good, honest, sensible woman, worried by family and financial cares, and accepted gratefully my suggestion of a small pension, during the period that her sister might be requiring medical care.

The interview with Agatha Milsom was a painful one to me. The woman is undoubtedly quite unbalanced, with a disagreeable sex-antagonism at the bottom of her mania. According to her, my father had treated his wife with abominable cruelty, and I was obliged to listen for a long time to her rambling accusations. The name of John Munting roused her to such excitement that I was afraid she would make herself ill; unfortunately, I could get nothing reliable out of her. For one thing, she was obsessed with the idea that he had designs upon her maiden modesty, and for another, many of her statements were so ludicrous that they cast suspicion over the rest.

As regards my father, however, I obtained one thing. I suggested that her memory of certain domestic incidents might be at fault, and in proof of her assertions she promised to get back from her sister, and send to me, all the letters she had written home during the previous two years.

It seemed to me that, since her mental deterioration had come on only gradually, the letters written at the time might possibly be considered to attain a reasonable level of accuracy. She kept her promise, and from this correspondence I selected the letters of relevant date, and these are the documents included in this dossier. It will be seen that great allowance must be made for bias; that much conceded, the statements may, I think, be accepted as having a basis in fact.

I need not say how distressing they were to me. They cast a light upon the miserable domestic conditions which my father had had to endure. I regretted most bitterly that

I had taken over that work in Central Africa, thus leaving him to the undiluted companionship of a selfish, discontented wife and a semi-demented and vulgar woman. My father was not a man to go abroad for the sympathy he could not find at home, and it was no wonder that he had welcomed the acquaintanceship of two young men who could, at least, make some pretence of entering into his interests.

But the thing which emerged from the letters with startling illumination was the intimate footing upon which Lathom had stood with the whole household. As may be seen by the few letters included above, my father was by no means a gossipy correspondent, and I had not realised that Lathom had become so much of a tame cat about the drawing-room. I had thought of him as being my father's friend almost entirely, and I believe that my father himself took that view, and, wittingly or unwittingly, gave me that impression. But it now seemed clear to me that this was not so, and that, what with my father's innocent pleasure in the apparent admiration and friendliness of this brilliant young man, and what with the perverse misconception of the wretched Agatha Milsom, we had all been 'led up the garden', as the expression is.

I saw now why both Lathom and Munting, standing by one another in a conspiracy of silence, had been able to deny with such obvious sincerity that there had ever been an undue intimacy between Munting and Margaret Harrison. Lathom had said that my father's last days had been free from suspicion; I saw now that this was possible. I also saw why Lathom had been so unwilling that I should ask Munting the same question, and why Munting had referred me back to Lathom for the answer. Munting must, I thought, be considered clear of any offence except a refusal to betray his friend's confidence; and I was obliged to confess that most people would think he had acted rightly. Lathom, too, had kept to the code of what is usually called honour in these matters. As for Margaret Harrison – but from her I had never expected anything but lies.

But if this was the truth, why should my father have committed suicide? For I still do not believe in the theory of accident. Either something must have opened his eyes during Lathom's visit to town, or else that other, darker suspicion, which I had hardly liked to glance at, was only too well-founded.

I am a business man. I have the business man's liking for facts. To me, an expert's knowledge is a fact. Experts occasionally make mistakes, but to me it appears far less probable that an expert should be mistaken than that an artist and a woman should be unprincipled. And I cannot make it too clear that my father's expert knowledge in the matter of fungi was to be trusted. I would as cheerfully stake my life on the wholesomeness of a dish prepared by my father as on the stability of a girder-stress calculated by my chief, Sir Maurice Berkeley. But I would not venture a five-pound note on the honesty of virtue of such people as Lathom and Margaret Harrison.

But to prove the truth of my suspicions, I needed more facts – the sort of facts that a jury would accept. To them, my father's knowledge of fungi would not be a fact at all.

I turned the matter over in my mind, and eventually came to the conclusion that, whether I liked it or not, I must see the woman Cutts. I hoped that she would come to me, but several days passed and I saw nothing of her. Either the creature had no facts to sell, or she was holding off in the hope of securing better terms. I saw through her artifice well enough, but I saw also that she had me at a disadvantage. Eventually, and with great reluctance, I wrote to her as follows, addressing the letter to Lathom's studio.

'Mrs Cutts –

'Madam, – When I saw you the other morning at Mr Lathom's studio, you suggested you might be in a position to do some work for me. I shall possibly be requiring some assistance of this kind in the near future, and shall be obliged if you would call on me one evening at my hotel to discuss the matter.'

On the second day after dispatching this, I was informed that a lad was waiting downstairs to see me. I went down and found a ferrety-eyed youth, who introduced himself as Archie Cutts.

'Oh, yes,' I said, 'you have come about the work I mentioned to your mother.'

'Yes, sir,' he replied. 'Mother says as she can't bring it 'ere, not 'avin' the tools by 'er, but if you was to come down to our place on Friday, the party as she obliges bein' out that night, she would be willing to make an arrangement.'

This was disagreeable.

'If I am to take that trouble,' said I, 'I shall want to know, first, whether your mother is likely to be able to do what I want.'

He looked cunningly at me with his shifty eyes.

'Mother says she could show you letters from a lady as you know very well, only she won't trust 'em to me, bein' valuable to 'er and not wantin' to lose 'em.'

'Oh, I see,' said I, loudly, 'testimonials, eh? Letters of recommendation. I see. And your mother thinks she understands what is required and would be able to give satisfaction?'

'Yes, sir.'

'Did she say anything about terms?'

'She says she'll leave that to you, sir, w'en you see the work.'

'Very well.' There was nothing to be got by argument. 'Tell your mother I will try and find time to call on her on Friday evening.'

'Yes, sir. Nine o'clock would suit mother best.'

I made the appointment for nine, and gave the lad a shilling for his trouble. At nine o'clock on the Friday evening I found myself knocking at a dilapidated door in the long drab street of very squalid houses. The ferret-eyed lad let me in, and I saw, with considerable repulsion, my former acquaintance, seated in some pomp at a round table, containing a lamp, a wool mat and a family Bible.

She greeted me with a condescending nod, and the youth withdrew.

'Well, now,' I said, 'Mrs Cutts, you have asked me to come and see you, and I hope you are not wasting my time, because I am a very busy man.'

This forlorn effort to establish my dignity made no impression on her.

'That's for you to say, sir,' said she. 'I wasn't for intrudin' on you. I am a respectable woman, thank God, and can maintain myself in my station by 'ard work, and never 'ad no complaints. Not but wot I'd be willin' to oblige a gentleman if 'e was requirin' my services, not bein' too proud to do a favour.'

'Quite so,' said I, 'and if you can do the work I want, I will see that it is made worth your while.'

'Wot sort of work was you thinkin' of, sir?'

'I gathered from what you said to me,' I answered, 'that you thought you might be able to throw some light on the circumstances of my father's death.'

'That's as may be. There's ways and ways of dyin'. Some is took, and some takes French leave, and others is 'elped out of life, ain't they, sir?'

'Have you got any information to show that my father was helped out of life?'

'Well, there, sir. I wouldn't go for to say sech a thing – nor yet for to deny it, 'uman nature bein' that wicked as you can see for yourself any Sunday in the *News of the World*. But wot I says is, w'en persons is wicked enough to 'ave goin's on be'ind a gentleman's back, there's no knowin' wot may come of it, is there?'

'You said you had letters to show me.'

'Ah!' she nodded. 'There's good readin' in letters sometimes, sir. There's letters as would be worth 'undreds of pounds in a court of law, to some people as one might name.'

'Come, come, Mrs Cutts,' said I, 'very few letters are worth anything like that.'

'That's not for me to judge, sir. If letters should turn out not to be worth nothin', why, they're easy destroyed, ain't they, sir? There's many a person I daresay wishes that 'e or it might be she, sir, 'ad destroyed the letters wot they 'ad written. I was never one for writin' letters myself. A word's as good, and leaves nothin' but air be'ind it, that's wot I say. And them as leaves letters about casual-like, might often be grateful for a word of warnin' from them as is wiser'n themselves.'

Her screwed-up eyes twinkled with consciousness of power.

'A word of warnin' is soon given, and may be worth 'undreds. I ain't got no call to press you, sir. I ain't dependent on anybody, thank God.'

'Look here,' I said briskly, 'it's no use beating about the bush. I must see these letters before I know what they're worth to me. For all I know they're not worth twopence.'

'Well, I ain't unreasonable,' said the hag. 'Fair and square is my motter. Ef I was to show you dockyments ter prove as your pa's missis was sweet on my young gentleman there, would that be worth anything to you, sir?'

'That's rather vague,' I fenced. 'People may be fond of one another and no great harm done.'

'Wot may seem no 'arm to some may be great 'arm to a right-thinking person,' said Mrs Cutts, unctuously. 'You can ask all about this neighbour'ood, sir, and they'll tell you Mrs Cutts is a lawful maried woman, as works 'ard and keeps 'erself to 'erself as the sayin' is. Not but wot there's a-many things as a 'ard-workin' woman in these parts 'as to shet her eyes to, and can't be blamed for wot is not 'er business. But there is limits, and w'en people is writin' to people as isn't their own lawful 'usbands about him bein' in the fambly way and about others as *is* their lawful 'usbands not 'avin' the right to exist, and w'en them lawful 'usbands dies sudden not so very long arter, then wot I ses is, it might be worth while for them as is right-thinkin' and 'ose place it is to interfere, to 'ave them there dockyments kep' in a safe place.'

I tried not to let her see how deeply I was interested in these hints.

'This is all talk,' I said. 'Show me the letters, and then we can get down to brass tacks.'

'Ah!' said Mrs Cutts. 'And supposin' my young gentleman should come 'ome and look for them letters, as it might be tonight, wot a peck of trouble I might be in. Do right and shame the devil is my mother, but motters won't feed a fambly o' children when a 'ard-workin' woman loses 'er job – now, will they, sir?'

I thought the time had come to lend an air of business to

the bargain. I drew a five-pound note from my pocket, and let it crackle pleasantly between my fingers. Her eyelids twitched, but she said nothing.

'Before we go any further,' I said, 'I must look at the letters and see that they are actually from the person you mention, and that they are of genuine interest to me. In the meanwhile, since I have put you to some trouble – '

I pushed the note towards her, but held my hand over it.

'Well,' she said, 'I don't mind lettin' you 'ave a look. Looks breaks no bones, as the sayin' is.' She fumbled in a remote pocket beneath her skirt and produced a small packet of papers.

'My eyes ain't so good as they was,' she added, with sudden caution. ' 'Ere, Archie!'

The ferrety youth (who must have been listening at the door) answered the summons with suspicious promptness. I noticed that he had provided himself with a formidable-looking stick and immediately pushed my chair back against the wall. Mrs Cutts slowly detached one letter from the bundle, and spread it out flat on the table, disengaging it from its folds with a well-licked thumb.

'W'ich one is this, Archie?'

The youth glanced sideways at the letter and replied:

'That's the do-something-quick-one, Mother.'

'Ah! and wi'ch is the one about the pore gentleman as was done in in a play?'

' 'Ere you are, Mother.'

She slid the letters across to meet my hand. I released the note; she released the letters and the exchange was affected.

These were the letters numbered 43 and 44, and dated August 2nd and October 5th respectively, as above. If you will glance back to them, you will see that they offered valuable evidence.

I at once recognised them for genuine documents in my stepmother's handwriting.

'How many letters have you?'

'Well there's more than I 'ave 'ere. But them as I 'old in my 'and w'ich makes eight, countin' them two, is the ones as 'ud interest anybody as wanted to know w'y a gentleman might die sudden.'

'Are there any that say definitely how he died or what he died of?'

'No,' said Mrs Cutts. 'I wouldn't deceive a gentleman like you, sir. Tell the truth, likewise fair and square. Them eight letters, sir, is wot they calls excitements to murder, and would be so considered by any party as might 'appen to receive them. But as for saying in so many words "weed-killer" or "prussic acid," I will not say as you will find them words in black and white.'

'That, of course, detracts from their value,' I said carelessly. 'These letters are evidence of sad immorality, no doubt, Mrs Cutts, but it's one thing to wish a person dead and another to kill him.'

'There ain't sech a great difference,' said Mrs Cutts, a little shaken. 'It says in the Bible – " 'E that 'ateth 'is brother is a murderer," now, don't it, sir? And there's some as sits on juries 'as the same way of thinkin'.'

'Maybe,' said I, 'but all the same, it's not proof.'

'Very good, sir,' said Mrs Cutts with dignity. 'I wouldn't contradict a gentleman. You 'and me them letters back, Archie. The gentleman don't want 'em. Ef Mr Lathom 'ad any sense 'e'd burn the rubbishin' stuff, and so I'll tell 'im, clutterin' up the place.'

'I don't say that, Mrs Cutts,' said I, holding on to the letters. 'They are of interest, but not of as much interest as I thought they might be. What value did you think of placing on them?'

'To them as knew 'ow to use 'em' – here Mrs Cutts appeared to size me up from head to toe – 'letters like them might be worth a 'undred pounds apiece.'

'Rubbish,' said I. 'I'll give you fifty pounds for the lot, and that's more than they're worth.'

I put the two letters back on the table and flicked at them disdainfully.

'Fifty pound!' shrieked Mrs Cutts, 'fifty pound! And me riskin' losin' a job as is worth more than that any day in recommendations and perks, not countin' my money regular every week!'

She gathered the letters together and began to tie the packet up again.

165

'Mr Lathom 'ud give five times that much to know as they wos safe,' she added.

'Not he,' said I. 'I doubt if he has as much as a hundred pounds in the world. Whereas, if your son likes to come round with me to my hotel, I can give him cash on the nail.'

'No,' said Mrs Cutts. 'I can't let them letters go. Supposin' Mr Lathom wanted to read 'em and they wasn't there.'

'That's your affair,' said I. 'If you don't want to sell them, you can keep them. If I were you I'd put them back quickly where you found them, and say nothing to Mr Lathom about it. There's such a thing as blackmail, you know, Mrs Cutts, and judges are pretty strict about it.'

Mrs Cutts laughed scornfully.

'Blackmail! Nobody ain't goin' to charge theirselves with murder, and don't you think it.'

'There's no murder there,' said I. 'Good-night.'

I rose to go. The woman let me get as far as the door and then came after me.

'See 'ere, sir. You're a gentleman, and I don't want to be 'ard on a gentleman wot's pore father 'as died sudden. Give me two 'undred pound, and I'll let yer take copies of 'em and Archie shall go with you and bring 'em back.'

'Copies don't count so well in a court of law as originals,' I said.

'They could be swore to,' said Mrs Cutts.

'Not at this time of night,' said I.

The youth Archie leaned across and whispered to his mother. She nodded and smiled her unpleasant smile.

'See 'ere, sir, I'll risk it. Archie shall bring you them letters to your 'otel in the mornin' and you shall take copies and 'ave them swore to afore a lawyer. I dursn't let you 'ave them, really I dursn't, sir. I'm takin' a sad risk as it is for a respectable woman.'

'Very well,' I replied. 'But copies are only worth a hundred pounds to me at the very outside.'

'You're makin' a very 'ard bargain, sir.'

'It's that or nothing,' said I.

'Well, sir, if you say so. I'll send Archie round at ten o'clock, sir.'

166

I agreed to this and walked away, glad to get out. I lay awake all night, fancying that Mrs Cutts would go to Lathom in the interval and make better terms with him.

However, Archie was there with the letters in the morning as agreed, and I took him and them round to a solicitor's where typed copies were made and sworn. I also made an affidavit that I recognised the writing of the originals as being in my stepmother's handwriting. I then paid the lad the agreed hundred pounds in Treasury notes, and dismissed him.

I have entered into all these details in order that there should be no doubt as to the genuineness of these copies, and to make quite clear why I am unable at the moment to forward the originals.

It is true that I could probably have forced Archie into handing the letters over, since he had no right to them. But several reasons urged me to take the other course. First, I had no legal right to them either, and was not clear how my action might be looked upon by the police. Secondly, and this was more important, I could hardly hope that Lathom would not discover their absence, and, if he did, he might take fright and leave the country and thus add great difficulties to my task. It would take some weeks, perhaps, to collect all the evidence I needed, and by the time I was ready to set the law in action, he might hide himself very effectually. Thirdly, I did not wish to alienate Mrs Cutts. I foresaw that she might be very useful, not only in bringing me fresh letters, if any arrived that threw further light on the business, but also in keeping watch on Lathom's movements. I suggested to Archie that there might be possibilities of further reward in the future, and cautioned him against alarming Lathom.

It is conceivable, however, that Mrs Cutts may consider it more advantageous to blackmail Lathom than to assist me. Up to the moment of writing, he is still living in Chelsea, and apparently feels himself safe. But for all I know, Mrs Cutts may have retained the letters and be blackmailing him on her own account. Or she may have delivered her warning, and he may have destroyed the letters and made himself (as he imagines) secure. In the latter case it will, of course, be impossible to produce the original documents in court, and then the certified copies will justify their existence.

Having obtained the evidence of the adultery, I now felt myself in a position to put pressure on Munting, and accordingly went round to see him again.

'I perfectly appreciate,' I said, 'the reasons for your silence at our last interview. But if I tell you that I have in my hands independent proof that Lathom was Margaret Harrison's lover, perhaps you will feel justified in assisting my inquiries.'

He shrugged his shoulders.

'My dear man,' he said, 'if you have proof already, I don't see what assistance you require. May I ask what you call proof? After all, one doesn't make these accusations without sufficient grounds.'

'I have got the letters written to Lathom by my stepmother,' I said, 'and they leave the matter in no doubt whatever.'

'Indeed?' said he. 'Well, I won't ask you where you got them from. Private detective work is not in my line. If you really believe that your father was driven to do away with himself, I am extremely sorry – but what can one do about it?'

'I do not think so,' I said. 'I believe, and these letters afford strong evidence to my mind, that my father was cruelly and deliberately murdered by Lathom at Margaret Harrison's instigation. And I mean to prove it.'

'Murdered?' he cried. 'Good God, you can't mean that! That's absolutely impossible. Lathom may be a bit of a rotter in some ways, but he's not a murderer. I'll swear he isn't that. You're absolutely mistaken.'

'Will you read the letters?'

'No,' he said. 'Look here. You're a man of the world. If things have got to this point, I don't mind admitting that Lathom did have some sort of an affair with Mrs Harrison. I did what I could to make him drop it, but, after all, these things will sometimes happen. I told him it was a poor sort of game to play, and when I got the opportunity – over that Milsom affair – I told him I'd shut up about it on condition

168

he cleared out. He assured me afterwards, in the most solemn way, that it was all finished with. Why, damn it, I asked him about it the very day we went down to Manaton, and he repeated that the whole affair was absolutely over and done with.'

'He was wise,' I said dryly, 'since he was taking you down there to view my father's dead body. Even you might have suspected something if you had gone to "The Shack" in the knowledge that it was to Lathom's interest to find what he did find.'

His face changed. I had touched him on the raw somewhere.

'Did you, as a matter of fact, believe Lathom?'

'I believed him – yes.' He turned his pipe thoughtfully over between his fingers. 'I believed that the affair had been put an end to. But I was not altogether sure that Lathom's affection for Mrs Harrison had ceased.'

'And when you found that my father had died so opportunely – did no suspicion enter your mind?'

'Well – I admit it did just pass through my mind that Harrison might have done it himself. I – I didn't want to believe it. I don't know that I did really believe it. But it did occur to me as a possibility.'

'Nothing more?'

'Absolutely nothing more.'

'Will you read the letters, and tell me if, after that, you still think there was nothing more?'

He hesitated.

'If you are so sure that Lathom is innocent, you may be able to prove his innocence.'

He looked at me doubtfully, and slowly put out his hand for the letters. He read the endorsement by the solicitor, and looked sharply at me again, but said nothing. I waited while he read the documents through – first quickly, then for a second time slowly and with greater attention.

'You will notice,' I said, 'that, shortly before the time when he told you the affair was over, Margaret Harrison had written him a letter clearly indicating that she believed herself to be about to have a child by him.'

'Yes, I see that.'

'And that he was not informed that this belief was erroneous, till after my father's death.'

'No.'

'Plenty of motive for murder there.'

'Plenty of motive, certainly. But motive by itself is nothing. Good heavens, man, if everybody committed murder because they had a motive, precious few of us would die natural deaths.'

'But you will admit that murder was being urged upon him, in various ways, in all these letters.'

'I wouldn't necessarily go so far as to admit that. Mrs Harrison is an emotional, imaginative woman. She picks up phrases out of books. Plenty of people talk in this vague way about love – about its being supreme, and justifying itself, and sweeping obstacles aside and so on, without ever intending to put their words into action. I've written that kind of thing myself – in books.'

'Very likely. As a modern novelist you need not be expected to uphold a high standard of morals. But in practice, I take it, you would not wish to excuse or justify murder.'

'No. I confess to an old-fashiioned prejudice against murder. It may be inconsistent of me, but I do. And so, I am sure, would Lathom.'

'Lathom is obviously very much under the influence of Margaret Harrison.'

'I should have said it was the other way round.'

'In some things. In theory, no doubt. But when it comes to doing things, I should say she was infinitely more practical – and more unscrupulous. But say, if you like, he is only under the influence of a strong passion – don't you think that might lead him to do things which conflicted with his principles, or prejudices, or whatever you like to call them? Come now, you have called me a man of the world. Murders are done every day, for much less motive than Lathom had.'

He drummed on the table.

'Well,' he burst out at last. 'I'll admit that. I'll admit – for the sake of argument – that Lathom *might* have murdered your father, though I don't believe it for a moment. But it was physically impossible. How could he? He was here in London all the time.'

'That's where you can help me. Why was it impossible? How do you know it was impossible? Can you prove that it was impossible?'

'I'm sure I can.'

'Will you let me have all the facts you know about the whole thing from the beginning?'

'Of course I will. Damn it all, if Lathom *did* do it, he deserves everything that's coming to him. He'd have to be an absolute swine. Mind you, Lathom and I didn't always get on together, but – it's absurd. He can't have done it. But we've got to kill the possibility.'

He began to walk up and down, visibly perturbed. I waited. We were interrupted by a servant announcing dinner.

'You'll stay?' said Munting. 'You must meet my wife. She has a very clear head for this kind of thing.'

I accepted, not wishing to lose a day in getting to the bottom of the matter. We did not, of course, talk about the subject while the maid was in the room, but after dinner we all went into the library, and there outlined the story to Mrs Munting. I mention her, not because she was able to contribute anything of great value to the discussion (though, being a woman, she was more willing than her husband to allow that a young man might murder an older one for a woman's sake), but because she fetched out the letters which Munting had written to her during his period of residence at Whittington Terrace, in order to verify facts and dates. In the end, she handed the letters over to me in case I might find in them any clue or suggestion which we had over-looked. Munting rather naturally objected to having his love-letters (if one can call these rambling effusions by that name) put into the hands of a comparative stranger, but his wife, with that curious lack of delicacy which virtuous women often display, laughed, and said she was sure I should not pay any attention to the personal passages.

'Mr Harrison is not proposing to publish your Life and Letters, you know,' she said.

This childish remark seemed to amuse Munting. He said: 'No; I fancy I'm safe with him,' and raised no further objection. Probably his vanity was sufficient to assure him that the exposure of his intimate feelings was bound to leave

171

a favourable impression. Indeed, it is obvious that, even in writing to his fiancée, he was writing for effect half the time and quite possibly with an eye to future publication. With young men like Beverley Nichols and Robert Graves prattling in public about their domestic affairs, we need hardly expect to find any decent reticence among the smart novelists of today.

Taking the question of *Motive* as settled for the moment, we proceeded to discuss the subjects *Means* and *Opportunity*. Under these heads, the Muntings put forward a number of objections to the murder theory, and I was bound to recognise that they looked sufficiently formidable. Here is the schedule which I drew up immediately after this conversation.

POINTS TO BE INVESTIGATED IN CONNECTION WITH
THE DEATH OF GEORGE HARRISON

A. *Means*

1. – *Did Harrison really die of muscarine poisoning?*

Muscarine (the poisonous principle of *Amanita muscaria*) was obtained in large quantities from (*a*) the viscera; (*b*) the bedclothes; and (*c*) the half-eaten dish on the table.

The appearance of the body and the symptoms of the illness, as deduced from the attendant circumstances, were both consistent with muscarine poisoning.

Sir James Lubbock stated on oath that the cause of death was muscarine poisoning.

Question: Could any other poison have produced similar effects or a similar chemical analysis? The analyst's attention having been specially directed to muscarine by the inquiries on the opening day of the inquest, did he, in fact, search for any poison other than muscarine?

NOTE: To write to Sir James Lubbock and put these points before him.

2. – *In any case, how did the muscarine get into the body,
if we exclude the hypotheses of accident and suicide?*

Supposing that Lathom had himself gathered the poisonous
fungi and surreptitiously added them to the dish while it
was in course of preparation, the murder might have been
very simply accomplished. If he had merely put them into
the basket with the genuine edible fungi gathered by my
father, the latter would certainly have discovered and thrown
them away when preparing the dish. It would, therefore,
be necessary to wait, and add them when the process of
cooking was already so far advanced that the fungi had lost
their characteristic colour and shape.

On any ordinary occasion it would have been easy for
Lathom to do this. It will be seen from the evidence at the
inquest that Lathom was often left at home in 'The Shack'
while Harrison went sketching or botanising.

In the actual case there are difficulties, some of which have
to be considered under the heading 'Opportunity'.

Question: Did Lathom know *Amanita muscaria* sufficiently well to be able to find it and know it for what it was?
(*Answer:* Quite possibly my father might have shown it to
him and warned him against it. Or he might have studied the
pictures in my father's books or in some other book.)

If not, can he have got some accomplice to procure the
fungus for him? (Not impossible, but unlikely. Country
people usually pay little attention to fungi, and the element
of risk involved would be very great.)

In what way was the dish of fungi cooked? It would be
easier to add a foreign substance to a stew, for example,
which is done slowly and needs little superintendence, than
to a grill or a fry, which takes only a few minutes and is
under the cook's eyes all the time. (*Answer:* Munting, speaking from memory, thinks the dish appeared more in the
nature of a stew. My father's letter to me (No. 15) of
October 22nd, 1928, is of interest in this connection.)

NOTE: To ask Sir James Lubbock if he can confirm this.

If Lathom was able to recognise and procure *Amanita
muscaria*, could he not have boiled it on some previous
occasion and added the poison to the stew in liquid form, so

as to run less risk of my father's recognising the intrusion of the wrong fungus?

(*Answer:* Very probably.)

(As regards the question of Means, therefore, it seemed clear that Lathom might readily have had access to the poison, and that there was no mechanical difficulty at all to prevent his having introduced it into the dish of mushrooms. When, however, we came to consider the subject of Opportunity, we were faced with a more important set of difficulties.)

B. *Opportunity*

   1. – *At what time was the poison actually administered to Harrison?*

A terminus *a quo* is provided by the evidence of Harry Trefusis, who saw Harrison alive and apparently well at 10.30 a.m. on Thursday. By this time, Lathom was presumably in the train and on his way to London.

The terminus *ad quem* can be stated with rather less accuracy. From the fact, however, that the shin of beef delivered that morning was afterwards discovered still wrapped in its original paper, it appears quite certain that Harrison was rendered incapable of seeing to any household affairs before the evening. From my knowledge of my father, I should be prepared to swear that he would certainly never have left meat in this condition overnight. He would have put it on to boil for stock, or, at the very least, would have transferred it to a plate – particularly in the case of shin of beef, which, being glutinous, has a habit of sticking to the wrapping-paper. When I stayed at 'The Shack' with my father, he was accustomed to have his evening meal about seven o'clock. After this, he would wash the crockery and tidy the place up, and put on any stock that might be required for the next day. He would then sit and read for an hour or two, retiring to bed about ten, possibly taking a cup of cocoa or some food before retiring.

It thus seems likely that the poison was taken between the hours of 10.30 a.m. and 8 p.m., and most probably at or about 7 p.m.

Question: What evidence have we that Lathom actually went to London by the 7.55 at all? Could he have returned to 'The Shack' surreptitiously during the interval? By hiring a motor-bicycle or car, he might easily have made his way back from Bovey Tracey or (if this might appear too obvious) from Bramley Halt, Heathfield, Teigngrace or Newton Abbot. He could then have lurked about in the neighbourhood of 'The Shack' till he saw Harrison go out, and taken the opportunity to add the poison to the dish or stock-pot.

NOTE: To inquire as to Lathom's movements in town. If anybody met him on Thursday morning, this hypothesis falls to the ground. If not, to find out whether he really entered the train at Bovey Tracey, and if anybody of his description hired any sort of motor vehicle at any point along the line. This would not, in fact, cover every contingency, for an active man might easily have walked the ten or twelve miles between Newton Abbot and 'The Shack'. A motor vehicle is perhaps more likely, as providing a quicker getaway after the crime.

2. – *Is it possible that the poisonous fungus, or liquid prepared from fungus, was added, not to the fungus gathered by my father on the Thursday, but to some other collection of fungus gathered the previous day?*

This appears unlikely, for three reasons. First: my father always made a great point of eating his fungi freshly gathered. It would have been quite unlike him to gather them overnight and eat them next day. He considered early morning the best time for picking fungus. He had stated his intention of gathering Warty Caps on the Thursday morning, and was, in fact, seen apparently doing so by the witness Coffin. Secondly: If the fungi eaten on Thursday night were gathered the previous day, what became of those gathered on Thursday morning? They were not found in 'The Shack'. Thirdly: For Lathom's purpose it was necessary that Harrison should have had the intention of gathering Warty Caps, and no other kind of fungus, since this is the only variety which could reasonably be confused with *Amanita muscaria*. It would appear, therefore, more than a coincidence that my father should have been seen gathering fungus in a spot where Warty Caps were usually to be found. Of course, Lathom's evidence on this point is suspect, and verification is necessary.

Question: Are Warty Caps (*Amanita rubescens*) actually plentiful in the spot where Harrison was seen by Coffin?

Can any of the contents of the dish of fungi actually be identified as *Amanita rubescens*?

When did Harrison mention to Lathom his intention of gathering *Amanita rubescens*? This question is important, because, if the poisonous fungi were introduced among the harmless ones in their natural state, it is absolutely necessary that the two varieties should bear at least a superficial resemblance to one another. Even in a half-cooked state, there could be no confusion between *Amanita muscaria* and, say, *Chantarelles* or *Bolitus edulis* or *Amanitopris fulva*. Unfortunately, no one can throw any light on this except Lathom himself, and it is not likely that he will tell the truth.

NOTE: To verify the habitat of *Amanita rubescens*, and, if possible, its presence in the actual dish of fungi analysed.

C. *Further Questions and Objections* (Miscellaneous)

If Lathom was guilty of administering poison to Harrison why did he return to 'The Shack' on Saturday? Would it not have been wiser to remain in town till the death was discovered?

This is an objection which to me appears to carry some weight. I can, however, see certain considerations which might account for a proceeding so apparently reckless from a practical point of view.

176

(*a*) Lathom may have wished to be on the spot to conceal any accidental traces of the crime. As we do not yet know his exact procedure, it is not certain what these could have been – a bottle, perhaps, containing extract of *Amanita muscaria*, a pan in which he had prepared it; a book or papers containing notes; traces of his previous arrival by motor-bicycle or otherwise; possibly some letter or message left by Harrison, containing his own suspicions as to the manner of his death.

NOTE: Munting's opinion is that Lathom originally intended to remain alone in 'The Shack' while he (Munting) went to fetch help, but when it came to the point found himself unable to face it. This is consistent with the above explanation, if we suppose that Lathom was overcome by fear or remorse at the sight of the body, and was thus prevented from carrying out his design. From Munting's own statement it will be seen that Lathom was in a nervous state from the moment of his meeting Munting in town, down to the time when the body was discovered.

(*b*) Supposing the plot had failed to work, Harrison would have been expecting Lathom's return. Let us say he had discovered an *Amanita muscaria* among his fungi – he would wonder how it had got there, and if Lathom never turned up might conceive such suspicion of him as would put him on his guard against any further attempts. On the other hand, he might have mentioned to people in the neighbourhood that Lathom was due to come back, in which case, the plot succeeding, Lathom's absence might have a suspicious look.

Further explanations suggested by the Muntings:

(*c*) Lathom (supposing him guilty) would probably have no idea when the death might be expected to take place. As Thursday, Friday and Saturday passed without news, he might be overcome by nervous restlessness and an overwhelming anxiety to see for himself what was going on. (I suppose that from artists and persons of unbalanced temperament, such behaviour may be expected, half-witted as it may appear.)

(*d*) The alleged hankering of a murderer to revisit the

scene of the crime. (This I hold to be pure superstition and quite baseless in fact.)

(e) Remorse. Perhaps Lathom regretted what he had done, and was making a belated effort to save Harrison's life by fetching medical assistance before it was too late. (In this suggestion, put forward by Mrs Munting, the wish is probably father to the thought.)

Why did Lathom take Munting down to 'The Shack' with him? This again seems to me to have been the act of a madman. Unless, indeed, he was cunning enough to foresee that this was exactly the appearance it *would* present, and was therefore the best defence he could put up against suspicion.

Further, of course Munting provided Lathom with a complete alibi for the whole of Saturday and an unprejudiced witness as to the discovery of the body. Suppose, for example, that Harrison, instead of having been dead six or seven hours, had been only just dead or on the point of expiring when they got there, Munting could have given evidence that they had found him in that condition on their arrival.

On the other hand, Lathom was running a very serious risk, not only of defeating his own ends, but of having the whole vile plot exposed. If they had found Harrison still alive, they would have had no choice but to summon a doctor immediately; the victim might have recovered, or at least recovered sufficiently to denounce Lathom.

NOTE: Is Munting entirely cleared from complicity in the murder? His behaviour has been suspicious, and he has withheld information as long as possible. Not to trust him too far.

Neither Munting nor his wife seem to find as much difficulty as I do about this part of the business. They agree that a man of Lathom's temperament, having committed a murder, would be afraid to be alone, and would take any risks to secure companionship. They instance Patrick Mahon's incredible rashness in taking Miss Duncan to sleep at the Crumbles on the very night after he had murdered Emily Kaye, and while her dead body was actually lying in the next room. These people are both novelists and are supposed to have studied human nature. They say it is full of inconsistencies and I daresay they are right. I admit that, to me, the mentality of men like Lathom is perfectly incomprehensible, and I am ready to believe anything.

* * *

It was late when I left the Muntings, taking away with me the letters they gave me, and having obtained from Munting a promise that he would draw up a statement of the course of events during the periods not covered by the letters, and containing, in particular, an exact account of what took place at 'The Shack'. This is the statement which forms part of this dossier, divided into cronological sections for greater ease of reference. I regret that it is so diffuse and adorned with so many unnecessary personal reflections and literary embellishments. It seems that the vanity of writers must be indulged at all costs, even where a straightforward summary of events would be far more useful. I have not, however, ventured to omit or alter anything, preferring to submit the documents exactly as they stand.

My next step was to write to Sir James Lubbock, raising the various points noted in the schedule for his consideration. In the course of a few days I received the following courteous reply.

HOME OFFICE
12 January, 1930

PAUL HARRISON, ESQ.

DEAR SIR,

I have your letter of inquiry with regard to the circumstances attending your late father's unfortunate death. I quite understand that you are anxious to have the fullest information about it, and will do my best to clear up the various points you raise.

You may rest fully assured that the death was in fact due to the cause stated at the inquest, viz.: poisoning my muscarine, the poisonous principle of the fungus *Amanita muscaria*. In such a case I should not confine myself to searching

179

for the particular poison suggested by the circumstances, but should search, as a matter of routine, for all the various classes of scheduled poisons, including not only the other vegetable alkalis but also the metallic poisons. The analysis was made with great care, and I can confidently state that every possibility was eliminated, except that of poisoning by muscarine. This poison, which was present in very considerable quantities, was unmistakably identified, while the symptoms and post-mortem appearances, as reported by the witnesses, were indubitably consistent with this form of poisoning.

I may add that preparations of the viscera, vomit, etc., and the unconsumed part of the dish of fungi have been preserved untouched, as is my invariable custom in such cases, so as to be available for future reference or analysis in case of any further question being raised. Humanly speaking, however, you may rely absolutely on the accuracy of my results.

With regard to the composition of the dish, I find, on referring to my notes, that this consisted of fungi exhibiting the structural features of *Amanita*, stewed whole in a preparation of beef broth, flavoured with garlic and pot-vegetables.

Your further question displays a slight misapprehension. The isolation of muscarine itself in a pure state from the fungus would be a chemical experiment of considerable difficulty, and has, so far as I know, been accomplished only by two men, Harnack and Nothnagel; their results have not, I believe, received confirmation as yet. Choline aurichloride and muscarine aurichloride have been obtained by Harnack from fractionation of extracts of the fungus, and, more recently, King obtained muscarine chloride from the same source. But I conceive your question to mean, simply, 'Could a poisonous liquid be produced by simply boiling the fungus in water of broth?' To this, my answer is, Yes; the liquid part of a stew made with *Amanita muscaria* would be equally poisonous with the solid part. In fact, according to Dixon Mann, the solid parts of the fungus, when thoroughly desiccated, are harmless, and are eaten with impunity in certain parts of the Continent, so that the juices when extracted by ebullition would probably contain a greater proportion of poisonous matter than the solid residue.

Trusting that these facts are what you require,

I remain,

Yours faithfully,

JAMES LUBBOCK

The ground being thus cleared for my investigations, I determined to clear up the Manaton end of the thing first. Munting having meanwhile undertaken to make inquiries as to Lathom's movements in London on the 17th and 18th of October.

'The Shack' had been locked up, and the key deposited with the local constable. Being the executor under my father's will, I had no difficulty in obtaining it, and took the opportunity of asking a few questions at the public-house. All I could gather was, however, that Mr Lathom had knocked them up on the Saturday night in a 'terrible state' and 'looking as though he had seen a ghost', and had announced that Mr Harrison had been found dead. As he seemed on the point of collapse, the publican had comforted him with strong drink and had himself summoned the police from Bovey Tracey, the village constable being, as it happened, absent on some duty or other. While waiting, Mr Lathom had recovered himself and had asked to make a trunk call to town. This was, of course, the call to Margaret Harrison. The telephone is in the landlord's private room, and the landlord had, with a proper delicacy, retired and shut the door on his guest, so that nothing had been overheard. On coming out, Lathom had seemed greatly agitated, and had explained that he had been breaking the news to the dead man's family. This was disappointing, as it would have been interesting to know in what words Lathom had announced the event. From Margaret Harrison's letter, however, it seems that he represented the thing as an accident. Yet she must surely have had her suspicions of a death occurring so opportunely and so pat upon her own instigations to murder. Possibly she managed to convince even herself by her hypocrisy – Munting thinks it not unlikely, and no doubt he has had experience of her type of mentality.

181

I next obtained the address of the labourer, Harold Coffin. His wife was at home, and informed me that I should find her husband at work carting some timber which had fallen in the recent gale. If I followed the lane leading down past 'The Shack' I could not miss him. Following these directions, I came upon him on the outskirts of a small wood. He was very ready to tell me all he knew, and led me at once to the spot, not very far away, where he had last seen my father.

It was, of course, too late in the season for *Amanita rubescens,* but the site which he pointed out seemed suitable enough for it, and he also, without being prompted, mentioned that he had often seen fungi growing there, of a reddish-brown colour with grey patches on the top. I took *Edible and Poisonous Fungi* from my pocket and asked him to look through it. He hesitated some time between the pictures of *Amanita rubescens* and *Amanita muscaria,* and finally said he thought it might be one of those two. The colour of *Amanita muscaria* seemed a bit overdone, he thought, but then, pictures in books wasn't always right, was they, sir? The wood, locally known as Five-Acre Wood, was a great place for toadstools, and he had often seen my father gathering the great *Hepatica* fungus from the trees – the huge liver-coloured lumps commonly known as 'Poor Man's Beefsteak'. Coffin was quite clear that my father was actually gathering fungi, and not merely looking for them. My father had spoken to him and said something about, 'Getting my supper, you see, Coffin. You ought to try some yourself; you're missing a treat.' Coffin had often thought of those cheerful words when he heard of the poor gentleman's death, and had taken them as a warning.

Coffin said he knew Mr Lathom quite well by sight, having met him from time to time in the public-house when having a friendly glass. He had never seen him in the Five-Acre Wood but once, and that was with Mr Harrison, about a week before the latter's death. His own work had lain in and about the Five-Acre during the first fortnight of October – he was employed by Mr Carey – all this round here was Mr Carey's land – and he thought he should have seen Mr Lathom if he had come there alone at any time.

Having thanked and rewarded Coffin, I made my way to 'The Shack'. Except for the removal of the bedclothes and other objects required for the inquest it was exactly as it had been left at the time of the death. The broken bedstead, with its terrible witness to my poor father's death-agony, still stood in a corner of the bedroom. Even Lathom's painting materials lay huddled in a corner. I suppose he had forgotten to remove them. A few roughly-daubed canvasses in oil contrasted strongly with my father's delicate water-colours, of which I found a number put away in a drawer. Dust had gathered thickly everywhere.

I made a careful search on shelves and in drawers for any notes or papers that might throw light on my problem, but found nothing except a few bills and the letter my father had received from me. There were one or two novels, a number of local guide-books and botanical books of reference, and some artist's catalogues. Delving among these, I at length came on a large scale-map of the district, with notes upon it in my father's handwriting. He had apparently used it as a kind of botanical chart, marking on it the localities in which various plants and fungi were to be found. Five-Acre Wood was clearly shown, and upon it my father had made a small cross accompanied by the note 'Amanita rubescens.' I looked for any mention of Amanita muscaria, but could see none; either my father had not found it in the district, or else he had concerned himself with edible varieties only.

One question, therefore, seemed clearly answered. My father *had*, without question, been gathering fungi for his supper on the 17th October, and the place where he had gathered them was a place in which he was accustomed to find Amanita rubescens.

I could find nothing further of any interest at 'The Shack', though I spent a whole day there. I passed the night at the inn, and next day departed to Bovey Tracey to check Lathom's movements.

My first interview was with the taxi-driver. This man's name is William Johnson and he lives in the High Street. He perfectly recollects having driven to Manaton on Thursday, 17th October, and taken Lathom to catch the 8.13. The circumstances had been strongly impressed upon his mind by the catastrophe that followed it so closely, and the fact that he had actually visited 'The Shack' and seen the victim, only two days before the discovery of the body, has naturally made him a kind of local hero.

He is positive that my father and Lathom parted on the best of terms. They shook hands, and my father said: 'Well, hope you have a good journey. See you back on Saturday. What train do you think you'll catch? Lathom answered that he wasn't quite sure, and added: 'Don't wait up for me if I'm late.'

This answers one of our questions, and makes it quite clear that at least one person besides my father knew that Lathom was expected back on the Saturday.

My next question was, At what time had Lathom ordered his taxi? The man remembered this too. A telephone message was put through to him from Manaton at about nine o'clock on the Wednesday evening. He can verify this, if necessary by his order-book.

This is interesting. It makes it seem likely that Lathom only decided to make this trip to town at the last moment – in fact, after hearing my father express his intention of gathering *Amanita rubescens* the following day.

Finally, I inquired whether Johnson had actually seen Lathom get into the train. By a stroke of good fortune he was able to answer this question definitely. He had put a parcel on the train for a printer at Bovey Tracey, and, while doing this, he had seen Lathom take his seat in a third-class smoker. As the train went out, Lathom leaned out of the window and shouted something to a porter – some question, he thought, about changing at Newton Abbot.

I hired this man's taxi, which was a reasonably good one, and interviewed the railway staff at the three intermediate stations between Bovey Tracey and Newton Abbot. Here, as was natural, the men found some difficulty in remembering the events of three months ago. I could not find anybody who recollected seeing Lathom. In each place I asked for a name of anybody in the village who might be likely to have a car or motor-cycle for hire, and went to see the proprietors of the vehicles, but without result. Nowhere could I find any record of such a transaction.

Newton Abbot is a larger place, and I anticipated difficulty. On the contrary, and greatly to my surprise, I got on to Lathom's trail almost immediately. No sooner had I mentioned his name to the station-master than he said at once:

'Oh, yes, sir – that was the gentleman who lost a pocket-book last October. Did he ever find it?'

Taking this cue as it presented itself, I replied that he had not, and that, being in the neighbourhood, I had promised to call and ask about it.

'Well, sir,' said the station-master, 'we made inquiries all down the line, and had several men out searching, but they never found it. They would have brought it to me if they had, for they were all decent fellows and Mr Lathom offered a reward. I'm afraid some tramp must have picked it up, sir. There's a lot of them about these days and they're not over-honest.'

'No doubt that was it,' said I. 'Let me see – whereabouts did he say he lost it?'

'Said he thought it must have fallen out from his breast-pocket when he was leaning out of the window. He couldn't say exactly where, but he thought it must be just the other side of Heathfield. Here's the note I made in my book, you see, sir, and here's the gentleman's name and address that he wrote down himself.'

I recognised the handwriting in which Lathom had written out Munting's address for me.

'Well, it was very tiresome,' I said, 'but I am sure you did all you could. There was money in the pocket-book, I suppose?'

'Yes, sir, and the gentleman's ticket to town. He was in quite a way about it, because he said he hadn't enough money on him to book again. So I spoke to the ticket-collector, and he said he would make it all right on the train, and Mr Lathom could settle it with the Company when he got to town.'

These inquiries had taken the greater part of the day, so I decided to stay that night in Newton Abbot and interview the ticket-collector the next day. He was still on the same train and perfectly recollected the affair of Lathom and his ticket. I went on up to Paddington with him, and there the friendly collector directed me to the official in the Inquiry Bureau who had dealt with the matter on the previous occasion. After considerable referring back and forth and ringing up the head office, it was clearly established that Lathom had duly arrived by the 1.15, without his ticket, had explained the circumstances and had left his name and address, promising to send the ticket on if it turned up. As a matter of fact, it never turned up, but as the booking-clerk at Bovey Tracey had clearly remembered issuing it and had identified Lathom on his next visit as being the person to whom the ticket had been issued, the Company accepted the explanation and allowed the matter to drop.

This was something of a blow. I had really reckoned more than I realised on finding that Lathom had left the train at some point and doubled back to Manaton. There was just one possibility. He might have hurried across to the down platform and taken the 1.30, which would land him back at Bovey Tracey at about half-past six. This would have meant very quick work, for the explanation to the authorities at Paddington must have taken him nearly ten minutes. And at the other end he would have had to get, somehow or other, to Manaton and then do the three miles out to 'The Shack', and then snatch his opportunity to rush in unseen, and drop the poison into the stew while my father's back was turned. It seemed almost impossible. Apart from everything else, it was inconceivable that he should not have been seen, either at Newton Abbot or at Bovey Tracey. He would have had to pass the barrier, and he would have had to hire a car, for nothing else would have got him to 'The Shack' before supper-time.

I turned it over and over in my mind and could make nothing of it. It seemed that I must abandon this whole theory. I returned to my hotel in a mood of deep depression, and found there, waiting for me, a letter from Munting, which I append here in its place.

50. *John Munting to Paul Harrison*

DEAR HARRISON,

A damnably awkward thing has happened. Lathom turned up here last night. The girl showed him straight into my study and I was caught without hope of escape.

He looked nervous and irritable, and came straight to the point.

'Look here,' he said, 'has this fellow Harrison been round to see you?' I hesitated, and he went on at once, 'Can't you say yes or no? What's the good of lying about it?'

'Yes,' I said, 'he came round.'

'What did he want?'

I said you were naturally anxious to have all available details about your father's death.

'Yes, that's all very well,' he cut in angrily. 'What have you been saying to him? Have you been discussing my private affairs?'

'I don't think,' I answered cautiously, 'I told him anything that he didn't know already.'

'Have you been spreading scandals about Mrs Harrison and me? Come on, out with it!'

'Sit down,' I said, 'it's no good shouting at me like that.'

'Sit down be damned! I suppose you've been chattering as usual. I should have thought you would have the decency to shut up about what wasn't your business. I warned you about him, didn't I? Why couldn't you keep the fellow out?'

'My dear man,' I said, 'if I'd refused to see him, he'd have thought there was something very suspicious about the business.'

'So I suppose you blabbed it all out like a good, virtuous little boy.'

'As a matter of fact,' I said, 'he seemed to know all about it.'

'Nonsense! How could he know, unless you told him?'

'Possibly,' I said, 'he gathered it from your manner, or from Mrs Harrison. Besides,' I added, feeling that attack was my only possible form of defence, 'I thought you told

187

me it was all over and done with. Isn't it? I assured Harrison that it was. I had only your word to go on. If it wasn't all over, what the devil did you mean by taking me down to Devon with you? You know perfectly well that if I'd known it was still going on, wild horses wouldn't have taken me down there.'

This brought him up all standing.

'Yes, well,' he said, 'of course it's all over. But why did you have to tell him anything about it at all?'

'Look here,' I said, 'you've not been straight with me, and I don't believe you now. I've had quite enough of this. You've dragged me into this business again. I've been your scapegoat once and I'm fed up. Do you expect me to go on taking the blame for your idiotic love-affairs? I've got my wife to consider.'

I was afraid he would go back to the very difficult question of how you got to know about the intrigue. I didn't want to tell him about the letters, which you had shown me more or less in confidence, and yet I felt a perfect cad for not warning him of his danger. It seemed abominable to have listened to such suspicions against a man, without giving him the chance to clear himself. Fortunately, he abandoned this point.

'What does the fellow want?' he went on. 'What's he think he's going to find out? The thing's clear enough, isn't it?'

'Well,' I said, 'to tell you the truth, Lathom, when I came to consider the thing I couldn't help suspecting – '

'Suspecting! My God, *you've* got your beastly suspicions now. What in the devil's name do *you* suspect?'

'I couldn't help suspecting,' I went on, as steadily as I could, 'that old Harrison had found out something and committed suicide.'

'Oh!' said Lathom. 'Well, what if he did? The man was a – ' (a word which I will spare you). 'The best thing he could do was to clear out from a place where he wasn't wanted. Damn good riddance. A good thing if he did have the sense to see it.'

'That's a pretty rotten thing to say, Lathom.'

'Don't be such a damned hypocrite.'

'I mean it,' I said. 'You're behaving like an absolute swine. Harrison was damned decent to you, and you seem to think that just because you can paint better than he could, you are perfectly justified in seducing his wife and then accepting his hospitality and driving him to commit suicide.'

'I hadn't anything to do with it,' he retorted, 'he was all right when I left him. You ask anybody down there who saw him. He was as cheery and friendly as could be. I'm not responsible for what he did behind my back. I was in London all the time. I can prove it.'

'I don't see that it needs proving,' said I.

'Oh, don't you?' he burst out violently. 'Well, I do. You'll be saying next that I had something to do with his death.'

He stopped suddenly and I caught him looking sideways at me, as if to see how I should take this suggestion. It turned me quite cold, and I had a curious sensation as if my stomach had turned right over.

'Well,' I said, 'if anybody heard you talking like this, they might be excused for thinking so.'

'Oh, might they!'

'It's dangerous to talk about wanting people out of the way, you know,' I went on, watching him.

'Punk!' he said. 'Now, I'll tell you, Mr Good Little Moral Boy, I'll tell you just exactly where I was all the time – all the time, do you hear? And then you can come and beg my pardon.'

'I don't want – ' I began.

'No, but I do. Got that? I do. And you may as well make a note of it. On Thursday, now – Thursday – have you got that? – I was at the dentist's at two o'clock, see? First thing I did when I got to town. You can verify that, I suppose? Or do you imagine I have bribed the dentist? You'd better write his address down. Get on with it.'

'Really, Lathom – '

'No, you won't. Any excuse not to believe me, I suppose. Well, I'll do it for you. Dentist, two o'clock, name and address, here you are. Seven o'clock – you'll allow that I couldn't get to Devon and back between two-thirty and seven, I suppose – or do you imagine I chartered an aeroplane?'

'I suppose nothing of the sort.'

'Damn it, suppose what you like. I can give you what I was doing at four o'clock. Come now, that's close enough, isn't it? I had tea with Marlowe. He's a painter, but even you will allow he's honest enough. Tea with Marlowe, four o'clock. At seven, I dined at the 'Ben Bourgeois', and paid by cheque – you can confirm that, you know – and went on to the first night of Meyrick's show. He saw me there. Is that good enough?'

He was writing all these times and places down, digging the pencil savagely into the paper. I said:

'You seem to remember it all very clearly.'

'Yes, that's one in the eye for you, isn't it, my lad? Sorry and all that, but you asked for it. I slept that night at the studio. I'm afraid I've only Mrs Cutts's word for it, and, of course, she'd say anything.'

'Very likely,' said I.

'That gives you a gleam of hope, doesn't it? But seeing I didn't get home till four ack emma, after celebrating with Meyrick's crowd – ask them – it doesn't leave much margin, does it? Particularly as I was up again at nine o'clock.'

'That's very unusual,' I said, trying to speak lightly. 'Whatever did you get up at nine for?'

'To spite you. And incidentally, to sign for a beastly registered letter. Providential, wasn't it?'

'Obviously,' said I.

'At ten-thirty I went to see my agent. You know him, don't you?' I admitted knowing the agent.

'I lunched at Lady Tottenham's. Went to see her about a sitting at twelve and stayed on. Anything fishy about Lady Tottenham?'

'Nothing, except her husband's income. Sardines, isn't it?'

'Damned witty. You ought to put that in your next book. Then I went round to Winsor & Newton's and paid a bill. By cheque. And ordered some stuff. No doubt they will be happy to show you their books.'

I was silent.

'Dinner at Holtby's. Very stately and all that. Old boy

thinks of presenting a portrait to Liverpool Town Hall. Most respectable party. Went on to the Aitchbone – not so respectable, but full of people. Spent the night with the Goodman boys. Breakfasted there. Came on. Looked you up, and you had me under your own bloody inquisitive eye for the rest of the day. Now then!'

I asked him why he was so anxious to tell me all this.

'To tell your pal Harrison,' he snapped back. 'He seems blasted anxious to stick his nose into my concerns. Tell him to keep out of it. I don't like the swine.'

'I don't see,' I said, 'why you should work yourself up into this extraordinary state of mind because a man has made a few ordinary inquiries about his father. Unless, of course, you have anything special to hide.'

This seem to sober him down. He pulled his face into something more nearly resembling amiability and then suddenly began to laugh.

'I'm sorry. I lost my temper rather. Anything to hide? Good God, no – except that I'm sorry Harrison has got on to – that business with Margaret, you know. She must have let something out, accidentally. But I'll swear the old man never knew a word about it. Not a damn thing. He was as right as rain – best of pals, and all that. But I don't like that pup of his.'

I put down the pen with which I had been fidgeting all this time, got up and went and stood by him on the hearthrug.

'Lathom,' I said, 'why did you come here?'

He looked at me, and for a moment I thought he was on the point of getting something off his chest. I had a horrible fear of what it might be. If he had spoken, I really do not know what I should have said or done. I might – I don't know. I was really quite horribly frightened.

But nothing came of it. He shifted his gaze and said, in a curious, embarrassed way:

'I've told you. I wanted to know what you'd done with Harrison – to find out how the matter stood. Afraid it's been awkward for you. I didn't quite realise. It can't be helped. He'd have to know sometime, anyhow. I'd better be going.'

He held out his hand. In the state things were in, I could not take it. Either I was being a perfect Judas Iscariot, in which case I hadn't the face to give him my hand, or else *he* was, in which case I felt I would rather be excused. It was all so involved that at the moment I was completely incapable of deciding anything.

'Oh!' he said. 'I've said one or two things, haven't I? All right. Sulk about it if you like. I'm damned if I care.'

He slammed out. After a moment I went after him. 'Lathom!' I called.

I don't know what I meant to say to him. The only answer was the bang of the outer door.

Honestly, Harrison, I don't know what to make of it. I don't know whether I've been a skunk or a moral citizen. I don't know whether I've warned a guilty man, or betrayed an innocent one, or the other way round. But I'm feeling like hell about it, because – well, frankly, because I cannot believe that an innocent man would have such a water-tight alibi.

It's perfectly obvious he came here to ram the alibi down my throat. But it *is* an alibi. I'm enclosing the paper with the names and addresses he wrote down so pat. You can investigate it all, if you like, but it's certain to be sound. He knew it. He was perfectly confident. Besides –

Anyway, I won't touch it. It makes me sick.

I've finished that statement, by the way. Here it is. I hope to God the whole thing comes to nothing and I never hear of it again. I ask you, as a favour, to leave me out of it if you can.

Yours very Truly,
J. MUNTING

51. *Statement of Paul Harrison* [Continued]

Disregarding the hysterical tone of his last few sentences, I felt that on the whole Munting was right, and had behaved with more discretion and public spirit than I had credited him with.

It was obvious to me that Lathom was losing his nerve.

As to his guilt, I had by now no shadow of a doubt. The blatant way in which he had marked his trail, right up from Manaton to London and back again, and his determination to let Munting know all about it, were actions entirely inconsistent with the carelessness of an innocent man. The trouble was that he was now on the alert. At any minute he might take alarm and bolt. On this account, I decided to waste no valuable time in checking his alibi. The fact that he had produced it with such confidence left me no hope of breaking it down; moreover, some of the inquiries were of a sort that could only be made satisfactorily by the police.

It was evident that I must abandon the whole idea of a return to Manaton. Only one possibility was left, namely, that the poison had been left in such a place that my father was bound to add it to the dish of fungi himself; and that this manoeuvre had been carried out before Lathom left for London.

I knew that all the foodstuffs in 'The Shack' had been carefully analysed and found harmless, with the exception of the half-eaten dish of fungi itself. I was, therefore, forced to conclude that the poison had been added to the beef stock in which the fungi were stewed. Anything else would be dangerous, for the presence of muscarine in, say, the salt or the coffee would be a circumstance so suspicious as to impress even the coroner's jury.

There was nothing difficult about this. The stock would have been prepared from Monday's delivery of shin of beef. It was my father's habit always to keep a pan of stock simmering on the hob. By Thursday morning there would probably be just sufficient left to cook his evening meal, after which he would boil up the new supply of shin for the rest of the week.

Now, in what form would the poison have been added? Not in the solid form, for my father would have noticed the presence of fungi in his stock. But a teacupful of poisonous liquid might easily have been poured in at any moment. I was, therefore, brought back to my previous idea that Lathom managed to procure the *Amanita muscaria* and decoct the poison during my father's absence from the hut.

But how I was ever to prove this, I did not know. I had plenty of evidence of motive and opportunity, but nothing that could put the crime beyond any reasonable doubt in the minds of twelve good and true jury-members. And besides, I was by no means satisfied of Lathom's ability to identify *Amanita muscaria* with certainty. Was there no easier and more reliable method by which he might have obtained the stuff? Was it possible, for instance, to buy muscarine? If so, and if one could trace the sale to Lathom, there would be genuine evidence of criminal intent. For what innocent reason could an artist require muscarine?

The difficulties of the thing stared me in the face. Even if muscarine was procurable commercially (which I thought very unlikely, for, so far as I know, it has no medicinal use), it was impossible for me, as a private individual, to broadcast an investigation among all the chemists in the country. Only the police could do that, and I could not set the police to work without producing the very evidence which was the object of the search. There were not only chemists – there were all the research laboratories, too. The thing seemed hopeless.

At this point the word 'laboratories' struck a chord in my mind. Had not there been something in the Munting correspondence about a laboratory?

I had not paid much attention to the passage when I first read it, because my mind had been taken up with the idea of Lathom's having gathered the fungus on the spot. And, indeed, the facts had been so buried in a lot of vague twaddle about the origin of life and other futile Muntingesque speculations that I had skimmed the pages over in disgust, but when I turned back to the letter I cursed myself for not having given it fuller consideration before.

Two facts emerged very clearly from the welter of surrounding nonsense:

1. That Lathom had been shown a collection of poisons, apparently kept where anybody could easily get at them; and

2. That Leader had drawn the special attention of the party to certain synthetic, or laboratory-made poisons, in-

distinguishable by analysis from natural vegetable products.

Here at last was something definite. Supposing that a bottle of muscarine had by any chance formed part of the collection, what was easier than for Lathom to have helped himself to it?'

I did not know whether it was possible for an outside person to penetrate the laboratories of St Anthony's College unchallenged, but this I could easily find out by the simple process of going there. Probably I should only have to ask to see some doctor or student. Lathom, for instance, could have asked to see this man Leader, whom he already knew. Leader might very well be able to give us some help in the matter. Munting was my point of contact with Leader, and the next step was obviously to go round and get a note of introduction.

Munting, of course, showed great unwillingness to interfere in the matter. His interview with Lathom seemed to have upset him badly. At length, however, I persuaded him that he had a duty in the matter.

'If you refuse to help me,' I said, 'and I am able to prove the murder, you will be something very like an accessory after the fact.'

Mrs Munting, who, in practical common sense, is worth ten of her husband, agreed with this point of view.

'It would be very unpleasant if you got into trouble about it, Jack. I do think if Mr Lathom really has done this dreadful thing, you oughtn't to stand in the way of getting it found out. A man like that is very dangerous. And they say that when a poisoner has once committed a murder and got away with it, he is very likely to try it again. It might be you or young Mr Harrison next time.'

'Do you really think so?' he muttered unhappily.

'I do. And oh, Jack! Do think of the awful cruelty of letting that poor man die such a painful, lingering death, all alone in that place, without a soul to come near him. Anyone who could do that would be an absolute monster. I don't care what excuse he had.'

'That's been haunting me,' said Munting – and he did look very white and ill. 'All right, Harrison. I'll see it through. Look here, I'll come along to the place with you.'

We walked in complete silence till we came to St Anthony's. There were numbers of people passing in and out through the wide entrance, and nobody took the slightest notice of us.

'I think the labs are up this staircase,' said Munting, leading the way. 'And here's where we hang up the hats and coats,' he added, rattling his umbrella into a hat-stand placed inside the heavy swinging door.

'Is that usual?' I inquired.

'We did it last time,' said Munting, 'I remember it distinctly. And as the idea is to see whether it's feasible to roam unchallenged about the place, we may as well look as much like the inhabitants as possible. If Lathom did come here poison-hunting, he'd scarcely omitted that precaution.'

Having thus shed the outward insignia of visitors, we found ourselves in a wide corridor, smelling faintly of chemists' shops, with numbered doors on either side. A few men in white overalls passed us, but took no notice of us. We walked briskly, as though with a definite objective, and, selecting at random a door near the end of the corridor, pushed it boldly open.

A big room, full of sinks and tables and well-lit by large windows, presented itself to our view. A student sat at a bench near us with his back to the door. He was boiling something in a complicated apparatus of glass tubes over a Bunsen burner. He did not look up. Over by the window four men were gathered round some sort of experiment, which apparently absorbed all their attention. A sixth man, mounted on a pair of steps, was searching for something in a cupboard. He glanced round as we entered, but, seeing that we did not look likely to assist him in finding what he wanted, ignored us, and, coming down, went up to the student with the apparatus.

'What's become of . . . ?' (something I didn't catch) he asked irritably.

'How should I know?' demanded the other, who was pouring some liquid into a funnel and seemed annoyed at the interruption. 'Ask Griggs.'

We backed out again, unregarded, and tried another door.

Here we found a small room, with a solitary, elderly man bending over a microscope. He removed his eye from the lens and looked round with a scowl. We begged his pardon and retired. Before we had closed the door, his head was back at the eyepiece again, while his right hand, which had never stopped writing, continued to take notes.

We intruded, with equal ease and equally unchallenged, into a lecture-room, where forty or fifty students were gathered round a demonstrator at a blackboard; into two more laboratories, one empty and the other containing two absorbed men and a dead rabbit, and finally into a fourth laboratory, where a dozen or so students were laughing and talking and seemed to be waiting for somebody.

One of these, having nothing particular to do, came forward and asked if we wanted anybody in particular. Munting replied that he was looking for Mr Leader.

'Leader?' said the student. 'Let me see. He's a second-year man, isn't he? Where's Leader, anybody know?'

A young man in spectacles said he fancied Leader was in Room 27.

'Oh, yes, to be sure. Try 27 – along the corridor on the right, up the steps and the second door on the left. If he's not there, I expect they'll be able to tell you. Not at all, pleasure.'

We found our way to Room 27, and there, among a group of students, found Leader, who greeted Munting with loud demonstrations of joy. I was introduced, and explained that I was anxious for a little information, if he could spare the time.

He led us to a quiet corner, and Munting reminded him of his previous visit with Lathom and the conversation about synthetic poisons. He was only too delighted to assist us, and led us along at once to another room, inhabited only by the usual couple of absorbed men in a far corner, who took no notice of us.

'Here you are,' said Leader, cheerfully, displaying an open cupboard stacked with glass bottles. 'Convincing demonstration of the way we've got Mother Nature beat. Synthetic thyroxin – some stuff you produce in your own throat, handy and available without the tedious formality of opening you up. A small daily dose gives you pep. Camphor, our own brand, cures cold and kills beetles. Take a sniff and admire the fine, rich, natural aroma. Cinchona, all my own work, or, strictly speaking, Professor Benton's. Adrenalin – that's the stuff to make your hair stand on end; full of kidney punch. Muscarine – not so pretty as scarlet toadstools, but just as good for giving you tummy-ache. Urea – '

'That's very interesting, isn't it?' said Munting.

'Very,' said I. My hand shook a little as I took the bottle from Leader. It was a squat, wide-mouthed glass jar, about half-full of a whitish powder, and clearly labelled 'Muscarine (Synthetic) $C_5H_{15}NO_3$'.

'It's rather deadly, I suppose,' I added, with as much carelessness as I could assume.

'Fairly so,' said Leader. 'Not quite as powerful as the natural stuff, I believe, but quite disagreeable enough. A teaspoonful would settle your hash all right, and leave a bit over for the dog. Nice symptoms. Sickness, blindness, delirium *and* convulsions.' He grinned fondly at the bottle. 'Like to try some? Take it in a little water and the income-tax won't bother you again.'

'What's it made of, Leader?' asked Munting.

'Oh – inorganic stuff, you know – all artificial. I couldn't say offhand. I can look it up if you like.' He hunted in a locker and produced a notebook. 'Oh, yes, of course. Cholin. You start with artificial cholin.'

'What's that? Something to do with the liver?'

'Well, yes, in the ordinary way. But you can make it by heating ethene oxide with triethylamine. That gives you your cholin. Then you oxidise it with dilute nitric acid – the stuff you etch with, you know. Result, muscarine. Pretty, isn't it?'

'And if you analyse it again chemically, could you tell the difference between that and the real stuff?'

'Of course not. It *is* the real stuff. I don't think we've got any of the natural muscarine about the place, or you'd see. But there's no difference at all, really. Nature's only a rather clumsy kind of chemist, don't you see. You're a chemical laboratory; your body, I mean – so am I – so's everybody –

only rather a careless and inaccurate one, and given to producing unnecessary flourishes and ornaments, like your face, or toadstools. There's no *need* to make a toadstool when you want to produce muscarine. If it comes to that, I don't suppose there's any real need for your face – from a chemical point of view. We could build you up quite easily in the labs if we wanted to. You're mostly water, you know, with a little salt and phosphates and all that kind of thing.'

'Come, Leader, that won't quite do. You couldn't make me walk and talk, could you?' (This was Munting, of course.)

'Well, no. There's a trifling hitch there, I admit – always supposing anybody wants to hear your bright conversation.'

'Then there is something – what I call Life – which you can't imitate.'

'Well, yes. But I daresay we shall find it some day. It can't be anything very out-of-the-way, can it? I mean, there's an awful lot of it knocking about. The trouble is, one doesn't seem to be able to find it by chemical analysis. If one could, you know, it would probably turn out to be something quite ordinary, and then one could make it.'

'The lost formula of *Rossum's Universal Robots*, eh?'

'Very likely,' said Leader, 'that's a play, isn't it? I never go to high-brow plays. All rot, you know – more in your line. But there it is. Analyse you and you're just so much dead matter. Analyse toadstools, and you get this muscarine stuff. Makes one think a bit less of the marvels of Nature, don't it?'

'Except,' said Munting, who had by now mounted on his usual hobby-horse, 'except for the small accident of Life, which is, as you say, a triviality, no doubt, but yet – '

I interrupted him.

'We don't want to waste Mr Leader's time with metaphysics.'

'No,' said Munting, obstinately, 'but what I want to know – '

A tremendous clattering of feet in the corridor heralded the throwing open of the door and the irruption of a large number of young men in overalls.

'Oh, Lord,' said Leader, 'we'll have to clear out.' He

199

looked at his watch. 'I say, do you mind if I barge off? There's a demonstration I've simply got to attend. Nuisance, but I'm rather behind with Dimmock's subjects. Must mug it up somehow. Awfully pleased to have seen you. Can you find your way out?'

'Just a moment,' said Munting. 'You remember the fellow I brought with me last year – Lathom – the artist?'

'Yes, of course – the fellow who was so keen on poisons. Asked such a lot of questions about the right dose, and was so struck with our synthetic stuff. Didn't seem able to get over the fact that you couldn't distinguish artificial muscarine from the natural product by chemical analysis. Very intelligent bloke I thought he was – for an artist. I remember him perfectly. Why?'

'Have you seen anything of him since?'

'No. Why?'

'I just wondered. He said something once about looking you up.'

'Well, he didn't. Perhaps he came in the vac. There's nobody here then, except the swots and the dunces trying to cram themselves for the exams. Tell him to come in termtime. I really must buzz along. I say, come and feed one night, won't you?'

Munting promised to do so, and Leader escaped, cannoning violently into the demonstrator as he dashed out. We followed, not wishing to be caught and interrogated.

'That was Benton,' said Munting, looking back at the closing door. 'I wish we could have had a word with him. If Leader – '

'About the origin of life, I suppose? You're cracked about the origin of life. It's the origin of death we're investigating. We've got what we came for. It's clear enough that anybody might have walked in and helped himself to a dose of that stuff. Look at those places we went into. No one to stop us – and it's term-time, too. In the vac. the place is absolutely deserted. If Lathom was over here in the vac. – and he was. Don't you remember those letters of Margaret Harrison's? He was here in July.'

'Yes,' agreed Munting, thoughtfully. 'Yes, I quite see that. But the difficulty is to *prove* it. Just because it's so easy to get in, it's a million to one against anybody having noticed you. And you can't expect a jury to accept a vague possibility like that. If there was any analysable difference between natural and synthetic muscarine, then, of course, you would have something genuine to go upon. Because it would be quite impossible to eat synthetic muscarine by accident – except in a laboratory. But apparently there is no difference.'

This sobered me. I had been feeling that we were well on the way to solve the problem. But now I saw very clearly that we were just as far away as ever. No jury in the world would accept this involved and unsubstantiated theory. True, people are ready enough to believe that an adulterer is very likely a murderer as well. But if it comes to the question of probability, which will they rather believe? That a man elaborately stole a rare and incomprehensible laboratory product which none of them have ever heard of, and elaborately administered it under involved and peculiar circumstances? Or that an eccentric experimenter with 'unnatural' foods accidentally poisoned himself with toadstools? The answer is obvious.

Moreover, to obtain a conviction, there must be no doubt possible. The murder theory must be overwhelmingly *more* likely than the accident theory. Judges are careful to point this out.

I was as certain that Lathom had poisoned my father with synthetic muscarine as that I was alive. But I began to be equally certain that Lathom had hit upon a method of murder that was utterly and completely proof against proof.

52. *Statement of John Munting*

[Additional and concluding portion.]
This damned business of Lathom's.

People write books about murders, and the nice young men and women in them enjoy the job of detecting. It is a good game and I like reading the books. But the emotions of

201

the nice young people are so well-regulated, or so perfunctory, or something. They don't feel like worms and get put off their dinners when they have succeeded in squeezing a damaging admission out of a friend. They don't seem to suffer from fits of retching terror for fear they should find out something definite. Nor, while struggling with these complicated miseries, do they ever have to fulfil contracts with publishers. Sometimes they are filled with a stern sorrow – a nice, Brutus-like sentiment. I envy their nerves.

My nerves went back on me about the time of our visit to St Anthony's. I took a kind of hysterical pleasure in pointing out that we had no proof of the murder. I didn't want proof. I didn't want to know. It was like writing one of those horrible letters which call for a decisive answer one way or another. You post it and wait, and you know that one morning you will see your correspondent's handwriting on an envelope, and feel as hollow as a piece of bamboo. And you wait. Nothing comes. And after a time you say, 'It's been lost in the post. Now I need not know. Not now, at any rate, I can still pretend that it's all right. Nothing will happen today. I can eat my dinner and listen to the wireless – and perhaps it will go on like that for ever.'

The answer to the Lathom problem seemed to have been lost in the post. We did not talk about it at home. My wife knew that I winced from it. It made other subjects impossible, too. Women, for instance, and the way they influence their lovers – we would start as far off as Gordon Craig's theatre-masks or *Gryll Grange* and Lord Curryfin's *echeia*, and before we had gone far, the figure of Clytemnestra would come bobbing over the horizon, and I would be talking hurriedly, dismissing it, rushing into technicalities about epode and stasimen, or about the chorus or the machines – anything. Or if Elizabeth merely asked what we should have for dinner, it seemed difficult to think of anything that was not flavoured with mushrooms or founded on beef-stock. We lived for a whole week on fish once, so sensitive did our minds become.

I got over it, more or less, after a time and, mercifully, Lathom let me alone. It was not till March that a faint reminding echo of the thing sounded faintly over the breakfast-table. I got a note from Mr Perry, the parson to whom I had once lent a volume of Eddington. At the sight of his name I got a kind of painful twitching in the sore place.

The note was to invite me to dinner. An old college friend of his, the extremely celebrated Professor Hoskyns, was coming over to spend the evening with him. Hoskyns is, of course, a very brilliant physicist, and Perry thought it would interest me to meet him. One or two other people were coming as well. If I could put up with a very simple meal, he thought we should enjoy a really enjoyable talk.

My first instinct was to refuse. I hated the idea of going into the district and of seeing anybody even remotely connected with the Harrisons. But the idea of meeting Hoskyns was fascinating. I have that kind of vaguely inquiring mind that likes to be told what is going on, even though I could not be troubled to make a single experiment myself, and should not have the vaguest idea what experiment to make. A pap-fed, negative, twentieth-century mind open on all sides and wind-swept by every passing gust. Elizabeth thought that a chat with a bunch of scientific men would do me good. We need not, she said, mention the Harrisons. In the end, I accepted, and I rather think Elizabeth must have conveyed some sort of warning to Perry, for the Harrisons were not mentioned.

Perry's shabby little sitting-room seemed crowded with men and smoke when I arrived. Professor Hoskyns, long, thin, bald, and much more human-looking than his Press photographs, was installed in a broken-springed leather arm-chair and called Perry 'Jim'. There was also a swarthy little man in spectacles whom they both called 'Stingo', and who turned out to be Professor Matthews, the biologist, the man who has done so much work on heredity. A large, stout, red-faced person with a boisterous manner was introduced as Waters. He was younger than the rest, but they all treated him with deference, and it presently appeared that he was the coming man in chemistry. Desultory conversation made it clear that Matthews, Hoskyns and Perry had been contemporaries at Oxford, and that Waters had been brought by Matthews, with whom he was on terms of the heartiest friendship and disagreement. A thin youth, with an eager manner and an irrepressible forelock, completed the party. He sported a clerical collar and informed me that he was the new curate, and that it was 'a wonderful opportunity' to start his ministry under a man like Mr Perry.

The dinner was satisfying. A vast beef-steak pudding, an apple-pie of corresponding size, and tankards of beers, quaffed from Perry's old rowing-cups, put us all into a mellow humour. Perry's asceticism did not, I am thankful to say, take the form of tough hash and lemonade, in spite of the presence on his walls of a series of melancholy Arundel prints, portraying brown and skinny anchorites, apparently nourished on cabbage-water. It rather tended to the idea of: 'Beef, noise, the Church, vulgarity and beer,' and I judged that in their younger days, my fellow-guests had kept the progs busy. However, the somewhat wearisome flood of undergraduate reminiscence was stemmed after a time with suitable apologies, and Matthews said, a little provocatively;

'So here we all are. I never thought you'd stick to it, Perry. Which has made your job hardest – the War or people like us?'

'The War,' said Perry, immediately. 'It has taken the heart out of people.'

'Yes. It showed things up a bit,' said Matthews. 'Made it hard to believe in anything.'

'No,' replied the priest. 'Made it easy to believe and difficult not to believe – in anything. Just anything. They believe in everything in a languid sort of way – in you, in me, in Waters, in Hoskyns, in mascots, in spiritualism, in education, in the daily papers – why not? It's easier, and the various things cancel out and so make it unnecessary to take any definite steps in any direction.'

'Damn the daily papers,' said Hoskyns. 'And damn education. All these get-clever-quick articles and sixpenny textbooks. Before one has time to verify an experiment, they're all at you, shrieking to have it formulated into a theory. And if you do formulate it, they misunderstand it, or misapply it. If anybody says there are vitamins in tomatoes, they rush out with a tomato-theory. If somebody says that gamma-rays are found to have an action on cancer-cells in mice, they proclaim gamma-rays as a cure-all for everything from old age to a cold in the head. And if anybody goes quietly away into a corner to experiment with high-voltage electric currents, they start a lot of ill-informed rubbish about splitting the atom.'

'Yes,' said Matthews, 'I thought I saw some odd remarks attributed to you the other day about that.'

'Wasting my time,' said Hoskyns. 'I told them exactly what they put into my mouth. You're right, Jim, they'd believe anything. The elixir of life – that's what they really want to get hold of. It would look well in a headline. If you can't give 'em a simple formula to cure all human ills and explain creation, they say you don't know your business.'

'Ah!' said Perry, with a twinkle of the eye, 'but if the Church gives them a set of formulae for the same purpose, they say they don't want formulae or dogmas, but just a loving wistfulness.'

'You're not up-to-date enough,' said Waters. 'They like their formulae to be red-hot, up-to-the-minute discoveries.'

'Why, so they are,' said Perry. 'Look at Stingo here. He tells them that if two unfit people marry, their unfitness will be visited on their children unto the third and fourth generation, after which they will probably die out through mere degeneration. We've been telling them that for three or four thousand years, and Matthews has only just caught up to us. As a matter of fact, you people are on our side. If *you* tell them the things, they may perhaps come to believe in them.'

'And possibly act on them, you think?' said Matthews. 'But we have to do all the work for them, just as you have to do the godly living.'

'That's not altogether true,' said Perry.

'Near enough. But we do get on a bit faster, because we can give reasons for things. Show me a germ, and I'll tell you how to get rid of plague or cholera. Call it Heaven's judgement for sin, and all you can do is to sit down under it.'

'But surely,' struck in the curate, 'we are expressly warned

205

in Scripture against calling things judgements for sin. How about those eight on whom the Tower of Siloam fell?'

'If it was anybody's sin,' said Perry, 'it was probably the carelessness of the people who built the tower.'

'And that's usually a sin that finds somebody out,' added Waters. 'Unfortunately, the sinner isn't always the victim.'

'Why should it be?' said Matthews. 'Nature does not work by a scheme or poetical justice.'

'Nor does God,' said Perry. 'We suffer for one another, as, indeed, we must, being all members one of another. Can you separate the child from the father, the man from the brute, or even the man from the vegetable cell, Stingo?'

'No,' said Matthews. 'It is you that have tried to keep up that story about Man in the image of God and lord of nature and so on. But trace the chain back and you will find every link hold – you yourself, compounded from your father and mother by the mechanical chemistry of the chromosomes. Back to your ancestors, back to prehistoric Neanderthal Man and his cousin, Aurignacian. Neanderthal was a mistake, he wouldn't work properly and died out, but the line goes on back, dropping the misfits, leaving the stabilised forms on the way – back to Arboreal Man, to the common ancestor Tarsius, to the first Mammal, to the ancestral bird-form, back to the Reptiles, the Trilobites, back to the queer, shapeless jellies of life that divide and sub-divide eternally in the waters. The things that found some kind of balance with their environment persisted, the things that didn't, died out; and here and there some freak found its freakishness of advantage and started a new kind of life with a new equilibrium. At what point, Perry, will you place your image of God?'

'Well,' said Perry, 'I should not attempt to deny that Adam was formed of the dust of the earth. And your ape-and-tiger ancestry at least provides me with a scientific authority for original sin. What a mercy the Church stuck to that dogma, in spite of Rousseau and the noble savage. If she hadn't, you scientists would have forced it back on her, and how silly we should all have looked then.'

'But it was all guess-work,' retorted Matthews, 'unless you call it inspiration, and very inaccurate at that. If the author of Genesis had said that man was made of sea-water, he would have been nearer the truth.'

'Well,' said Waters, 'he put the beginnings of life on the face of the waters, which wasn't so very far off.'

'But how did life begin?' I asked. 'After all, there is a difference between the Organic and the Inorganic. Or there appears to be.'

'That's for Waters to say,' said Matthews.

'I can't be very didactic about that,' said the chemist. 'But it appears possible that there was an evolution from Inorganic or Organic through the Colloids. We can't say much more, and we haven't – so far – succeeded in producing it in the laboratory. Matthews probably still believes that Mind is a function of Matter, but if he asks me to demonstrate it for him, I must beg to be excused. I can't even show that Life is a function of Matter.'

'The Behaviourists seem to think that what looks like Intelligence and Freewill are merely mechanical responses to material stimuli,' I suggested.

'That's all very well,' said Hoskyns, emerging with a grin from a cloud of tobacco-smoke, 'but all you people talk so cheerfully about Matter, as if you know what it was. I don't, and it's more or less my job to know. Go back again, go past your colloids and your sea-water. Go back to the dust of the earth and the mass of rotating cinders which was before the ocean even began. Go back to the sun, which threw the planets off so unexpectedly, owing to a rare accident which might not happen in a million light-years. Go back to the nebula. Go back to the atom. Do some of the famous splitting we hear so much about. Where is your Matter? It isn't. It is a series of pushes or pulls or vortices in nothingness. And as for your train of mechanical causation, Matthews, when you come down to it, it resolves itself into a series of purely fortuitous movements of something we can't define in a medium that doesn't exist. Even your heredity-business is fortuitous. Why one set of chromosomes more than any other? Your chain of causation would only be a real one if all possible combinations and permutations were worked out in practice. Something is going on, that is as certain as anything can be – that is, I mean, it is the fundamental assumption we are bound to make in order to reason at all – but how it started or why it started is just as mysterious as it was when the first thoughtful savage invented a god to explain it.'

'Why should it ever have started at all?' said Matthews. 'As Matter passes from one form to another, so forces change from one to another. Why should we suppose a beginning – or an end if it comes to that? Why not a perpetually shifting kaleidoscope, going through all its transformations and starting again?'

'Why, my lad,' replied Hoskyns, 'because in that case you will come slap up against the second law of thermodynamics, and that will be the end of you.'

'Oh!' said Mr Perry, 'the formula that starts so charmingly about "Nothing in the statistics of an assemblage" – that appears to be all the Law and the Prophets nowadays.'

'Yes,' said Hoskyns. 'It's general meaning is that Time only works in one direction, and that when all the permutations and combinations have been run through. Time will stop, because there will be nothing further by which we can distinguish its direction. All the possibilities will have been worked out, all the electrons will have been annihilated, and there will be nothing more for them to do and no radiant energy left for them to do it with. That is why there must be an end. And if an end, presumably a beginning.'

'And the end is implicit in the beginning?' said I.

'Yes; but the intermediate stages are not inevitable in detail, only overwhelmingly probable in the gross. There, Perry, if you like, you can reconcile Foreknowledge with Freewill.'

'Life, then, I suppose, is but one more element of randomness,' said I, 'in the randomness of things.'

'Presumably,' said Hoskyns.

There was a pause.

'What is Life?' I asked, suddenly.

'Well, Pontius,' said Waters, 'if we could answer that question we should probably not need to ask the others. At present – chemically speaking – the nearest definition I can produce is that it is a kind of bias – a lop-sidedness, so to speak. Possibly that accounts for its oddness.'

208

'I've said that kind of thing myself,' I said, rather astonished, 'just as a sort of feeble witticism. Have I hit on something true by accident?'

'More or less. That is to say, it is true that, up to the present, it is only living substance that has found the trick of transforming a symmetric, optically active compound into a single asymmetric, optically active compound. At the moment that Life appeared on this planet, something happened to the molecular structure of things. They got a twist, which nobody has ever succeeded in reproducing mechanically – at least, not without an exercise of deliberate selective intelligence, which is also, as I suppose you'll allow, a manifestation of Life.'

'Thank you,' said Perry. 'Do you mind saying the first part over again, in words that a child could understand?'

'Well, it's like this,' said Waters. 'When the planet cooled, the molecules of that original inorganic planetary matter were symmetric – if crystallised, the crystals were symmetric also. That is, they were alike on both sides, like a geometrical cube, and their reversed or mirror-images would be identical with themselves. Substances of this kind are said to be optically inactive; that is to say, if viewed through the polariscope, they have no power to rotate the beam of polarised light.'

'We will take your word for it,' said Perry.

'Oh, well, that's quite simple. Ordinarily speaking, the vibrations in the aether – need I explain aether?'

'I wish you could,' said Hoskyns.

'We will pass aether,' said Perry.

'Thank you. Well, ordinarily the aetheric vibrations which propagate the light takes place in all directions at right angles to the path of the ray. If you pass the ray through a crystal of Iceland spar, these vibrations are all brought into one plane, like a flat ribbon. That is what is called a beam of polarised light. Very well, then. If you pass this polarised light through a substance whose molecular structure is symmetric, nothing happens to it; the substance is optically inactive. But if you pass it through, say, a solution of cane sugar, the beam of polarised light will be twisted, and you will get a spiral effect, like twisting a strip of paper

209

either to the right or to the left. The cane sugar is optically active. And why? Because its molecular structure is asymmetric. The crystals of sugar are not fully developed. There is an irregularity on one side, and the crystal and its mirror image are reversed, like my right hand and my left.' He laid the palm of the right hand on the back of the left to show his meaning. We all frowned and practised on our own hands.

'Very good,' continued Waters. 'Now, we can produce in the laboratory, by synthesis from inorganic substances, other substances which were at one time thought to be only the products of living tissues – camphor, for instance, and some of the alkaloids used in medicine. But what is the difference between our process and that of Nature? What happens is this. The substance produced by synthesis always appears in what is called a racemic form. It consists of two sets of substances – one set having its asymmetry right-handed and the other left-handed, so that the product as a whole behaves like an inorganic, symmetric compound; that is, its two asymmetries cancel one another out, and the product is optically inactive and has no power to rotate the beam of polarised light. To get a substance exactly equivalent to the natural product, we have to split it into its two asymmetric forms. We can't do that mechanically. We can do it by the exercise of our living intelligence, of course, by laboriously picking out the crystals. Or we can do it by swallowing the substance when our bodies will absorb and digest the dextro-rotating form, of, for example, glucose, and pass the laevo-rotating form out unchanged. Or we can get a living fungus to do it for us, such as blue mould, which will feed on and destroy the dextro-rotatory half of the racemic form of paratartaric acid and leave unchanged the laevo-rotatory half, which is the artificial, laboratory-made half. But we can't, by one mechanical laboratory process, turn an inorganic, inactive, symmetric compound into one single, asymmetric, optically active compound – and that is what living matter will do cheerfully, day by day.'

Waters finished his exposition with a smart little thump of the fist on the table. I knew what that was. It was the postman's knock, bringing the answer to that letter of mine. A horrid sinking feeling at the solar plexus warned me that in a very few minutes I should have to ask a question. Why need I do it? The subject was remote and difficult. I could easily pretend not to understand. If there really was a difference between the synthetic and the natural product, it was not my business to investigate it. Waters was changing the subject. He had gone back to the first day of creation. Hang him! Let him stay there!

'So that, as Professor Japp said, as long ago as 1898, "The phenomena of stereo-chemistry support the doctrine of vitalism as revived by the younger physiologists, and point to the existence of a directive force, which enters upon the scene with Life itself and which, in no way violating the laws of the kinetics of atoms" – that ought to comfort you, Hoskyns – "determines the course of their operation within the living organism. That is that at the moment when Life first arose, a directive force came into play – a force of precisely the same character as that which enables the intelligent operator, by the exercise of his will, to select one crystallised enantiomorph and reject its asymmetric opposite." I learnt that passage by heart once, as a safeguard against cocksureness and a gesture of proper humility in face of my subject.'

'In other words,' said Matthews, 'you believe in miracles, and something appearing out of nowhere. I am sorry to find you on the side of the angels.'

'It depends what you mean my miracles. I think there is an intelligence behind it all. Else, why anything at all?'

'You have Jeans on your side anyway,' put in Hoskyns. 'He says, "Everything points with overwhelming force to a definite event, or series of events, of creation at some time or times, not infinitely remote. The universe cannot have originated by chance out of its present ingredients." I can't tell you what produced the first molecules of gas, and you can't tell me what produced the first asymmetric molecules of Life. The parson here may think he knows.'

'I don't know,' said Perry, 'but I give it a name. I call it God. You don't know what the aether is, but you give it a name, and deduce its attributes from its behaviour. Why

211

shouldn't I do likewise? You people are making it all very much easier for me.'

It was no good. I had to ask my question. I burst in violently, inappropriately, on this theological discussion:

'You mean to tell me,' I said, 'that it is possible to differentiate a substance produced synthetically in the laboratory from one produced by living tissue?'

'Certainly,' said Waters, turning to me in some surprise, but apparently accepting my tardy realisation of this truth as mere vagary of my slow and unscientific wits. 'So long, of course, as the artificial substance remains in the first or racemic form, for this would be optically inactive, while that form the living tissues would rotate the beam of polarised light, when viewed in the polariscope. If, however, that racemic form had been already split up by the intelligent operator, or some other living agency, into its two dextro- and laevo-rotary forms, it would be impossible to distinguish between them.'

I saw a path of escape opening up. Surely the synthetic muscarine at St Anthony's would have had this other operation performed on it. There was no reason at all why I should interfere. I relapsed into silence, and the conversation wandered on.

I was recalled to myself by a movement about me. Matthews was explaining that he had to be getting home. Waters rose to accompany him. In a minute he would be gone and the opportunity lost. I had only to sit still.

I got up. I made my fatuous farewells. I said I had a perfectly good wife to go home to. I thanked my host and said how much I had enjoyed the evening. I followed the other men out into the narrow hall, with its loaded umbrella-stand and ugly, discoloured wall-paper.

'Dr Waters,' I said.

'Yes?' He turned smiling towards me. I must say something now or he would think me a fool.

'May I have a word with you?'

'By all means. Which way do you go?'

'Bloomsbury,' said I, hoping desperately that he lived at Hendon or Harringay.

212

'Excellent, I am going that way myself. Shall we share a taxi?'

I murmured something about Professor Matthews.

'No, no,' said he, 'I'm going by tube to Earls Court.'

We found our taxi and got in.

'Well, now?' said Waters.

I was in for it now. I told him the whole story.

'By God,' he said, 'that's damned interesting. Fine idea for a murder. Of course, any jury in the country would be only too ready to believe it was accident. Tempting Providence, and all that. And unless your man was fool enough to use the synthetic muscarine in its racemic form, you know, I'm very much afraid he's pulled it off. There's a chance, of course. They may not have gone further than that. Why didn't you ask Benson while you were about it?'

'I thought of doing so,' I admitted. 'At least, I didn't know about this racemic business, but I thought there might be some way of telling the artificial stuff from the real. But Harrison seemed satisfied – '

'He would be. I know these people. Wrapped up in their own subjects. An engineer – *he* ought to know something about molecular structure. But no. He's no occasion to study Organic, so it doesn't occur to him that there's anything to know about it. The word of a first-year student at Anthony's is enough for him. You have more imagination. Why didn't you – ?'

'I don't know that I quite wanted to.'

'Let bad alone, eh? But damn it, it's interesting. I say, what a scoop for the papers, if it comes off! "First murder ever caught by the polariscope." Better than Crippen and the wireless. Only they'll have a bit of a job explaining it. Now, look here, what are we going to do about it? Who did the analysis?'

'Lubbock.'

'Oh, yes – Home Office man, of course. We'll have to get on to him. It's chance if he's kept the stuff by him. What? Oh, he has. That's all right then. We've only got to take a squint at it and then we shall know. I mean, if the stuff really is racemic, we shall know. If Not, we never shall.

213

What's the time? Quarter-past eleven. No time like the present. Here, driver!'

He thrust his head out of the window and gave an address in Woburn Square.

'It's all on our way, and Lubbock never goes to bed before midnight. I know him well. He'll be keen on this.'

His energy swept me up, feebly protesting, and in a few minutes' time we were standing on Sir James Lubbock's doorstep, ringing the bell.

The door was opened by a manservant, of whom Waters inquired whether Sir James was at home.

'No, sir. He is working late tonight, sir, at the Home Office. I think it's the arsenic case, sir.'

'Oh, of course. That's luck for us, Munting. We'll run down and catch him there. You might give him a ring, Stevens, and say I'm coming down to see him on an urgent matter. You know who I am?'

'Oh, yes, sir. Dr Waters. Very good, sir. You'll find him in the laboratory, sir.'

'Right. We'd better hurry up, or we may just miss him.'

We plunged back into the taxi.

'Shall we find any difficulty in getting in?'

'Oh, no. I've been there before. We're making very good time. Provided he hadn't started before Stevens got through to him, he'll wait for us. Ah! here we are.'

We drew up at a side door in the big Government building. After a short colloquy with the man on duty, we were passed through. I stumbled at Waters's heels through a number of dreary corridors, till we fetched up in a kind of small anteroom.

'I feel strongly persuaded,' I said, 'that I am on a visit to the dentist.'

'And you hope very much he'll say there's nothing to be done to you this time. I, on the contrary, hope very much that it's something malignant and unusual. Have a fag.'

I accepted the fag. I tried to think of Harrison, perishing horribly in his lonely shack, but instead I could only see Lathom with his hair rumpled and his teeth set, painting with his usual careless brilliance. I got the idea that God or Nature or Science or some other sinister and powerful

214

thing had set a trap for him, and that I was pushing him
into it. I thought it was ruthless of God or whoever it was.
Pom, pomty; pom, pomty; pom, pomty; pom, pomty – I was
nervously humming something and I couldn't think what.
Oh, yes – Haydn's *Creation* – that bit, where the kettle-
drums thump so gently, so ruthlessly, on one note – 'And-
the-spi-rit-of-God (pomty) moved-upon-the-face-of-the-
waters-(pom)' – only apparently it wasn't the spirit of God,
but an asymmetric molecule, which didn't fit the rhythm.
Somebody was walking down the corridor, with a soft,
muffled beat, rather like kettle-drums. 'Let there be light
(pomty-pom) and there was – '

The door opened.

I recognised Sir James Lubbock at once, of course,
though now, in a white overall and pair of crimson carpet
slippers, he presented an appearance less point-devise than
he had done at the inquest. He greeted Waters cordially
and received my name with a faint look of puzzledom.

'Mr Munting? Yes – let me see, haven't we met before?'
I reminded him of Manaton.

'Of course, of course. I knew I knew your face. Mr
Munting, the novelist. Delighted to make your acquaintance
under more pleasant auspicies.'

'I don't know that they are much more pleasant,' said
Waters. 'As a matter of fact, it's the Harrison case we
wanted to see you about.'

'Really? Has something fresh turned up? You know, the
other day I had a letter from the man's son. Rather an odd
letter. He seemed to have got the idea that there was more
in the case than met the eye. Hinted that we might have
found something else – strychnine or something. Quite
ridiculous, of course. There wasn't the faintest doubt about
the cause of death. Muscarine poisoning. Perfectly straightforward.'

'Just so. By the way, Lubbock, did it by any chance occur
to you to give that muscarine the once-over with the
polariscope?'

'With the polariscope? Good heavens, no. Why should it?
That wouldn't tell one anything. You know all about muscarine. Dextro-rotatory. Nothing abstruse about it.'

'Oh, quite. But we've been having a little discussion, and – as a matter of fact, Lubbock, it would relieve Mr Munting's mind – and mine – considerably, if you would just check up on that point.'

'Well, if you insist, there's nothing easier. But what's the mystery?'

'Nothing at all, probably. Just an extra bit of collateral evidence, that's all.'

'You've something at the back of your mind, Waters. Can't I be allowed to know?'

'I'll tell you after you've done it.'

Sir James Lubbock shook his handsome grey head.

'That's Waters all over. He's like Sherlock Holmes. Never can resist a touch of the dramatic.'

'No,' said Waters. 'It's just native caution. Don't want to commit myself and be made to look foolish.'

'Oh, well, come along and we'll get it over.'

'Aren't we interrupting your work?' I said. I hope this question was prompted by politeness, but I think I spoke in a vain hope of delaying the crisis.

'Not a bit. I'd just finished – was packing up, in fact, when I got your message.'

We traversed some more corridors and eventually came out into a large laboratory, faintly lit by a single electric bulb. An attendant was just locking a cupboard. He turned as he saw us.

'It's all right, Denis. I'll see to things. You can trot away home.'

'Very well. Good-night, Sir James.'

'Good-night.'

Sir James switched on some more lights, flooding the gaunt room with what Poe has called somewhere a 'ghastly and inappropriate splendour.' Stepping across to a tall cupboard labelled with his name, he unlocked it with a key that hung upon his watch-chain.

'Here's my bluebeard's chamber,' he said, smiling. 'Relics of all kinds of crimes and tragedies. Bottled murders. Bottled suicides. Plenty of plots for novels here, Mr Munting.'

I said I supposed so.

216

'Here we are, Harrison. Extract from stomach. Extract from vomit. Extract from dish of fungus. Which is it you particularly want Waters?'

'Doesn't matter. Try the extract from the dish of fungus. It'll be less open to – that is, it is possibly better for our purpose. What's this, Lubbock?'

'That? Oh, that's a fresh solution of muscarine I made myself for control purposes, to assist in determining the strength.'

'Made from the fungus?'

'Yes. I don't altogether guarantee that I've isolated the principle. But it's near enough.'

'Oh, yes. I'd like to have a look at that, too, if I may.'

'By all means.'

He brought the bottles out and set them on one of the laboratory tables. In appearance they were indistinguishable – the same white salt that I had seen before in the laboratory at St Anthony's.

Sir James Lubbock unlocked another cupboard, and produced a large heavy instrument, rather like a telescope fixed to a stand. He put it down beside the two bottles and departed in search of water. While he was preparing solutions from the respective bottles of muscarine, Waters turned to me.

'You'd better have this quite clear in your mind – I mean, you'd like to know what you may expect to see, exactly.'

'Yes,' I said. 'At present I feel rather like the good lady in *The Moonstone*, who wanted to know when the explosion would take place.'

'I'm afraid it won't be so exciting at that. Cheer up, man, you look as white as a sheet. At the further end of the instrument is a thin plate of the semi-transparent mineral, tourmaline. You've seen it in jewellers' shops. Pretty stuff, and all that, and, what is more to the purpose, it has a very finely foliated structure. In a ray of ordinary light, the vibrations take place in all directions, but when passed through a slice of tourmaline they are confined to one plane, and the light is then polarised. We talked about that at dinner – you remember. This slice of tourmaline is called the polariser. Right. Now at this end, near the eyepiece, is a

217

second slice of tourmaline, which can be rotated, and which is called the analyser. Now, when the analyser is turned so that its foliations are parallel to those of the polariser, light will pass through both, but if the analyser is turned so that its foliations are at right angles to those of the polariser, then no light will pass and there will be darkness. All clear so far?'

'Perfectly.'

'Very well. Now, if, when the analyser is thus turned to darkness, I place the solution of an optically active substance between the two slices of tourmaline the light will – you can tell me that yourself – it's a *band* of light, remember.'

'I remember. Yes. The band of light will be rotated as it passes through.'

'That's right. It will come round into line with the foliations of the analyser, and –'

'Come through!' said I, triumphantly.

'Thank God for a man of intelligent mind. As you rightly say, it will come through. And therefore you will see – '

'Light!' said I.

(Pom, pomty; pom, pomty – if I could have got rid of that relentless drum-beat. My heart seemed to be going very heavily too.)

'But if,' went on Waters, with his eye on Sir James, who was stirring his solutions with a glass rod over the sink, 'if the substance should be optically inactive – if, for example, it should turn out to be a synthetic product, prepared from inorganic substances in the laboratory – then it will not rotate the beam of polarised light. The darkness will persist.'

I saw that.

'Well, now you perfectly understand. If, when we put the muscarine solution in the polariscope, we get light, it proves nothing. Either the stuff is natural, or else the synthetic preparation has already been split up into its two active forms, and we can make no pronouncement about it. But if we get darkness – then it's a pretty dark business, Mr Munting.'

I nodded.

'Well, Waters,' said Sir James, cheerfully, 'finished your lecture?'

'Quite. The pupil is highly commended.'

'Good. Now, I'm in your hands, Waters. What do you want me to do?'

'I think we'll have the control solution first, if you don't mind. Now, Mr Munting, you will see how this substance, prepared from the living tissue of a fungus, rotates the beam of polarised light. Right you are, sir.'

Sir James handed me a glass cylinder, filled with a colourless solution. I sniffed at it, but it had no smell.

'I shouldn't taste it if I were you,' said Sir James, a little grimly. He struck a match and lit a Bunsen burner, the flame of which played upon a small mass of something held above it by a platinum projection.

'Sodium chloride,' said Waters; 'in fact, not to make unnecessary mystery about it, common salt. Shall I switch off?'

He snapped off the lights, and we were left with only the sodium flame. In that green, sick glare of a face floated close to mine – a corpse-face – livid, waxen, stamped with decay– sharp-shadowed in the nostrils and under the orbits – Harrison's face, as I had seen it in 'The Shack,' opening a black mouth of complaint.

'Spectacular, isn't it?' said Sir James, pleasantly, and I pulled myself together and realised that I must look just as ghastly to him as he to me. But for the moment the face had been Harrison's, and from that moment Lathom was nothing to me any more.

Sir James settled down to his experiment with comfortable deliberation. He placed the cylinder containing the solution in the polariscope, adjusted the eyepiece and looked. Then he turned to Waters.

'So far,' he said, dryly, 'the laws of Nature appear to hold good. Do you want to see?'

'I should like Mr Munting to see,' said Waters. 'Here you are. Wait a minute. We'll take the cylinder out for a moment. Come along. You shall do it yourself.'

My heart *was* thumping. To my excited imagination it

219

seemed to shake the table as I took Sir James's place before the polariscope.

'We'll start,' said Waters, 'with the analyser parallel to the polariser. Right you are. You see your beam of light? Now here's the adjustment. Turn it yourself.'

I turned it, and the light vanished.

'Hold on to it,' said Waters, cheerfully, 'so that you can be sure there's no hanky-panky. I'm putting the muscarine solution in again. Now then!'

As he slipped the glass cylinder into place the circle of light returned.

'Yes,' I said, 'I see it.'

'Convincing demonstration of a miracle,' said Waters, 'and the lopsidedness of things in general. That's all right, then. Now we'll have a look at the stuff that killed Harrison. No. Respect for our governors, teachers, spiritual pastors and masters. We'll let Sir James have a go first.'

Sir James, with a shrug, took my place at the instrument. Waters put his hand on my arm.

With maddening deliberation, the analyst set the first cylinder carefully on one side and took up the other. My mouth was dry as I watched him. He put the cylinder into the polariscope and looked. There was a pause. Then a grunt. Then his hand came up, feeling for the adjustment. There was another pause and an exclamation of impatience. Then his eye was jerked back from the eyepiece and his head peered round to examine the exterior of the instrument. Water's grip on my arm became painful in its tightness. Sir James's hand came round again, feeling, this time, for the cylinder. He took it out, held it up, looked at it and replaced it with very great care. He looked again, and there was a long silence.

Then came Sir James's voice, queer and puzzled.

'I say, Waters. There's something funny here. Just have a look, will you?'

With a final squeeze, Waters loosened his grip of me and took Sir James's place before the instrument. He moved the cylinder back and forth once or twice and said, in a judicial tone, 'Well!'

'What do you make of that?' said Sir James.

'One of two things,' said Waters, briskly, 'either it's a suspension of the laws of Nature, or this muscarine of yours is optically inactive.'

'What *do* you suggest?' demanded Sir James.

'I suggest,' said Waters, 'that this is a synthetic preparation in racemic form.'

'But how could – ?' Sir James broke off, and in the corpse-light I watched his face as he revolved the possibilities in his mind. 'You know what that means, Waters.'

'I might hazard a guess.'

'Murder.'

'Yes, murder.'

There was another pause, in which the silence seemed to become absolutely solid. Then Sir James said, very slowly:

'The man was murdered. My God, this is a lesson to me, Waters. Never to overlook anything. Who would ever have thought – ? But that's no excuse. I shall have to – I must verify it first, though. Do the preparations again. But – what put you on to this?'

'Let's go and get a drink,' said Waters, 'and we'll tell you all about it. You'd better have a look at this first, Mr Munting.'

I looked through the instrument. Dead blackness. But if the thing had shown all the colours of the rainbow, I should have been in no state to draw any conclusion from it. I sat stunned while somebody switched on the lights, extinguished the Bunsen burner and locked all the apparatus up again.

Then I found myself straggling after the other two, while they talked about something or other. I had an idea that I came into it, and presently Waters turned back and thrust his arm into mine.

'What you want,' he said, 'is a double Scotch, and no soda.'

I don't very well remember getting home, but that, I think, was not due to the double Scotch, but to bewilderment of mind. I do remember waking my wife up and blurting out my story in a kind of confused misery, which must have perplexed and alarmed her. And I remember saying that it was quite useless to think of going to bed, because I should never sleep. And I remember waking this morning very late, with the feeling that someone was dead.

I have written all this down. I don't know whether it is necessary, because, of course, Sir James will be doing something about it by now. But I promised a statement, and here it is.

One other thing has happened. As I was reading it through to see if it was coherent, the telephone rang. My wife answered it. I heard her say:

'Yes? – Yes? – Yes? – who is it speaking, please? – Oh, yes – I'm not sure – I'll go and see – Will you hold the line a minute?'

She put her hand over the mouthpiece and said, almost in a whisper:

'It's Mr Lathom, asking to speak to you.'

'Oh, God!' I said.

If I warned him now – there would still be time – and the man had been at school with me – and we had lived in the same rooms – and he was a great painter – something would be lost to the world if they hanged Lathom.

Elizabeth did nothing. She stood with the receiver in her hand.

'Tell him – '

'Yes?'

'Tell him I am out.'

She turned back to the instrument.

'I am so sorry, my husband is out. Can I give any message? No, very well. You'll ring up again. Good-night.'

She came over and stood by me.

'Elizabeth, tell me, am I an unutterable sweep?'

'No. There was nothing else you could do.'

I want to know whether Lathom knows the sort of woman he did it for. I want to know how much she really knows or suspects. I want to know whether, when she wrote that letter which drove him to do it, she was deceiving him or herself. I want to know whether, in all these months, he has been thinking that she was worth it, or whether, in a ghastly disillusionment, he has realised that the only real part of

222

her was vulgar and bad, and the rest merely the brilliant refraction of himself. What is the good? Whatever he realised, he must have gone on telling himself she was worth it, or he would have gone mad.

Perry would say that this was God's judgement. Life outraged, vindicating itself against the powers of death and hell. Or no, Perry expressly refuses to recognises judgements. Besides, if Lathom had known just a little more about chemistry, he could have defeated the judgement. Ignorance is no excuse in law. Nor in the law of Nature. Well, we know that. All the same, if I were in Lathom's place, I would hate to have been tripped up by a miserable asymmetric molecule.

I hope Lathom will not ring up again.

53. *Note by Paul Harrison*

This statement concludes the evidence, which I have to lay before you. You have already, I understand, received a brief communication from Sir James Lubbock, confirming the account of his experiment with the synthetic muscarine. Munting's narrative is of some value as indicating the lines on which such an experimental proof, though unusual and somewhat technical in character, might be presented to a jury of reasonably intelligent persons.

The unsatisfactory part of the case is, as you will see, that which concerns the woman, Margaret Harrison. As the letter No. 46 shows, she has taken pains to protect herself against any suspicion of complicity. Although, morally, she is quite equally guilty with Lathom, and though I have personally no doubt that the letter is an impudent hypocrisy, it will probably be difficult to bring home to her a guilty knowledge of the actual commission of the crime. That she instigated and inspired it is, to my mind, certain; but Lathom will strenuously deny this, and I have failed to secure any reliable evidence against her. I trust that you will use every possible endeavour to prevent this abominable woman from getting off scot-free.

I re-open this parcel to add that I have received a message from Mrs Cutts. Lathom, she tells me, has given a week's notice to his landlord. This may mean everything or nothing, but prompt action seems advisable.

Sir Gilbert Pugh, Director of Public Prosecutions, turned the last page of the manuscript, and sat for a few minutes in silence. Mentally he watched his expert witnesses displaying an asymmetric molecule to a jury of honest tradesmen, under a withering fire of commentary by the counsel for the defence.

He sighed. This sort of case always meant a lot of work and bother.

'Simmons!'

'Yes, sir.'

'Get me the Chief Commissioner on the phone.'

[Pinned to the portfolio at some subsequent date.]

Extract from the 'Morning Express' of November 30th, 1930

MANATON MURDERER HANGED

The execution took place in Exeter Gaol, at 8 a.m. today, of Harwood Lathom, who was convicted in October of the murder of George Harrison at 'The Shack,' Manaton, by poisoning him with muscarine.

THE END

C I T Y P A C K
Sydney

By Anne Matthews

Fodor's

Fodor's Travel Publications
New York • Toronto • London • Sydney • Auckland

WWW.FODORS.COM

Contents

About this book

CityPack Sydney is divided into six sections to cover the six most important aspects of your visit to Sydney. It includes:

- The author's view of the city and its people
- Itineraries, walks, and excursions
- The recommended top 25 sights to visit
- Sections on what makes the city special
- Detailed listings of restaurants, hotels, stores, and nightlife
- Practical information

In addition, easy-to-read side panels provide extra facts and snippets, highlights of places to visit, and practical advice.

CROSS-REFERENCES

To help you make the most of your visit, cross-references, indicated by ➤ , show you where to find additional information about a place or subject.

MAPS

The fold-out map in the wallet at the back of the book is a comprehensive street plan of Sydney. All the map references given in the book refer to this map. For example, the State Parliament House in Macquarie Street has the following information: ✚ ciii; K5 indicating the grid square of the map in which that building will be found.

The city-center maps found on the inside front and back covers of the book are for quick reference. They show the top 25 sights described on pages 24–48, which are clearly numbered (**1**–**25**, not by page number).

ADMISSION CHARGES

An indication of the admission charge for all attractions is given by categorizing the standard adult rate as follows: ✋ expensive (over A$10), ✋ moderate (A$5–A$10), and ✋ inexpensive (under A$5).

SYDNEY *life*

INTRODUCING SYDNEY

Geography and climate

Sydney's greatest assets are its climate and setting. The harbor is by no means the only waterway—to the north lie Pittwater and the Hawkesbury River, while the southern city limits are bounded by Botany Bay and other inlets. Golden beaches and unspoiled bushland add to the beauty. Sydney's "warm temperate" climate translates into warm to hot summers and mild winters.

If you could summarize Sydney in just four words, the most appropriate selection would be: cosmopolitan, diverse, energetic, and easygoing. Blessed with a long, sheltered harbor and a sunny, temperate climate, it is a blend of colonial heritage, dazzling modern buildings, and a free-wheeling lifestyle. People live life out of doors and pursue cultural and sporting activities with a zesty dedication.

The great irony of this city of freedom is that it started life as a penal settlement for Britain's overcrowded jails. Perhaps this is the point: far from the limitations of England, these reluctant pioneers laid the foundations for a new society which could simply invent itself. Within the central business district, the lifting of height restrictions has led to a growth in skyscraper architecture and, while these dominate the city vista, other forces have moved to conserve its historic past, most notable in Macquarie Street and The Rocks. As host venue for the 2000 Olympic games, dubbed the "best ever" by the International Olympic Committee president, Sydney portrayed itself as a city that could mix with the world's best.

A Bondi Beach lifeguard

Sydney is warm, vibrant, yet somewhat brash. Its attractions are on shimmering display—an easy place to get to know and like. For the people who live here it's the "best address on earth," relatively safe, clean, and unpolluted, and Australians are generally relaxed and easygoing. The often-heard expressions "No worries, mate" and "She'll be right" say much about the attitudes here. Society embraces people of all races and nationalities and, although this certainly isn't a multicultural utopia, the principles of the once racist "White Australia" laws have long been buried. While not many Aboriginal people live in Sydney,

Sydney Harbour Bridge— the "Coathanger"

Asian faces are everywhere and you could easily find yourself overhearing conversations in Italian, Cantonese, Japanese, or Vietnamese.

Come to Sydney with an open mind and you'll probably be surprised. It's not entirely the rather clichéd expectations of sun, beaches, surf, sport, and the great outdoors—there are world-class museums and galleries, and designer shops like Tiffany's and Cartier. You will find great cuisine and some of the world's best wines. There's also plenty to do at night—take in an opera or ballet at the Sydney Opera House, see a first-class theatrical production, dance the night away in a trendy club, or spend the evening sampling fine local beers in a historic sandstone hotel.

Don't expect too many grandiose buildings, broad European-style avenues, or the ultimate in service (Australians are often cheerfully laid-back). Also lacking, however, are overcrowded streets, over-stressed people, and excessive formality. Sydneysiders tend to live life at a faster pace than people in other parts of Australia, so be prepared to get lost in a rapid delivery of the colloquial English known as "Strine," spoken in the typically nasal Australian accent. Fortunately, celebrities like Paul Hogan have been "throwing shrimps on barbies" and "downing Fosters" long enough on television for it not to be a complete mystery.

Getting around

Although the metropolitan region is vast (around 42 miles north–south and east–west), Sydney's central business district (CBD) is very compact and the most important sights are centrally located. Buses serve most parts of the city; a monorail serves the Chinatown, Darling Harbour, and central Pitt Street area; a new light rail system runs between Central Railroad station and Star City casino via Darling Harbour; and a comprehensive rail network covers all but the northeast area. Ferries operate across much of the harbor and even upriver to the historic city of Parramatta.

7

PEOPLE & EVENTS FROM HISTORY

Olympics 2000

Sydney's growing status as a world-class city was confirmed by its choice (in September 1993) as the venue for the 2000 Olympic games. In some ways this Olympics represented a coming of age for the nation, which celebrated the centenary of federation on January 1 2001.

THE FIRST FLEET

The most bizarre birth of any nation on earth might so easily have been a disastrous false start, but Sydney and the nation have thrived, thanks initially to Governor Phillip and the people who sailed on the First Fleet of 11 ships from England. These reluctant pioneers of 1788—including 568 male and 191 female convicts, and 200 marines and their wives and children—suffered incredible hardships to set this isolated colony on its feet.

GOVERNOR MACQUARIE

When Scotsman Lachlan Macquarie (1761–1824) arrived in Sydney as governor of New South Wales in 1810, fortunes changed dramatically. In just 12 years, Macquarie's inspired vision and determination converted the struggling colony into a thriving community. Evidence of his building program, executed by pardoned convict architect, Francis Greenway, remains today, particularly in Macquarie Street, and he is even credited with naming Australia.

GOLD FEVER

Although declared a city in 1842, it was not until the 1851 discovery of gold near Bathurst, beyond the Blue Mountains, that Sydney really earned its new status. Prospectors arrived from all over the world and Sydney boomed—the population virtually doubled in a decade. The ensuing wealth created grand buildings and prosperity, changing the city for ever.

The gold rush in 1853: diggings at Sheep Station Point on the Turon River

CONTEMPORARY SYDNEYSIDERS

KEN DONE

One of Australia's most successful designers and artists, Ken Done spent many years as a creative director of various advertising agencies before starting his designer clothing and furnishing business and, more recently, his art career. He has held numerous solo and group exhibitions in galleries throughout Australia, Japan, and France and his awards are numerous, including Father of the Year 1989 and an Australia Medal in 1992. Born in Sydney in 1942, Done is a goodwill ambassador for UNICEF Australia.

COLLEEN McCULLOUGH

Her major best-seller and later TV series, *The Thorn Birds*, rocketed Colleen McCullough into the literary spotlight. Born in 1937, she was educated in Sydney and once worked here as a neurophysiologist. Today, she lives on Norfolk Island where she has written several histories of ancient Rome, including *The First Man in Rome* (1990) and *Caesar's Women* (1996).

PAT O'SHANE

Queensland-born in 1941, Pat O'Shane holds an impressive list of "firsts": she became the nation's first Aboriginal barrister in 1976, the first Aboriginal woman to head a state government department (NSW Aboriginal Affairs) in 1981 and, in 1986, the first indigenous Australian to become a magistrate. Not surprisingly, O'Shane is a role model for many Aborigines and is a well-respected member of the Sydney community.

BRYCE COURTENAY

At 26 he was Australia's youngest creative director, yet recognition for Bryce Courtenay came only after his retirement, in 1993. Born in South Africa in 1933, his first successful novel, *The Power of One* (1989), was a major Hollywood movie and an international best-seller. *The Potato Factory* (1995), the first of an Australian trilogy that was completed in 1999, is still, in 2001, Australia's top-selling novel. *Meeting at the Smoky Joe Café* (2001) has been released as an e-book.

Famous Sydneysiders

For many, being famous at home is too tame; heading overseas to hit the big time is therefore an enduring Australian tradition. Some of Sydney's most famous exports are supermodel Elle "The Body" Macpherson, actors Mel Gibson, Nicole Kidman, and Judy Davis, author and TV personality Clive James, and art critic Robert Hughes.

The Packers

Headed by Kerry (easily Australia's richest man), the Sydney-based Packers are one of the nation's most powerful families. Kerry Packer, also known for his high-stakes gambling and love of polo, inherited the Australian Consolidated Press and Channel 9 media group from his father, Sir Frank. James, Kerry's son, now continues the long family tradition of business and the art of making money.

9

A CHRONOLOGY

40,000–50,000 years ago	Aborigines arrive from Southeast Asia.
April 29, 1770	Captain James Cook and the crew of the *Endeavour* arrive at Botany Bay.
1779	After transportation to America ends in 1776, suggestions are made in England that New South Wales could become a penal colony.
May 13, 1787	The "First Fleet" sails from Portsmouth, England. The 11 ships carry over 1,400 people.
1788	On January 20 the First Fleet sails into Botany Bay. The commander and first governor of the colony, Captain Arthur Phillip, deems the site unsuitable and on January 26 moves his settlement north to Port Jackson (Sydney Harbour). The colony of New South Wales is proclaimed.
1790	The Second Fleet arrives.
1793	The first free settlers land in Sydney.
1804	An uprising of 400 Irish convicts occurs at Castle Hill, Sydney. Australia's second major settlement is founded at Hobart, Tasmania.
1810	Lachlan Macquarie, known as the "Father of Australia" for his building and planning works, becomes governor and remains so until 1821.
1813	A route over the previously impenetrable Blue Mountains is finally discovered by explorers Wentworth, Lawson, and Blaxland.
1817	Governor Macquarie first refers to the colony as "Australia" in official correspondence.
1832	Assisted passages over the next 140 years help millions of people, mainly Britons, to emigrate to Australia.
1840	Convict transportation to New South Wales ends.
1851	Gold is discovered near Bathurst, and Sydney's population doubles in 10 years.

1888	Sydney celebrates its centenary with the opening of Centennial Park.
1900	Bubonic plague breaks out in The Rocks.
January 1, 1901	The Commonwealth of Australia is proclaimed at Centennial Park, joining the six Australian colonies into a federation.
1923	Work begins on Sydney Harbour Bridge.
March 1932	Sydney Harbour Bridge is opened.
1934	Australia's national airline, Qantas, begins scheduled flights between Sydney and London.
1939–45	Australian troops fight overseas during World War II.
1947	Post-war immigration from Europe begins, giving industry much needed skilled labor.
1973	Queen Elizabeth opens Sydney Opera House.
January 26, 1988	Bicentenary of European settlement.
1992	The 150th anniversary of Sydney's city status.
1992	Sydney Harbour Tunnel opens, relieving the Harbour Bridge of some of its traffic.
January 1994	Bushfires ravage the city's outer suburbs.
1995	Sydney's first legal casino opens.
1996	Paul Keating's Labor government loses the federal election to the Liberals. John Howard, a Sydney resident, becomes prime minister.
1997	After an absence of 39 years, trams return to Sydney in the form of a light rail system.
1999	Australia votes against becoming a republic.
2000	Sydney becomes the first Australian city to host the Olympic Games since Melbourne in 1956.

Sydney in Figures

Aboriginal presence

Aborigines have lived on the Australian mainland for over 40,000 years, and many of their descendants can be found living in Sydney, particularly in the suburbs of Redfern and La Perouse. Shops are full of arts and crafts from Aboriginal communities nationwide, but all that remains of Aboriginal culture in the Sydney region are shell middens on harbor foreshores, rock-carvings in surrounding national parks, and place-names such as Woolloomooloo, Maroubra, Turramurra, and Parramatta.

- Sydney was established on January 26, 1788, after the arrival of the 11 ships of the First Fleet from England.

- From the 1,400 people who arrived on the fleet, Sydney's population has grown to 3.8 million. This represents well over half of the New South Wales population of almost 6 million.

- The Sydney metropolitan region covers a vast area of over 1,640 square miles.

- Sydney Harbour contains 144 miles of foreshore, while the city region's coastline extends for 36 miles.

- At 33 degrees 55 minutes south, Sydney lies at a similar latitude to Los Angeles, Cape Town, Buenos Aires, Osaka, Beirut, and Casablanca.

- Sydney is 9,615 miles from New York, 10,305 miles from London (via Singapore) and 10,165 miles from Berlin.

- The city's tallest structure is the 825 ft-high AMP Centrepoint Tower, completed in 1981.

- Observatory Hill, the city center's highest point, is a mere 119 feet above sea level.

- The roof of Sydney Opera House is covered by more than one million Swedish ceramic tiles.

- The Sydney Harbour Bridge's area of steelwork is the equivalent of 60 soccer fields, with one coat of paint requiring 6,800 gallons.

- Chinese, in its various forms, is Sydney's second language. Around 70 percent of Sydneysiders are a combination of at least two ethnic backgrounds, while 36 percent are foreign born.

SYDNEY
how to organize your time

ITINERARIES

One of Sydney's sightseeing advantages is that the center is small—just six of the top 25 sights are more than a 20-minute walk from a CBD hotel.

ITINERARY ONE	**THE CBD: NORTH**
Morning	The Rocks (► 28) and Observatory Hill (► 48), with coffee at Gumnut Tea Garden (► 68).
or	Sydney Harbour Bridge (► 25), the Museum of Contemporary Art (► 40) and Sydney Opera House (► 24); coffee at MCA Fish Café (► 68).
Lunch	Sydney Cove Oyster Bar (► 64), Botanic Gardens Restaurant or picnic in Royal Botanic Gardens (► 42).
Afternoon	Royal Botanic Gardens (► 42), Sydney Opera House (► 24) and the Museum of Sydney (► 44).
	THE CBD: SOUTH
Morning	Darling Harbour area—Aquarium (► 29), Powerhouse Museum (► 34), National Maritime Museum (► 37), Chinese Garden (► 38)—including Chinatown.
Lunch	Jordons Seafood Restaurant (► 64).
Afternoon	Australian Museum (► 41) and the Art Gallery of New South Wales (► 43); tea at Hyde Park Barracks Café (► 68).
or	Queen Victoria Building (► 32), AMP Centrepoint Tower (► 31) and Macquarie Street; tea as above.
ITINERARY TWO	**HEADING EAST**
	The eastern suburbs include some of the city's best shopping, and the Bondi & Bay Explorer bus (► 19) is the best way to see the sights.
Morning	Elizabeth Bay House (► 54), Kings Cross, and the Sydney Jewish Museum (► 53).
Lunch	Golden Dog (► 68), Narai Thai (► 65), or picnic.
Afternoon	Centennial Park and Paddington/Woollahra (► 16); tea at Centennial Park Café.
ITINERARY THREE	**FURTHER EAST**
	The Bondi & Bay Explorer bus (► 19) covers this area and is the best way to see the sights.
Morning	Vaucluse House (► 47), Nielsen Park (► 47), and Watsons Bay (► 51).
Lunch	Doyles on the Beach (► 64) or Thai Flora (► 65).
Afternoon	Bondi Beach (► 30) with an option for a swim.

An alternative here is the walk along the harbor-side track to Bronte Beach. The lookout at Mackenzies Point provides panoramic views.

ITINERARY FOUR

OVER THE HARBOUR BRIDGE
Unless you have a vehicle, these are best visited as three separate excursions, traveling by ferry from Circular Quay (➤ 43).

Morning Walk across the Harbour Bridge (➤ 25) to Milsons Point and Mary MacKillop Place, then return by train to Circular Quay (➤ 27).

Lunch Fish at the Rocks (➤ 64) or Rossini's (➤ 67).

Afternoon Ferry to Taronga Zoo (➤ 36).

ITINERARY FIVE

WEST TO PARRAMATTA
Parramatta was founded in 1788, a few months after the nation's first white settlers arrived.

Morning Take a ferry from Circular Quay (➤ 27) for the one-hour journey to Parramatta Wharf and then take the Parramatta Explorer bus to see the sights, including Elizabeth Farm, Experiment Farm Cottage, and St. Johns Church.

Lunch Local restaurant or picnic.

Afternoon Visit Old Government House, then return by ferry to Circular Quay.

Sydney Opera House

Traveling west
Many travelers neglect western Sydney, with its vast suburban spread, but there are a few attractions here. In addition to Parramatta, you could visit the 2000 Olympics site (➤ 55) and Bicentennial Park at Homebush Bay, the colorful, multicultural suburbs of Leichhardt and Newtown or take a stroll along Glebe Point Road.

WALKS

INFORMATION

Distance 24 miles
Time 2 hours (5 hours if you spend some time in the Opera House and Art Gallery)
Start and end point Circular Quay
🚏 bii; J5
🚇 Circular Quay

Shopping in Paddington

CIRCULAR QUAY TO NSW ART GALLERY

Pack a picnic to eat in the Royal Botanic Gardens or stop at the Art Gallery café.

Walk from the ferry terminals at Circular Quay and follow the water's edge to the Opera House. The foreshore here provides some of the best views back to the city and towards the Harbour Bridge. At the Opera House, be sure to climb the steps of the forecourt and, for an interesting look inside the halls and theaters, take a guided tour. Walk to Bennelong Point at ground level to watch the passing water-traffic.

Enter the Royal Botanic Gardens at their northernmost point, next to the Opera House. Walking east, follow the water's edge all the way around Farm Cove to Mrs Macquaries Point and check out the views of the harbor. Turn inland and stroll along any of the garden paths to see tree and plant displays and specimens. Don't miss the visitor center (beside Mrs Macquaries Road), where exhibitions of a botanical nature are often held: works of botanical illustrators, collections of plant specimens, displays of books on plants, and so forth.

Allow plenty of time to view the exhibitions at the nearby Art Gallery of New South Wales, including its excellent Yiribana Gallery of Aboriginal art (► 43). To complete your circuit, head west, parallel to the Cahill Expressway, keeping within the gardens. Be sure to see the tropical plant pyramids at the Macquarie Street end. Turning right onto this street and walking almost its entire length before turning left brings you back to Circular Quay.

PADDINGTON & WOOLLAHRA

Paddington and Woollahra grew up around the 1841 Victoria Barracks (► 55), and by the 1880s the working-class suburb was crammed with terraced houses. These restored terraces, with their iron lacework balconies, are what make modern Paddington so charming. At Centennial Square, turn left off Oxford Street (which continues to Bondi Junction) onto Queen Street. With its exclusive antique shops, this is the heart of desirable and expensive Woollahra. Take a left turn onto Moncur Street, cross Jersey Road down onto Hargrave Street; you are now in the important National Trust conservation area of Paddington. Turn left onto Elizabeth Street, right onto Paddington Street and right again onto Cascade Street, which has some particularly good examples of the local architecture.

Walk down Cascade Street, left onto Gurner Street, turn right at the end onto Glenmore Road, and continue to Five Ways. Approximately 180 yards further along Glenmore Road, turn left onto steep Ormond Street, which has more of the historic terraced houses. Take Ormond Street to the end and you are back on Oxford Street. Stop to admire the architecture before turning left to reach the main Paddington shopping and café strip. This section of Oxford Street contains some of Sydney's most interesting clothing stores, as well as book, music and jewelry outlets, and deserves a browse. The Paddington Bazaar is held here, with its stalls and street performers, and is worth a visit (➤ 74).

If you wish, you can easily continue to the suburb of Bondi and its famous beach (➤ 30) after visiting Paddington and Woollahra.

THE SIGHTS

- Queen Street, Woollahra
- Paddington's architecture (➤ 55)
- Oxford Street (➤ 71)

INFORMATION

Distance 2 miles
Time 45 minutes–2 hours
Start point Corner of Queen and Oxford streets
🚉 M8
End point Oxford Street—main shopping/café area between William Street and Jersey Road
🚉 L8
🚌 378, 380 or 382 to/from Oxford Street (or continue to Bondi Junction by catching a 380 or 382 bus east from anywhere on Oxford Street)

Bondi beach

EVENING STROLLS

Take a friend

Walking in some areas (particularly
back streets) at night is not
recommended, but the Opera
House stroll includes a well-
frequented area, while most of the
Kings Cross/Wooloomooloo district
is also crowded in the evenings.
Both strolls would nevertheless be
best done with a companion.

DAWES POINT TO SYDNEY OPERA HOUSE

With its views this harbor stroll provides one of the best night-time panoramas in Sydney.

From George Street, walk towards the Harbour Bridge and across Dawes Point Park, just under the southern pylon of the bridge to Hickson Road—there is a particularly good view of Port Jackson and bridge from here. Continue past the Park Hyatt Hotel and Campbells Cove, onto lower George Street around Sydney Cove towards Circular Quay. From here you can follow the the waterside walkway past the Colonnade, a new retail and cinema precinct to Bennelong Point and the Opera House.

KINGS CROSS TO WOOLOOMOOLOO

Although the Kings Cross section of this area is somewhat seedy, the evening bustle makes this an interesting part of the stroll.

From Kings Cross station, walk north along Darlinghurst Road to the El Alamein Fountain. From here, Macleay Street, Potts Point, has many cafés and bistros. Continue past the Landmark Hotel, turn left onto Challis Avenue, and walk to Victoria Street, which has good views of the city skyline, grand houses, and trendy cafés and bars. Make your way back down Victoria Street and take the walkway just before Challis Avenue towards Wooloomooloo Bay. Walk west along Cowper Wharf Road, going past the navy docks, to the new W Hotel complex for a meal or coffee at the hotel or the wharf promenade.

ORGANIZED SIGHTSEEING

Sydney Harbour ferries

There are innumerable organized tours in and around Sydney. The following are just a few recommendations (also ➤ panels on 54 and 58).

NSW TRAVEL CENTRE
At the state-operated travel center, you can book everything from a bus trip to the Blue Mountains to adventure tours and visits to wildlife parks.
☎ 9231 4444

SYDNEY EXPLORER
Including 26 of the most important sights, the red Sydney Explorer buses are a great way to get around. Buses run daily every 20 minutes.
☎ 131 500

BONDI & BAY EXPLORER
This bus service covers 20 stops in harbor suburbs such as Watsons Bay and the beaches of Bondi and Coogee, returning via Paddington.
☎ 131 500

QUAYSIDE BOOKING CENTRES
These centers, at Circular Quay and Darling Harbour, handle bookings for ferry rides, harbor cruises, and sailing on tall ships.
☎ 9247 5151

AAT KING'S TOURS
This company is good for guided bus tours to the Blue Mountains, Parramatta, and the northern beaches.
☎ 9252 2788

Ride a Harley
An exciting way to get around Sydney is on the back of a Harley Davidson motor bike. You and your driver/guide can take in the city sights, northern beaches, or Royal National Park, or travel further afield to the Hunter Valley and the Blue Mountains. For more information, contact Eastcoast Motorcycle Tours (☎ 9544 2400) or Blue Thunder Bike Tours (☎ 9977 7721).

19

EXCURSIONS

INFORMATION

Blue Mountains

Distance Around 36 miles from
Sydney to Katoomba

Time Allow a full day (8 hours
minimum for the bus tour)

🚆 Train from Central Station

ℹ Blue Mountains Visitor
Information centers: Great
Western Highway,
Glenbrook, and Echo Point
Road, Katoomba ✉ PO
Box 228, Leura, NSW 2780
☎ 1300 653 408

**Ku-ring-gai Chase National
Park & the Hawkesbury River**

Distance 15 miles to Ku-ring-gai
(a further 21 miles to
Brooklyn)

Time Allow a full day (the drive to
Ku-ring-gai takes 30–40
minutes)

ℹ Bobbin Head Information
Centre ☎ 9457 9310

*The Blue Mountains
offer spectacular views*

BLUE MOUNTAINS

Cooler than Sydney in summer and bracingly
cold in winter, the Blue Mountains are famed
for an excellent range of guest accommodations,
top eating establishments, and grand scenery.
Visitors flock to the towns of Leura, Katoomba,
Springwood, Wentworth Falls, Blackheath, and
Mount Victoria to take in the panoramic vistas,
walk the trails, shop for arts, crafts, and antiques,
and to generally enjoy the unique mountain
ambience. Many of the superb mountain gardens
are open to the public and the cool-climate
Royal Botanic Gardens at Mount Tomah are a
blaze of color in fall and replete with flowers in
the spring and summer.

KU-RING-GAI CHASE NATIONAL PARK
& THE HAWKESBURY RIVER

Bordering Pittwater, but reached from farther
west, Ku-ring-gai Chase is undoubtedly one of
Sydney's gems. This 37,065-acre area of unspoiled bushland, creeks, walking trails, and
Aboriginal sites has been a national park since
1894 and contains a fantastic variety of wildlife.
Ranger-guided walks are available and you can
rent a boat at Bobbin Head. The Kalkari Visitor
Center provides leaflets detailing Aboriginal
heritage and nature walks. This region is
accessible only by car, and you can continue
north up the highway to Brooklyn to take a
cruise on the magnificent Hawkesbury River,
with its rugged bush scenery and many pretty
bays and inlets.

BOTANY BAY & THE ROYAL NATIONAL PARK

Captain Cook and the crew of the *Endeavour* landed at Botany Bay on April 29, 1770 and were followed by the First Fleet, which arrived on January 20, 1788. There are several interesting historic sites here—at the south Sydney suburb of La Perouse visit the museum, the 1882 Bare Island Fort, 1820s Macquarie Watchtower, and other monuments, while across the bay the Kurnell Peninsula offers the Discovery Centre and various Captain Cook-related sites. La Perouse, named after the Comte de la Perouse, a French explorer who arrived in Botany Bay a few days after the First Fleet, is also the home of one of Sydney's largest Aboriginal communities; you can buy arts and crafts here. Continue south to the Royal National Park, with its bushland, remote water holes popular with swimmers and picnickers, and lovely beaches. You can also visit the adjoining Heathcote National Park and Sydney Tramway Museum. You need your own transportation for this trip.

HUNTER VALLEY

The Hunter Valley vineyards are just three hours north of Sydney, near the old coal-mining town of Cessnock. A good range of bus tours is available from Sydney and, given the nature of the main activity here, this is the preferred means of travel. A well-established circuit travels past the cellar doors of dozens of wineries, where visitors are encouraged to sample the different products and are often invited to meet the winemakers in their cellars. Many fine restaurants are located in the area, where visitors can savor a good meal accompanied by a variety of excellent local wines.

INFORMATION

Botany Bay & the Royal National Park
Distance 18 miles to the Royal National Park entrance
Time Allow a full day
La Perouse Museum
✉ Anzac Parade
☎ 9311 3379
The Discovery Centre
✉ Kurnell
☎ 9668 8431
Royal National Park
☎ 9542 0632

Hunter Valley
🚌 Bus from Sydney
Distance 72 miles each way
Journey time Bus trip takes 3 hours
ℹ Hunter Valley Tourist Information Centre
✉ PO Box 132, Cardiff, 2285 ☎ 4941 1115

WHAT'S ON

Sydneysiders need no excuse to party. The best way to find out what's on is to check the entertainment pages of the *Sydney Morning Herald*. On Fridays this newspaper publishes the 20-page *Metro* guide, detailing everything from opera to free outdoor events. Other useful publications are *This Week in Sydney* and *What's on in Sydney*, which are distributed free through hotels, tourist information booths, and many of the city's attractions. The following is a brief rundown of some of the major events in the Sydney calendar.

January	*Festival of Sydney*: A month-long celebration. *Test cricket matches*: Sydney Cricket Ground. *Australia Day* (Jan 26): Includes fireworks.
February	*Gay and Lesbian Mardi Gras*: The city's most glittering parade. *Chinese New Year*: Fireworks and feasting in Chinatown.
March/April	*The Golden Slipper*: A well-known horse race. *Anzac Day* (Apr 25): War Veterans Parade. *Royal Easter Show*: Agriculture show, Homebush.
August	*City-to-Surf* (date to be announced): An 8-mile fun run to Bondi Beach.
September	*Rugby Grand Finals*: League and union teams battle it out in their respective finals.
October	*Manly Jazz Festival*: Music by the sea.
November	*Melbourne Cup* (1st Tue): The country's top horse race brings the nation to a halt for 15 minutes.
December	*Sydney to Hobart Race* (Dec 26): A spectacular start to one of the world's great yacht races.

The Festival of Sydney

The city's major celebration is the Festival of Sydney, an array of theater, music, arts, and outdoor events in January—make sure you catch one of the free concerts held in The Domain. The festival reaches its climax on Australia Day (January 26), the nation's birthday.

SYDNEY's
top 25 sights

The sights are shown on the maps on the inside front cover and inside back cover, numbered **1–25** *in recommended viewing order*

SYDNEY OPERA HOUSE

This once controversial, yet ethereal, sail-roofed building rising from the water on its prominent harborside site, epitomizes the free-spirited nature of this young and vibrant harbor city.

Sydney's most recognizable building The opera house was conceived by Danish architect Joern Utzon, who won a design competition in 1959. It took 14 years to create this masterpiece, which was opened in 1973 by Queen Elizabeth II, although the project was fraught with technical and political problems and Utzon eventually resigned. The building holds four performance halls—for theater, dance, symphony concerts, opera, and other events—restaurants and bars, and a maze of backstage areas. It also houses the Performing Arts Library and Archives. The roofs are covered with more than a million ceramic tiles, and the vast stone base and terraces are modeled on the Mayan and Aztec temples of Mexico. You can enjoy the exterior at any time; a walk around gives you a chance to view the building from many perspectives.

The interior While the architect's vision for the interior was never fully realized, there is much to

see here including a John Olsen mural, *Salute to Five Bells*, in the northern foyer of the Concert Hall, and a Michael Tjakamarra mural, titled *Possum Dreaming*, in the foyer of the Opera Theatre. If possible, attend a performance or take a guided tour to fully appreciate this place.

HIGHLIGHTS

- Location on Bennelong Point
- Ceramic-tiled roof
- Concert Hall
- Opera Theatre
- *Five Bells* mural, by Australian artist John Olsen
- *Possum Dreaming* mural

INFORMATION

- ✚ ci; K4
- ✉ Bennelong Point
- ☎ Tours 9250 7250. Box office 9250 7777
- 🕐 Tours daily 9–4. Performances most days. Closed Good Fri, Dec 25
- 🍴 Four restaurants and cafés
- 🚇 Circular Quay
- 🚌 Sydney Explorer
- ⛴ Circular Quay
- ♿ Good
- 💲 Moderate
- ↔ Sydney Harbour (➤ 26), Circular Quay (➤ 27), The Rocks (➤ 28), Museum of Contemporary Art (➤ 40), Royal Botanic Gardens & The Domain (➤ 42), Museum of Sydney (➤ 44)
- ❓ Tours daily; free outdoor concerts

SYDNEY HARBOUR BRIDGE

Affectionately called "the coat hanger" by locals, the Sydney Harbour Bridge is one of the most famous symbols of this harborside city. Take a climb to the top of the bridge for great harbor views.

All things to all people The Sydney Harbour Bridge is an essential link between the south and north sides of the harbor, the perfect postcard backdrop to the Opera House, and a great spot to take in the harbor panorama. The world's widest long-span bridge was opened in March 1932, and is 1,360 feet long and 130 feet wide, with eight road lanes, two railroad tracks, a cycleway, and a footpath. Crossing by car, bus, or train just isn't the same—by far the best experience is walking across. From the city side, access to the walkway is via Argyle Street in The Rocks, while the northern entrance is near Milsons Point station; a ferry service operates between Milsons Point and Circular Quay. Paul Hogan, star of the film *Crocodile Dundee*, was once a Harbour Bridge rigger.

The Pylon Lookout The highlight of a walk across the bridge is a stop at the southeast pylon. There is an interesting display here on how the bridge was constructed, and the 200-step climb to the lookout is well worthwhile, for the views of the harbor and the city are magnificent.

HIGHLIGHTS

- The walk across
- View from the Pylon Lookout
- Pylon Lookout display
- Close-up look at the structure

INFORMATION

- J4
- Pylon Lookout
- 9247 3408, 9218 6923
- Daily 10–5. Closed Dec 25
- Circular Quay (southern side)
- Sydney Explorer
- Milsons Point (northern side)
- Circular Quay (southern side)
- Walkway free. Pylon Lookout inexpensive
- Mary McKillop Place (► 52), Sydney Opera House (► 24), Circular Quay (► 27), The Rocks (► 28), Sydney Observatory (► 48)

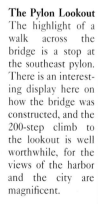

Harbour Bridge detail

3

SYDNEY HARBOUR

HIGHLIGHTS

- Ferry ride or cruise
- Fort Denison
- Views from South Head and North Head
- Goat Island
- The Spit to Manly walk (➤ 51)
- Picnic on Shark Island

INFORMATION

- ➕ L4
- ✉ Fort Denison, Sydney Harbour
- 🕐 Tours daily from Circular Quay
- 🚉 Circular Quay
- 🚌 Sydney Explorer to Circular Quay
- 🚢 From Circular Quay
- ↔ Sydney Opera House (➤ 24), Sydney Harbour Bridge (➤ 25), Circular Quay (➤ 27), The Rocks (➤ 28), Royal Botanic Gardens & The Domain (➤ 42)
- ❓ For guided tours and cruises to Shark, Clark, Goat, and Rodd Islands, contact National Parks ☎ 9555 9844

Spectacular Sydney Harbour, officially Port Jackson, undoubtedly makes this city special. You get stunning water views from the most unexpected places and the still waters are a wonderful place for sailing and swimming. Be sure to take a ferry ride to Manly.

Sydney Harbour With a shoreline that stretches for 149 miles, Sydney's harbor is guaranteed to delight. The best way to enjoy this setting is to take a ferry ride or cruise (➤ 19), most of which depart from Circular Quay; you can travel on anything from a square-rigged schooner to a high-speed JetCat. You can visit beautiful Cremorne Point, Taronga Zoo (➤ 36), Manly (➤ 35), and Watsons Bay (➤ 51), or take an evening cruise to view the spectacular city lights. Harborside walks, such as those around North Head or South Head, are also popular, while Sydney Harbour National Park (➤ 51) encompasses Shark, Clark, Goat, and Rodd islands, which can be toured or booked for picnics (see panel). After you have taken in the more obvious attractions of the main part of the harbor, head west beyond the Harbour Bridge or take a RiverCat trip upriver to Parramatta, or travel by ferry to the suburbs of Balmain, Birchgrove, Greenwich, Hunters Hill, and Meadowbank.

Fort Denison This harbor island was once known as "Pinchgut," after the practice of marooning disobedient convicts here with extremely meager rations. By 1857, the island had become Fort Denison, constructed to defend Sydney against possible Russian invasion during the Crimean War. The historic buildings can be visited on a guided tour.

CIRCULAR QUAY

The epicenter of Sydney's maritime life since European settlement, Circular Quay is today a bustling pedestrian precinct with ferry, bus, and rail terminals. Be sure to check out the galleries, stores, and restaurants in nearby Customs House.

Circular Quay The city's ferry terminal is a great place to sit and watch the boats and buskers, or enjoy a coffee. The covered walkway from the Opera House includes Writers Walk, with plaques that commemorate some prominent Australian authors, poets, and playwrights.

Circular Quay West The surrounding precinct of Circular Quay West contains Cadman's Cottage, the city's oldest building. Dating from 1816 and originally home to the governor's boat crew, it is now a National Parks and Wildlife information center. Also in this area is First Fleet Park, commemorating the nation's first settlers, and the large Overseas Passenger Terminal, the berth for cruise ships.

Customs House From 1845 to 1990 this was home to the Customs Service, but today the building's interior has been refurbished as a major cultural center. Included here are galleries, cafés, studios, and a performance space.

HIGHLIGHTS

- Customs House
- Ferry terminal
- Cadman's Cottage
- Writers Walk
- Buskers
- Harbor views
- Galleries

INFORMATION

- ✚ J5
- ✉ Circular Quay
- ☎ Customs House information line 9247 2285
- 🕐 Daily, except Good Fri, 25 Dec
- 🍴 Cafés and restaurants
- 🚉 Circular Quay
- 🚌 Various
- ♿ Moderate
- ↔ Sydney Opera House (▶ 24), Sydney Harbour (▶ 26), The Rocks (▶ 28), City Center (▶ 33), Museum of Contemporary Art (▶ 40)

Top: Circular Quay
Left: Customs House

THE ROCKS

INFORMATION

- bi; J4–J5
- The Rocks Heritage & Visitor's Centre, 106 George Street
- 9255 1788
- Daily 9–5
- Many cafés and restaurants nearby
- Circular Quay
- Sydney Explorer, 431, 432, 433
- Circular Quay
- Generally good
- Free
- Sydney Harbour Bridge (➤ 25), Sydney Harbour (➤ 26), Circular Quay (➤ 27), Museum of Contemporary Art (➤ 40), Sydney Observatory (➤ 48)
- Rocks walking tours start from the Heritage & Visitor's Centre

The district known as The Rocks, Sydney's first "village," has a fascinating history as a colonial port area. Many of the restored old buildings now house interesting stores and galleries.

A Rocky Start Named after the rocky shore where convict tents were erected in January 1788, The Rocks is Sydney's most intriguing and picturesque area. It was once the province of seamen and traders, thieves and prostitutes, and the scene of a 1900 outbreak of bubonic plague that claimed over 100 lives. More destruction was wreaked during the 1920s, as entire streets were demolished in order to make way for the southern approach to the Harbour Bridge. Meticulous and detailed restoration since 1970, however, has transformed the district into Sydney's tourist hub, the delights of which are equally appreciated by the locals. The area is packed with attractions which will easily fill a day—there are many 1900s buildings to admire, narrow streets such as Nurses Walk and Suez Canal to explore, and plenty of stores and cafés. Campbells Cove, with its historic warehouses, and Dawes Point Park under the Harbour Bridge are both good waterfront spots. As if this wasn't enough, The Rocks also offers many museums and galleries that are well worth exploring (➤ 52 for more details).

The Rocks Heritage and Visitor's Centre Perhaps the best place to start your visit is at the Heritage and Visitor's Centre. Housed in the restored Sailors Home built in 1864, this information and tour-booking outlet contains a shop and an illuminating upstairs display that covers the history of The Rocks. You can also take a Rocks walking tour from here.

6

AQUARIUM & DARLING HARBOUR

Encounter sharks and crocodiles at close quarters, marvel at the species diversity of the Great Barrier Reef, and explore Australia's marine environments at this world-class aquarium. Don't miss the nearby IMAX Theatre.

Aquatic Fun The real thrill here is walking through transparent plastic tunnels beneath the two vast floating oceanariums, watching fish, rays, eels, and sharks glide above you. The Great Barrier Reef display features fish and coral of impossibly bright colors, while the saltwater crocodiles are awesome. Seals frolic in the Marine Mammal Sanctuary, and children can pick up marine creatures in the touch pool.

Darling Harbour The eastern part of Darling Harbour offers several attractions, including the Panasonic IMAX Theatre and Sega World Sydney. The eight-story screen IMAX Theatre is housed in a distinctive eye-shaped building. Sega World is Sydney's first indoor family theme park, giving access to virtual-reality and high-tech rides. Pyrmont Bridge (1902), which links the two sides of Darling Harbour, is the world's oldest electrically operated swingspan bridge, and is still in use.

HIGHLIGHTS

* Sharks in "The Open Ocean"
* Great Barrier Reef display
* Saltwater crocodiles
* Touch pool
* Marine Mammal Sanctuary
* Pyrmont Bridge

INFORMATION

➕ J6

✉ **Aquarium** Aquarium Pier.
IMAX Theatre 491 Kent Street.
Sega World Harbour Street

☎ **Aquarium** 9262 2300.
IMAX Theatre 133–IMAX, 133 462.
Sega World 9273 9111

🕐 **Aquarium** daily 9:30–9.
IMAX Theatre daily 10–10.
Sega World Sun–Thu 10–10; Fri, Sat, school hols 10AM–midnight.

🍴 **Aquarium** restaurant.
IMAX Theatre Star Grill

🚉 Town Hall

🚌 Sydney Explorer

🚝 Monorail to Darling Park

⛴ Aquarium Wharf

♿ Very good

💲 All expensive

🔄 Sydney Harbour (➤ 26), Powerhouse Museum (➤ 34), National Maritime Museum (➤ 37), Chinese Garden & Chinatown (➤ 38), Darling Harbour (➤ 60)

Shark encounters

BONDI BEACH

HIGHLIGHTS

- Beach
- Cafés on Campbell Parade
- Exhibitions and events in Bondi Pavilion
- Clifftop walk to Bronte Beach
- Golf overlooking the ocean
- Surfing

INFORMATION

- ✚ Off map to east
- ✉ Bondi Beach
- ☎ Bondi Pavilion 9130 3325
- 🕐 Daily 24 hours
- 🍴 Many good cafés and restaurants
- 🚉 Bondi Junction, then bus 380, 382
- 🚌 Bondi & Bay Explorer, 380, 382, 389
- ♿ Generally good
- 💲 Free
- ↔ Bronte Beach (➤ 57)
- ❓ Frequent festivals, exhibitions, and events on the beach and at Bondi Pavilion

Just off Australia's most famous beach

Enjoy Sydney's outdoor life at this world-famous strip of surf and sand. Regardless of the season, join the locals as they swim, sunbathe, jog, eat, drink, or simply stroll along the water's edge. This is also a great place for people-watching.

Bondi beach Summer or winter, Bondi is quintessential Sydney. This is one of the world's most famous strips of surf, sand, and beach life, and there is no better way of understanding how the locals enjoy themselves than by heading down to Bondi. The Aboriginal name roughly means "the noise of tumbling waters," a description that aptly sums up this beach and its rolling surf. Perfect for a summer sunbathing and surfing session, or a brisk winter walk along the clifftop path to Tamarama and Bronte beaches. Bondi is Sydney at its very best. In summer you are likely to witness a surf carnival or other beach event, while the Bondi Pavilion often holds musical and theatrical performances and art exhibitions.

Beachside Bondi Street life is just as entertaining, with its bars, pubs, and cafés, as well as a good bookstore and surf and beach clothing shops. You can even play golf overlooking the ocean at the public Bondi Golf Course. Bondi is also a great place to stay, with a growing range of accommodations to suit all budgets.

8

AMP CENTREPOINT TOWER

This 1,000 foot-high structure, soaring dizzily above the city, is the best place to view Sydney's layout. The incredible panorama from the tower's viewing levels extends to the Blue Mountains on a clear day.

The structure Completed in 1981, gold-topped Centrepoint Tower, as it is known locally, a member of the World Federation of Great Towers, is anchored to the Centrepoint shopping center below by 56 stabilizing cables, each of which weighs almost eight tons. "AMP" was added to the name when this financial services company bought the naming rights to the building. This is one of the tallest public buildings in the southern hemisphere, and contains two revolving restaurants, an observation level, and a coffee shop. A ride in the high-speed elevator—a journey that takes a mere 40 seconds—is an experience in itself. While here, a visit to Centrepoint is also worthwhile. This large complex has over 170 stores (mainly clothing and fashion items) on four levels, several cafés, and a reasonably priced basement food court.

The views The 360-degree views are incredible, and a visit to the tower is a starting point to becoming familiar with the city's layout. You will see the harbor, beyond to the ocean, the Blue Mountains 50 miles west, and south towards Botany Bay, you can clearly see aircraft taking off and landing at the airport. The observation level features high-powered binoculars and free guided tours. There are also special glass windows for glare-free photography. The views down into the city streets are no less fascinating, and a visit after dark is magical. Try dining in one of the tower's restaurants to appreciate the glittering night-time panorama.

HIGHLIGHTS

- View of Sydney Harbour, the city buildings and south to Botany Bay
- Night views
- Revolving restaurants
- High-speed elevator

INFORMATION

- ✚ biv; J6
- ✉ 100 Market Street
- ☎ 9229 7444
- 🕐 Sun–Fri 9:30–9:30; Sat 9:30AM–11PM
- 🍴 Two restaurants, coffee lounge
- 🚇 St. James
- 🚌 Any Circular Quay-bound bus
- ♿ Good
- 💲 Moderate
- ↔ Queen Victoria Building (➤ 32), Hyde Park Barracks (➤ 45), Hyde Park (➤ 60), Martin Place (➤ 60)
- ❓ Audio and guided tours

9

QUEEN VICTORIA BUILDING

HIGHLIGHTS

- Building's facade
- Floor tiles on the first floor
- Central dome
- Stained-glass windows
- Replica Crown jewels display on third floor
- Chinese jade bridal carriage on second floor
- Victorian-era toilets on second floor

INFORMATION

- biv; J6
- Corner of George, York, Market, and Druitt streets
- 9264 9209
- Daily. Shops generally 9–6
- Many food stands, cafés, and restaurants
- Town Hall
- Sydney Explorer, any Circular Quay-bound bus
- Very good
- Free
- Aquarium and Darling Harbour East (➤ 29), AMP Centrepoint Tower (➤ 31), City Center (Town Hall ➤ 33)

The delightfully restored interior of Sydney's most imposing Victorian-era building prompted French fashion guru Pierre Cardin to describe the structure as "the most beautiful shopping center in the world."

The building Constructed to commemorate Queen Victoria's golden jubilee and completed in 1898, the domed Romanesque-style QVB was originally used to house markets downstairs and offices upstairs. The building fell into decline during the 1960s and 1970s, and there were even moves to demolish this remarkable piece of history to make way for a civic center and underground parking lot. Fortunately, it survived and in the 1980s, courtesy of a Malaysian company, meticulous restoration transformed the seven-level sandstone structure into a historic attraction and a delightful shopping center. Capped by a central glass dome, the 180ft-long building, occupying an entire city block and containing over 180 stores, cafés, and restaurants, features beautiful stained-glass windows, patterned floor tiles, and period colors and appointments, while the four main floors are divided into elegant Victorian-fronted shops.

Shopping in the QVB Shopping in such attractive surroundings is a pleasure. The lower-level food court and first-floor stores are more run-of-the-mill, but the upper floors contain outlets for international labels such as Ralph Lauren and Papoucci, as well as excellent local designers and a wide range of quality souvenir shops. On Victoria Walk (third floor), there is an interesting collection of historical objects. Here you can admire a replica of the British Crown jewels, an incredibly ornate Chinese jade bridal carriage, the "Royal Clock," and a jade tree.

CITY CENTER

Sydney's colonial-era and Victorian buildings have been restored and many are open for inspection. Walk around the city center, with its splendid parks and malls, to view some architectural gems and don't forget the interesting little backstreets.

Colonial and Victorian Sydney From its origins as a convict settlement, Sydney has always had fine public and commercial buildings which were progressively replaced with grander and newer versions as the years went by and the population increased. Fortunately, a few colonial buildings, such as the Hyde Park Barracks and St. James Church, remain, as do splendid examples of 19th-century architecture that were built using local sandstone. One such is the Town Hall in George Street, an elaborate 1869 building. You can look at the richly decorated vestibule and the grand hall with its powerful organ at any time, or join one of the guided tours that take place on most days. Next door is St. Andrews Cathedral, while St. Marys Cathedral is on the eastern side of Hyde Park.

Art Deco Sydney A number of buildings survive, but the Anzac War Memorial, in the southern section of Hyde Park, and the Archibald Fountain, in the northern section, are the most accessible and classic of all structures from this era.

Modern Sydney While many of the city's modern structures are not considered architecturally important, some buildings are worth seeking out, including Chifley Tower at Chifley Square and the Harry Seidler-designed buildings, the MLC Centre in Martin Place, and Australia Square in George Street.

HIGHLIGHTS

- Sydney Town Hall
- Harry Seidler buildings
- Hyde Park
- Hyde Park Barracks
- St. Andrews Cathedral
- Sydney Mint Museum
- Chifley Tower

INFORMATION

- ✚ J6
- ☎ Town Hall tours 9231 4629
- ◷ Tours daily
- 🍴 Town Hall, Museum
- ♿ Few
- 💲 Free
- ↔ Circular Quay (▶ 27), AMP Centrepoint Tower (▶ 31), Australian Museum (▶ 41), Royal Botanic Gardens (▶ 42), Museum of Sydney (▶ 44), Hyde Park Barracks (▶ 45), Chifley Tower (▶ 54)

Central station is one of many fine sandstone buildings in the CBD

POWERHOUSE MUSEUM

HIGHLIGHTS

- Decorative Arts section
- Boulton and Watt engine
- King's Cinema
- "Space: Beyond this World"
- Transportation section
- Powerhouse Garden Restaurant

INFORMATION

- ✚ H7
- ✉ 500 Harris Street, Ultimo
- ☎ 9217 0111
- 🕐 Daily 10–5. Closed Dec 25
- 🍴 Restaurant, outdoor kiosk and tables
- 🚇 Central
- 🚌 Sydney Explorer
- 🚝 Monorail to Haymarket
- ⛴ Aquarium Wharf, Darling Harbour
- ♿ Excellent
- 💲 Moderate; free 1st Sat of every month
- ↔ Aquarium & Darling Harbour East (➤ 29), National Maritime Museum (➤ 37), Chinese Garden & Chinatown (➤ 38), Harris Street Motor Museum (➤ 52), Darling Harbour (➤ 60)
- ❓ Guided tours, regular films, courses, and display demonstrations

Sydney's most innovative museum is housed in a cavernous old power station with modern extensions. Interactive audiovisual displays are combined with fascinating historical exhibits.

The building During the 1980s the 1899 Ultimo Power Station was transformed into Sydney's largest museum. Displays are housed in the vast boiler, turbine, and engine houses, as well as the new Neville Wran Building, which was inspired by grand 19th-century exhibition halls and railroad stations.

The collection The award-winning museum contains much of the Museum of Applied Arts and Sciences' extensive collection, which originated in the 1880s. Grouped into five themed areas—Creativity and Australian Achievement, Decorative Arts, Everyday Life in Australia, Bringing People Together, and Science, Technology and People—the contents range

from the enormous 18th-century Boulton and Watt steam engine to historic gowns, audiovisual presentations, sound effects, holograms, and dozens of hands-on scientific displays. You can even sit in King's Cinema, a re-creation of a 1930s art deco cinema, and watch a silent movie, accompanied by the bells, whistles, and gadgetry of an electrically and air-activated Fotoplayer. Be sure to see the Garden Restaurant, painted by the Sydney artist Ken Done.

The Powerhouse caters for all ages and interests

MANLY & OCEANWORLD

The slogan "seven miles from Sydney and a thousand miles from care" originated in the late 1880s, when ferries greatly shortened the previously cross-country journey to Manly, a favorite beachside suburb. Sydneysiders have flocked here ever since.

Manly The strangely titled suburb of Manly owes its name to Governor Phillip, who remarked on the "manly" appearance of Aborigines here in 1788. It first became a beach resort in the late 1800s, and today it's just a short ferry ride or JetCat trip from the city. In summer, Manly and its excellent beaches, such as Shelly, draw surfers and swimmers, but there is plenty to do here at any time. The Manly Art Gallery and Museum has a good collection, and you can stroll around the modern Manly Wharf, with over 65 stores and cafés, as well as watch free street-entertainment. Continue to North Head and visit the historic Quarantine Station, or take a bus excursion to the wonderful northern beaches, such as Palm Beach or Mona Vale.

Oceanworld A good focus for your trip to Manly is a visit to Oceanworld. This big aquarium features colorful fish of the Great Barrier Reef, as well as corals, sharks, seal shows, and giant stingrays. The sharks are hand-fed twice a day.

HIGHLIGHTS

Manly
● Main beach and Shelly Beach
● Weekend Arts and Crafts Market
● Manly Art Gallery and Museum

Oceanworld
● Great Barrier Reef display
● Seal shows
● Stingrays
● Divers hand-feeding sharks

INFORMATION

✠ Off map to northeast
✉ Oceanworld, West Esplanade, Manly
☎ 9949 2644
🕐 Daily 10–5:30. Closed 25 Dec
🍴 Café
🚇 Manly
⌘ Few
💲 Moderate
↔ Sydney Harbour (► 26), North Head (► 51), The Spit to Manly Walk (► 51), Quarantine Station (► 52)
❓ Guided tours, special aquarium shows, and various Manly events and festivals (for information ☎ 9977 1088)

Manly's amuseument park

13

TARONGA ZOO

HIGHLIGHTS

- Western Lowland gorillas
- "Koala Walkabout" and photos with the koalas
- Snow leopards
- Seal shows
- "Orang-utan Rainforest"
- White Sumatran tiger
- Platypus and echidna
- Views from the cable car
- Night zoo in October
- Discovery Park

INFORMATION

- M3
- ✉ Bradleys Head Road, Mosman
- ☎ 9969 2777
- 🕐 Nov–Sep: daily 9–5. Oct: daily 9–5; 5:30–9:30
- 🍴 Variety of cafés and kiosks
- 🚌 247
- 🚢 Taronga Zoo
- ♿ Good
- 💰 Expensive
- ↔ Sydney Harbour (➤ 26), Mosman (➤ 55), Cremorne Point (➤ 58)
- ❓ Guided tours, special zoo-keeper presentations, and talks

Located in Sydney Harbour, Taronga Zoo is a conservation leader. Although it doesn't limit itself to native animals, it's the Australian fauna most visitors come to see. Its superb site, spectacular outlook, and the ferry ride to get there, are all bonuses.

Australian fauna Set in natural foreshore bushland, Taronga (an Aboriginal word meaning water view) dates from 1916 and has long been at the forefront of keeping animals in less restrictive enclosures. Arrive by ferry and take the cable car up the zoo's steep incline to the top entrance. This is a great place to meet native Australian wildlife—you can see kangaroos, wallabies, dingoes, emus, wombats, the carnivorous Tasmanian devil, crocodiles, and many brightly colored birds. As always, the koalas are a must-see, particularly as you can have your photo taken next to one of these endearing creatures. Don't miss the spiky echidna and the aquatic platypus (examples of monotremes—strange, egg-laying mammals). Other highlights include Western Lowland gorillas, the very entertaining seal shows, and the Discovery Park, which gives children (and adults) the opportunity to meet and even touch some of the feathered and furry residents. Taronga has a strong educational bias, and a variety of animal presentations and keeper talks take place each day on anything from what koalas eat to the habits of giraffes. A night zoo operates throughout October.

Creatures from other countries Taronga's strong support for wildlife conservation is evident in its endangered species breeding program; the zoo is home to Sumatran tigers, Himalayan snow leopards, red pandas, and orang-utans. You will also see more familiar zoo animals such as elephants, giraffes, and chimpanzees.

A possum

14

NATIONAL MARITIME MUSEUM

This comprehensive display of Australia's maritime heritage, from the arrival of the First Fleet to the modern voyages of Vietnamese boat people, documents Australia's inextricable links with the ocean.

Indoor displays Opened in 1991, the museum features six themed sections—Discovery, Commerce, Passengers, Leisure, Navy, and Linked by the Sea—which contain thousands of items in displays as diverse as early beach fashions, the yacht *Australia II* (winner of the America's Cup in 1983), and migrant voyages. Other highlights include a section on Aboriginal people and the sea, the maritime links between Australia and the U.S.A., and an intriguing display on how a Sydney man built the world's fastest boat in his back garden. You can also see what life was like on board a convict ship, discover why surfboards have become shorter, play with high-tech computer games, or watch a film in the museum's movie theater. As well as the thousands of exhibits in the permanent collection, temporary exhibitions are presented in the North Gallery and Mazda Gallery.

Outdoor displays Once you've seen what's on offer inside, go to the outdoor displays, moored at the museum's wharves. The 12 historic vessels include HMAS *Vampire*, the last of the Royal Australian Navy's big gunships, and one of Russia's Cold War submarines, both of which you can tour. Among the other interesting craft here are the *Arkarana*, an 1888 racing cutter, a Vietnamese refugee boat that reached northern Australia, a lugger from the pearling port of Broome in Western Australia, and *Krait*, a World War II commando boat. From the wharves you can admire the building's unusual architecture.

HIGHLIGHTS

- HMAS *Vampire*
- Hands-on exhibits
- Vietnamese refugee boat
- Museum computer games
- America's Cup display
- Discovery section
- U.S.A. Gallery
- Russian submarine

INFORMATION

- ✚ H6
- ✉ Darling Harbour West
- ☎ 9552 7777. Recorded information 0055 62 002
- 🕐 Daily 9:30–5. Closed Dec 25
- 🍴 Good café
- 🚇 Town Hall
- 🚌 Sydney Explorer
- 🚝 Monorail to Harbourside
- 🚢 Aquarium Wharf
- ♿ Excellent
- 💰 Moderate
- ↔ Sydney Harbour (➤ 26), Aquarium and Darling Harbour East (➤ 29), Powerhouse Museum (➤ 34), Chinese Garden & Chinatown (➤ 38), Darling Harbour (➤ 60)
- ❓ Guided tours (included in admission price), films, maritime library, good shop

15

CHINESE GARDEN & CHINATOWN

HIGHLIGHTS

- Garden's pavilions, lakes, and waterfalls
- Pumphouse Brewery and Tavern (► 80)
- Sydney Entertainment Centre
- Paddy's Markets (► 74)
- Dixon Street
- Capitol Theatre (► 78)

INFORMATION

- ✚ J6–J7
- ✉ Chinese Garden: Darling Harbour
- ☎ 9281 6863. Darling Harbour infoline 0055 20261
- 🕙 Daily 9:30–dusk
- 🍴 Cafés and restaurants nearby
- 🚇 Town Hall
- 🚌 Sydney Explorer
- 🚌 Monorail to Haymarket
- ⛴ Aquarium Wharf, Darling Harbour
- ♿ Good
- 💲 Inexpensive
- ↔ Aquarium & Darling Harbour (► 29), Powerhouse Museum (► 34), National Maritime Museum (► 37), Darling Harbour (► 60)

The colorful Chinese quarter, part of the city since the 1860s, is a great place for diverse Asian cuisines and specialty shopping. The Chinese Garden, just a few steps away from Chinatown, offers a calm retreat in the middle of busy downtown Sydney.

The Chinese Garden The largest of its kind outside mainland China, this tranquil garden was designed by Chinese landscape architects from Guangdong Province, a New South Wales sister state, and features Cantonese-style pavilions, lakes, waterfalls, and bridges. With its shrubs, flowers, and trees, including maples, this is a delightful spot in which to relax after seeing Darling Harbour's myriad attractions. Its other name is the Garden of Friendship, symbolizing the enduring links between China and Australia.

Chinatown Centered on Dixon, Hay, and Sussex streets, Sydney's Chinatown is a bustling area of Asian food and clothing stores, as well as many moderately-priced restaurants. Paddy's Markets are held here at weekends and the area includes the city's largest performance venue, the Sydney Entertainment Centre. The beautifully restored 1928 Capitol Theatre, home of major musical and theatrical events, is nearby on Campbell Street; it's worth seeing a show to appreciate the extraordinarily ornate interior. Adjacent to the Chinese Garden, the Pumphouse Brewery and Tavern brews its own beer, and you can take a tour of the brewery. Chinese New Year (January or February) is a particularly exciting time to be in the area, when you will see fireworks, dragon dances, and street processions.

16

SYDNEY STAR CASINO

This hotel/casino complex, the latest addition to Darling Harbour, offers four levels dedicated to games of chance, fine dining, and a variety of specialty shops.

A long time coming Thanks to puritanical, if hypocritical, lawmakers and politicians, Sydney's gamblers waited many years for a legal gambling palace, putting up with illegal establishments that were often raided by the police. All that is in the past as the glitz and glamor of international standard gaming is only a short hop from Darling Harbour and is serviced by the new light rail service from Central Station.

State of the art Gamblers are encouraged to try their luck at international games such as blackjack, roulette, *pai gow*, and *sic bo* or take their chances at the old Aussie favorite, two-up. The main floor groans with the weight of 1,500 slot machines (called "pokies" by Australians, after the card game of poker) which entertain their patrons beneath a ceiling sparkling with abstract, multi-colored sculptures of Australian landscapes. At night, the tall-building silhouette of the city's western facade presents a dramatic view from the terraced balconies that cascade down the front of the casino.

Not just for gamblers Host to a range of international entertainers, the 2,000-seat Lyric Theatre is Sydney's newest major theater. In addition, a range of cuisines is presented in the many restaurants and cafés throughout the complex. The harbor views from Astral, the premier restaurant, contribute to a memorable meal. A good selection of specialist shops, retail outlets, restaurants, and cafés is located on the concourse level, including a florist, hairdressers, jewelers, food store, and clothing store, as well as a store selling casino merchandise.

HIGHLIGHTS

- 1,500 slot machines
- Blackjack, roulette, etc
- International entertainment
- Specialist shops
- Five-star hotel

INFORMATION

- H5
- 80 Pyrmont Street, Pyrmont
- 1800 700 700
- Daily 24 hours
- Various
- Star City Light Rail
- Good
- Powerhouse Museum
  (► 34), National Maritime
  Museum (► 37), Chinatown
  (► 38), Darling Harbour
  (► 60)

17

MUSEUM OF CONTEMPORARY ART

INFORMATION

- ✚ bi; J5
- ✉ Circular Quay West
- ☎ 9252 4033. Recorded information 9241 5892
- ◉ Daily 10–5. Closed Good Fri, Dec 25
- 🍴 Café
- Circular Quay
- 🚌 Sydney Explorer, 431, 432, 433
- Circular Quay
- ♿ Excellent
- Moderate
- ↔ Sydney Harbour Bridge (➤ 25), Sydney Harbour (➤ 26), Circular Quay (➤ 27), The Rocks (➤ 28), Sydney Observatory (➤ 48)
- ❓ Guided tours daily at noon and 2; special movies, talks, and performances

The MCA is a modern art gallery full of surprises. Stunning installations, audacious photography, fine Aboriginal art, and special performances all conjoin to astound and entertain.

The museum In a superb location overlooking the harbor, the MCA contains Australia's finest collection of contemporary art. Established in 1991 by the University of Sydney through a bequest of John Wardell Power, and by the provision of the building by the state government, the MCA contains more than 4,000 works. International traveling exhibitions, ranging from photography to 3-D installations, are a highlight, and often occupy most of the gallery space, sending much of the permanent collection into temporary storage.

The permanent collection The Australian and international art exhibits date from the 1960s and include indigenous art from the Northern Territory's Arnhem Land, the Contemporary Art Archive and work by overseas artists such as Andy Warhol and Roy Lichtenstein.

The building This historic building was once home to the Maritime Services Board. The structure was designed in 1939 but was not completed until 1954 due to the war and shortages of building materials. This makes it the last art-deco style building in Sydney. The fine MCA Fish Café offers magnificent views of the Opera House.

Top: exhibition of contemporary Australian art

Right: Circular Quay

AUSTRALIAN MUSEUM

Rated among the world's top natural history museums, the Australian Museum highlights the country's unique fauna, geology, and the origins and history of Australia's indigenous people.

The collection Housed in an 1849 building, with more recent additions, the museum has an excellent Aboriginal area, a showcase of native birds, insects, and mammals, and an informative display on gems and minerals. In other rooms you can discover more about human evolution, dinosaurs, and Pacific and Indonesian peoples and their customs, including a traditional Indonesian gamelan orchestra, and try some enjoyable hands-on computer displays. One of the most interesting sections is the Skeletons room, where the internal organs of various creatures, including a cycling human, can be examined. And don't miss Eric, a 110- to 120-million-year-old plesiosaur; this opalised marine reptile was, incredibly, excavated far inland, at dusty Coober Pedy in South Australia.

Other highlights The excellent changing exhibitions here generally focus on environmental and cultural heritage topics. The College Street Diner has a lively atmosphere and the museum shop sells books on Australia, as well as unusual cards, gifts, and souvenirs.

HIGHLIGHTS

- Aboriginal Australia display
- Planet of Minerals room
- Eric
- Australian birds, especially the parrots
- Human evolution displays
- Skeletons room
- Gamelan orchestra

INFORMATION

- ✚ K6
- ✉ 6 College Street
- ☎ 9339 8111. Recorded information 0055 29408
- ◷ Daily 9:30–5. Closed Dec 25
- ⑪ Two excellent cafés
- ⊙ Museum
- ⊟ Sydney Explorer, 311, 380, 382
- ♿ Very good
- ⑨ Moderate. Free after 4PM
- ↔ AMP Centrepoint Tower (➤ 31), Art Gallery of New South Wales (➤ 43), Anzac War Memorial (➤ 54), Hyde Park (➤ 60)
- ❓ Free tours daily; performances, special events, and exhibitions; museum shop

Eric the plesiosaur

19

ROYAL BOTANIC GARDENS & THE DOMAIN

HIGHLIGHTS

- Sydney Tropical Centre
- Sydney Fernery
- Palm Grove
- Visitor Centre and Gardens Shop
- Charlton Pool
- Government House (➤ 60)
- Walk around Farm Cove to Mrs Macquaries Point
- Views from Mrs Macquaries Point

INFORMATION

- ✚ ci–cii; K5–K6
- ✉ Behind Farm Cove, and off Mrs Macquaries Road
- ☎ Botanic Gardens 9231 8111, 9231 8125. Government House infoline 9931 5200
- ◑ Gardens daily 8AM–dusk. Glasshouses daily 10–4. Closed Good Fri, Dec 25. Government House Fri–Sun 10–3
- 🍴 Gardens restaurant
- 🚇 Circular Quay/Martin Place
- 🚌 Sydney Explorer, 888 (to The Domain)
- 🚢 Circular Quay
- ♿ Very good
- 💲 Free
- ↔ Sydney Opera House (➤ 24), Sydney Harbour (➤ 26), Art Gallery of New South Wales (➤ 43), Hyde Park Barracks (➤ 45)
- ❓ Free guided walks, exhibitions

To escape the crowds of the city center, visit the glorious Botanic Gardens, once an Aboriginal sacred site, then take a stroll in the adjoining Domain, a harbor-side haven for kookaburras, cockatoos, and fruit bats.

Royal Botanic Gardens Extending inland from the curve of Farm Cove, these lovely gardens were the site of the first, rather unsuccessful, government farm back in 1788. The gardens were founded in 1816 and now contain a fine collection of native and foreign plants. The highlights include the lush Sydney Fernery and the Sydney Tropical Centre with its ultra-modern glasshouses. The center explains the wonders of tropical ecosystems and features a verdant display of plants from around the world. You can also wander through the delightful Palm Grove, or visit the beautifully laid-out Herb Garden, the Visitor Centre and Gardens Shop, and the National Herbarium, established in 1985 to study Australia's native plants. The impressive Government House, once the official residence of the governor of NSW, lies within the gardens and is open to the public.

The Domain The northern section of The Domain (the remainder fronts the Art Gallery on the other side of the Cahill Expressway and is used mainly by lunchtime joggers and for open-air concerts in summer) is part of the land laid out in 1810 as the "domain" of Governor Macquarie. This narrow, tree-lined area is a lovely spot for picnics and waterfront strolls. In summer, you can have a dip at the open-air Andrew "Boy" Charlton swimming pool and walk to Mrs Macquaries Point, named after the governor's wife who, not surprisingly, enjoyed the wonderful view from this promontory.

ART GALLERY OF NEW SOUTH WALES

The Aboriginal material is a particularly exciting part of the wonderful collection of Australian, Asian, and European art exhibited here. The local works of art offer a disparate view of Australian society and culture.

The collection The original Victorian building has been greatly extended (most recently to mark the 1988 bicentennial) to showcase the gallery's diverse permanent collection and the high-quality visiting international exhibitions. Besides work by European artists and fine Australian painters such as Frederick McCubbin, Arthur Streeton, Elioth Gruner, Lloyd Rees, Tom Roberts, and Sidney Nolan, the gallery has an excellent Asian art section, whose ceramics are highly rated among connoisseurs. European highlights include works by Picasso, Van Gogh, Degas, and Rodin, while the prints and drawings room and the photography gallery are also well worth visiting.

The Yiribana Gallery This newest exhibition is an exciting addition to the complex. It contains Australia's most comprehensive collection of Aboriginal and Torres Strait Islander art. More than 200 items, ranging from the most contemporary paintings to sculptures and traditional works on bark, are housed here. In addition, Aboriginal dance and music performances take place in the gallery at noon from Tuesday to Friday.

HIGHLIGHTS

- Yiribana Gallery
- Thai bronze Buddhas (Asian Art room)
- Elioth Gruner's *Spring Frost*
- Lloyd Rees's paintings
- Photography gallery
- Tom Roberts's paintings

INFORMATION

- ✚ ciii; K6
- ✉ Art Gallery Road, The Domain
- ☎ 9225 1744. Recorded information 9225 1790
- 🕐 Daily 10–5. Closed Good Fri, Dec 25
- 🍴 Excellent restaurant and café
- 🚉 St. James/Martin Place
- 🚌 Sydney Explorer, 888
- ♿ Excellent
- 💲 Free
- ↔ City Center (➤ 33), Royal Botanic Gardens & The Domain (➤ 42), Hyde Park Barracks (➤ 45)
- ❓ Free tours daily, lectures, movies and performances; library and shop; Aboriginal dance and music

The Buddha enthroned under seven-headed naga (19th-century gilt bronze from the Thai, Bangkok period)

21

MUSEUM OF SYDNEY

This unusual museum leads you on an illuminating journey of discovery from the local Aboriginal occupation and the earliest convict days of the late 18th century to the emerging Sydney of the 1850s and beyond.

HIGHLIGHTS

- *Edge of the Trees* sculpture and the public square
- Original Government House foundations
- Video wall
- Eora story
- Sydney environment displays

INFORMATION

- ✚ biii; J5
- ✉ Corner of Bridge and Phillip streets
- ☎ 9251 5988
- 🕐 Daily 10–5. Closed Good Fri, Dec 25
- 🍴 Café
- 🚇 Circular Quay
- 🚌 Any Circular Quay-bound bus
- ⛴ Circular Quay
- ♿ Excellent
- Moderate
- ↔ Sydney Opera House (➤ 24), Circular Quay (➤ 27), Royal Botanic Gardens & The Domain (➤ 42)
- ❓ Guides available in the museum; exhibitions, lectures, performances; museum shop

The site Where the museum is located forms an integral part of this exciting A$29 million museum, opened in May 1995, for it was here the nation's first, modest Government House was built in 1788. Home to the first eight governors, the building was demolished in 1846, but excavations have revealed the original foundations, part of which can be viewed through the paving. Emphasizing the nation's mixed origins, the dramatic forecourt sculpture, *Edge of the Trees*, consists of 29 columns, remnants of Aboriginal and early European occupation.

The museum Divided into several themed areas and laid out in an imaginative minimalist style, the three-level Museum of Sydney aims to interpret the city's history from 1788 to 1850. Stories of the local Eora Aborigines and the early European days are told through artifacts found during the excavations, computer displays, an extraordinary 33-screen video wall, and spoken history.

Top: exhibits in the Museum of Sydney
Left: Edge of the Trees sculpture

HYDE PARK BARRACKS

This building, once inhabited by convicts, was designed by the brilliant ex-forger turned architect Francis Greenway. Now a museum, the building has remarkable displays covering convict life and Sydney's early years.

The barracks Located on historic Macquarie Street, Hyde Park Barracks (1819) is perhaps the city's most charming building. This three-story example of Georgian architecture originally accommodated convicts, and later became a home for destitute women. The building is now a fascinating museum, focusing on the lives of these occupants and providing a glimpse into Sydney's early days. Changing exhibitions are mounted on the ground-floor Greenway Gallery, and you can even spend the night here (in a hammock) to get a feel of convict life. The most enjoyable way to appreciate the simple but elegant building, however, is by taking a coffee or meal at the delightful Hyde Park Barracks Café in the courtyard.

Queens Square and Macquarie Street The city's finest and most historically significant avenue, Macquarie Street, begins outside the barracks at Queens Square, which is anchored by an 1888 statue of Queen Victoria. This area contains the city's oldest church, the 1822 St. James (another Francis Greenway building), the modern Law Courts, and other historic structures such as the 1816 Sydney Mint Museum. To appreciate thoroughly Macquarie Street's charms, walk past Victorian Sydney Hospital, the Mint Museum, and State Parliament House (1816) to the State Library. Beyond Bent Street you can view the 1819 Greenway-designed Conservatorium of Music, which adjoins the Royal Botanic Gardens.

HIGHLIGHTS

- ● Elegant architecture
- ● Exhibitions in the Greenway Gallery
- ● Historic Macquarie Street
- ● St. James Church
- ● Spending the night in a barracks hammock

INFORMATION

- ✚ ciii; K6
- ✉ Queens Square, Macquarie Street
- ☎ 9223 8922. Overnight bookings 9692 8366
- 🕐 Daily 10–5. Closed Good Fri, Dec 25
- 🍴 Hyde Park Barracks Café (➤ 68)
- 🚇 Martin Place/St. James
- 🚌 Sydney Explorer, 311
- ⛴ Circular Quay
- ♿ Few
- 💰 Moderate
- ↔ AMP Centrepoint Tower (➤ 31), Royal Botanic Gardens & The Domain (➤ 42), Art Gallery of New South Wales (➤ 43), Museum of Sydney (➤ 44), Sydney Mint Museum (➤ 53)
- ❓ Guided tours, exhibitions, special tours, and events

CENTENNIAL PARK

INFORMATION

- M8–L9
- Centennial Park, off Oxford Street, Woollahra
- 9331 5056
- Daily during daylight hours
- Excellent café
- Bondi Junction
- Bondi & Bay Explorer, 378, 380, 382
- Very good
- Free. Inexpensive for walks
- Victoria Barracks (➤ 55), Moore Park Golf Club, Sydney Cricket Ground and Sydney Football Stadium (all ➤ 82)
- Ranger-guided walks; occasional concerts, and special events

One of Sydney's largest green spaces, Centennial Park is perfect for picnicking, walking, jogging, cycling, horse riding, or rollerblading. The fashionable suburbs of Paddington and Woollahra are nearby.

The park Originally known as Sydney Common and used for grazing animals, Centennial Park is the inner-city's largest expanse of greenery. Although it is relatively crowded on weekends, and a hive of activity before and after work hours during the week, Centennial Park is quiet during the day and a good place for a picnic or just relaxing. You can lose yourself among lakes, grassland, woods, or the swamp, or spot some of the 200 species of birds that have been recorded seasonally. If you'd like a tour, there are ranger-guided nature and heritage walks, or you can rent bicycles, inline skates, and horses to circle the 2.5 mile Grand Drive. The Federation Pavilion, which was opened in 1988 (Australia's bicentenary year), commemorates the nation's federation ceremony, which took place in the park in 1901.

Paddington and Woollahra These neighboring suburbs (➤ 16) provide much to do, with interesting clothing and antique stores, excellent cafés, quaint streets, and, on Saturdays, the famous Paddington Bazaar.

One of the peaceful lakes in Centennial Park

VAUCLUSE HOUSE & VAUCLUSE

Visit this charming old eastern suburbs harborside mansion to have a look at its distinctive Gothic-style architecture and its authentic interior furnishings, and to enjoy the well-tended gardens and old-fashioned tearooms.

The house and grounds Much of modern-day Vaucluse, one of Sydney's most desirable harborside suburbs, was once part of the large estate of William Charles Wentworth. Set in 27 acres of grounds, most of Gothic-style Vaucluse House was constructed in the 1830s for Wentworth, a prominent citizen, barrister, and explorer (one of the first men to cross the Blue Mountains in 1813), and the father of the Australian Constitution. The house contains 15 rooms, furnished in the style of the mid-19th century, including an impressive entertaining suite as well as a particularly well presented kitchen. The large drawing room is splendid, with opulent fabrics and furnishings and a bay window that is framed by the shady veranda. Look out for the unusual corridor bedroom on the second floor—it is partitioned off from the hallway by a screen of cupboards. Little remains of the original estate, but the gardens and tearooms are delightful.

The best of Vaucluse This expensive suburb, named after Vaucluse in the south of France and first settled in 1803, is full of large homes, green, leafy streets, and wonderful harborside spots. Parsley Bay is a favorite family beach, while the sand and gardens at Shark Beach and Nielsen Park are packed in summer. This latter beach is within Sydney Harbour National Park (▶ 51), and was once part of the Vaucluse House estate. You can take a scenic walk, with great views, around the foreshore.

HIGHLIGHTS

- The architecture
- Kitchen, drawing room, and gardens
- Nielsen Park's beach and foreshore walk
- Parsley Bay
- Vaucluse House tearooms

INFORMATION

- Off map to east
- Vaucluse House, Wentworth Road, Vaucluse
- 9388 7922
- Tue–Sun, hols 10–4:30. Closed Good Fri, Dec 25
- Famous tearooms
- Bondi & Bay Explorer, 325
- Watsons Bay (then bus 325)
- Moderate
- Sydney Harbour (▶ 26), Watsons Bay and South Head (▶ 51)
- Performances and special events in the gardens

25

SYDNEY OBSERVATORY

INFORMATION

- ✚ ai; J4
- ✉ Sydney Observatory, Observatory Hill, Millers Point
- ☎ 9217 0485 (Mon–Fri only)
- 🕐 Mon–Fri 2–5; Sat, Sun 10–5 (evenings Thu–Tue). Closed Good Fri, Dec 25
- 🍴 Café nearby
- 🚇 Circular Quay
- 🚌 431, 432, 433
- 🚢 Circular Quay
- ♿ Few
- 🅿 Free; charge for night viewing
- ↔ Sydney Harbour Bridge (➤ 25), Circular Quay (➤ 27), The Rocks (➤ 28)
- ❓ Guided tours, night viewing, talks, exhibitions, and movies

Sydney's glittering night skies, so different from those in the northern hemisphere, are as intriguing now as they were for Australia's early astronomers, who erected this fine building high on Observatory Hill in 1858.

The Observatory and Observatory Hill The Observatory, now a museum of astronomy and related sciences, provides a fascinating glimpse into those studies through entertaining hands-on exhibits and other displays. This is also the location for one of Sydney's most unusual tourist activities—night-sky viewing, which must be reserved in advance. Observatory Hill is the city center's highest point (119 feet), and was the site of Fort Phillip (1803), the original 1821 Observatory and the Signal Station (1848), which still stands today. There are great inner-harbor views from the hill and you can walk behind the Observatory to visit the National Trust Centre, with its S.H. Ervin Gallery and excellent tearooms. The gallery features changing exhibitions of Australian art and culture, ranging from watercolor paintings to photography.

Argyle Place Just below Observatory Hill and flanked by historic houses and the 1840 Gothic-revival Garrison Church is Argyle Place, the city's only village green. Also here is the sandstone Lord Nelson Hotel (1834), licenced since 1842 and Sydney's oldest watering hole. A stroll down nearby Lower Fort Street reveals more 19th-century terraced houses and the charming, oddly shaped Hero of Waterloo Hotel (1844), the city's second-oldest pub. From just above Argyle Place, you can walk, via the covered steps, on to the Sydney Harbour Bridge walkway.

SYDNEY's *best*

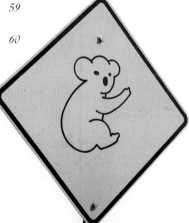

THE GREAT OUTDOORS

Adventure activities

Few cities in the world can offer outdoor adventures just minutes from downtown. In Sydney you can hike, dive, windsurf, or sail, or even go rappeling on various cliffs. Details of operators are available from the NSW Travel Centre (☎ 9231 4444), or contact Australian Adventure Activities (☎ 9523 0955).

CREMORNE POINT RESERVE

This walk reveals a portion of the city that visitors seldom see, and lies just a short ferry ride from Circular Quay. From the wharf, turn left and walk along the reserve's western section, which gives fine views of the city. By walking up the steps opposite the wharf and heading to the left, you can stroll around the harborside, past lush gardens and homes with superb outlooks, to tranquil Mosman Bay. From here, the ferry will take you to Circular Quay.

➕ L3 ✉ Cremorne 🕐 Daily ⛴ Cremorne Point 🏷 Free

LADY BAY BEACH

For some, the ultimate in getting back to nature involves stripping off and spending the day at a nudist beach. This idyllic harborside area is one of Sydney's most popular *au naturel* spots, and lies just a short walk from Camp Cove at Watsons Bay.

➕ Off map to east ✉ Watsons Bay 🕐 Daily 🍴 At Watsons Bay 🚌 9324, 325 (or ferry to Watsons Bay) 🏷 Free

Life's a beach around Sydney Harbour

NORTH HEAD

The impressive national park-protected outcrop of North Head looms above Manly and the harbor, with incredible views from its various lookouts.

⬛ Off map to northeast ☎ 9977 6229 🕐 Daily 🍴 In Manly
🚢 Manly 💲 Free

NORTHERN NATIONAL PARKS

The greater Sydney region contains no less than 10 national parks, as well as many other natural reserves. In the north you can visit Cattai, Lane Cove, Garigal, and magnificent Ku-ring-gai Chase (▶ 20), although you need to have your own vehicle or take a tour to fully appreciate these superb wilderness areas.

⬛ Off map to north ☎ 9457 9322 🕐 Daily 🍴 Kiosks and picnic areas 💲 Inexpensive

SOUTHERN NATIONAL PARKS

The city's southern national parks—Botany Bay and the Royal (▶ 21), Georges River, Thirlmere Lakes, and Heathcote—offer scenery ranging from freshwater lakes to spectacular beaches. Again, your own transportation is necessary, or contact Allambie Mini Buses ☎ 9451 8500 for group reservations.

⬛ Off map to south ☎ 9542 0666 🕐 Daily 🍴 Kiosks and picnic areas 💲 Inexpensive

THE SPIT TO MANLY WALK

This 5 mile harborside walk takes three to four hours and passes through undeveloped bushland and the waterfront suburbs surrounding Manly; views of the harbor and city are magnificent. Further information is available from the National Parks Service.

⬛ Off map to north ✉ From the Spit Bridge, Middle Harbour
☎ National Parks Service 9977 6522 🕐 Daily 🍴 At Manly
🚌 178, 180, 182, 190 💲 Free

SYDNEY HARBOUR NATIONAL PARK

Designated in 1975, Sydney Harbour National Park encompasses islands and pockets of remarkably unspoiled bushland around the harbor. There are many beaches to enjoy, walks in the bush, historic sites, and even Aboriginal carvings.

⬛ N2–N4 ☎ 9337 5511 🕐 Daily 🍴 Kiosks and picnic areas
💲 Free

WATSONS BAY AND SOUTH HEAD

In the early 1800s Watsons Bay was a fishing hamlet and military base. Today, this charming suburb has retained its village atmosphere. There are great views of the harbor, swimming at Camp Cove, and an enjoyable walk to South Head National Park.

⬛ Off map to east ☎ 9337 5511 🕐 Daily 🍴 Cafés and restaurants 🚌 324, 325 🚢 Watsons Bay 💲 Free

Sydney's beaches

Sydney's great outdoors is epitomized by the many beaches dotted along its harbor and extensive coastline. Popular harbor beaches are Nielsen Park (▶ 47) and northside Balmoral. Other than Bondi and Manly, good surf beaches include Coogee, Maroubra, and Cronulla to the south, and the wonderful northern beaches that stretch from Manly to Palm Beach.

GALLERIES & MUSEUMS

See Top 25 Sights for
ART GALLERY OF NEW SOUTH WALES (▶ 43)
AUSTRALIAN MUSEUM (▶ 41)
HYDE PARK BARRACKS (▶ 45)
MUSEUM OF CONTEMPORARY ART (▶ 40)
MUSEUM OF SYDNEY (▶ 44)
NATIONAL MARITIME MUSEUM (▶ 37)
POWERHOUSE MUSEUM (▶ 34)

Museums in The Rocks

The Rocks contains several small but interesting museums. The best are the Merchants' House (✉ 43 George Street), featuring a collection of rare children's books and toys; Susannah Place (✉ 58–64 Gloucester Street), an entire terrace of four restored houses; and the Westpac Museum (✉ 6–8 Playfair Street), which tells the story of Australian banking.

The Justice and Police Museum

52

HARRIS STREET MOTOR MUSEUM
Located not far from the Powerhouse (▶ 34), this intriguing museum is dedicated to the display of around 200 classic motor cars, commercial vehicles, and bikes, and tells the story of the automotive industry over the past century or so.
🚇 H6 ✉ 320 Harris Street (corner of Allen Street), Pyrmont ☎ 9552 3375 🕐 Wed–Sun (daily during school hols) 10–5 🍴 Nearby 🚝 Monorail to Convention Centre ♿ Moderate

JUSTICE AND POLICE MUSEUM
Originally the Water Police Court (1856), these atmospheric old buildings now house a museum of legal and police history. The complex includes the Magistrate's Court, exhibitions in the cells, and a museum of crime, the latter featuring mug shots of some of early Sydney's criminals.
🚇 cii; K5 ✉ 8 Phillip Street ☎ 9252 1144 🕐 Sun (Sun–Thu in Jan) 10–5 🍴 Nearby 🚝 Circular Quay ♿ Moderate

MARY MACKILLOP MUSEUM
Beatified in 1995, Mary MacKillop was a determined leader who made a huge contribution to the status of the poor in Australia. State-of-the-art electronics, animatronics, and powerful theatrics show Mary's life, and how in 1866, at the age of 24, she opened her first Josephite school and founded an institute for women. Also found at this museum is Mary MacKillop's tomb and memorial chapel, Alma Cottage, where she lived and, in 1909, died.
🚇 J2 ✉ Mary MacKillop Place, 7 Mount Street, North Sydney ☎ 9954 9688 🕐 Sun–Fri 10–4; Sat noon–4. Closed Dec 25 🍴 Coffee shop 🚝 North Sydney ♿ Moderate

QUARANTINE STATION
Used since the 1830s to protect Sydney from smallpox, bubonic plague, and other contagious diseases by quarantining migrants, the station is now an unusual museum. You can see the burial grounds, rock engravings, and various displays, while nighttime ghost tours of the reputedly haunted complex, complete with tales of strange happenings, are a spooky alternative.
🚇 Off map to northeast ✉ North Head, Manly ☎ 9977 6229 🕐 Tours daily 1:10PM 🚢 Manly, then bus 135 ♿ Moderate

Charge Room in the Justice and Police Museum

SYDNEY JEWISH MUSEUM

The ground floor of this museum is devoted to Australian Jewish history and documenting the gradual development of a community. Other intriguing displays explain special festivals and customs, and provide a glimpse into the Jewish religion and the traditional emphasis on family values. Upstairs is a memorial to the six million Jews who perished in the Holocaust.

✚ J4　✉ Corner of Darlinghurst Road and Burton Street, Darlinghurst　☎ 9360 7999　🕓 Mon–Thu 10–4; Fri 10–noon; Sun 11–5　🍴 Nearby　🚃 Circular Quay　♿ Moderate

SYDNEY MINT MUSEUM

Housed in the colonial Georgian-style 1816 Mint building, originally a wing of the Rum Hospital (at which time it was the first branch of the Royal Mint outside London), this museum concentrates on the discovery of gold in the 1850s and its dramatic effect on Australia's history. A large range of gold and silver objects are on display, and you can visit the coining factory where nuggets were made into coins from 1851 until 1927. The shop sells coins, jewelry, bullion, and other gold products.

✚ ciii; K6　✉ The Mint, Macquarie Street　☎ 9217 0311　🕓 Daily 10–5　🍴 Nearby　🚃 Martin Place　♿ Moderate

THE WHITELEY MUSEUM

This museum and gallery, opened in 1995, is a tribute to Brett Whiteley, one of Australia's most important and controversial modern artists, who died of a drug overdose in 1993. His studio, now refurbished by the NSW government, is full of his sculptures, paintings, drawings, and memorabilia.

✚ K8　✉ 2 Raper Street, Surry Hills　☎ 9225 1740　🕓 Sat, Sun 10–4　🍴 Nearby　🚌 302, 304　♿ Moderate

Commercial art galleries

If you are interested in exploring the modern Australian art scene, pay a visit to some of Sydney's commercial galleries, including Savill Galleries (✉ 156 Hargrave Street, Paddington); Barry Stern Galleries (✉ 19–21 Glenmore Road, Paddington); and the Roslyn Oxley Gallery (✉ Soudan Lane, off 27 Hampden Street, Paddington).

ARCHITECTURE & INTERIORS

See Top 25 Sights for
CITY CENTER (► 33)
HYDE PARK BARRACKS (► 45)
QUEEN VICTORIA BUILDING (► 32)
SYDNEY OPERA HOUSE (► 24)

Walking tours

If you are interested in Sydney's historic areas and architecture, join a guided walking tour. Such tours operate in The Rocks (► 28), while Sydney Guided Tours (☎ 9660 7157) can take you on informative strolls to places such as historic churches, the suburb of Balmain, and Sydney University.

ANZAC WAR MEMORIAL

This huge 1934 Art Deco structure, decorated with poignant sculptures, is Sydney's tribute to those who died during World War I. Inside, the domed ceiling is covered with stars representing World War I volunteers, while the lower level features a photographic exhibition.

✚ J6 ✉ Hyde Park South ⏰ Mon–Sat 10–4; Sun 1–4. Closed Good Fri and Dec 25 🍴 Nearby 🚇 Museum 💲 Free

CHIFLEY TOWER

Nearly all of Sydney's newer skyscrapers have interesting rooflines. Chifley Tower, built in 1993, is one of them, and also has some very chic stores and marble and terrazzo walkways inside.

✚ biii; J5 ✉ Chifley Square ☎ 9221 4500 ⏰ Daily 🍴 Cafés and restaurants 🚇 Martin Place 💲 Free

ELIZABETH BAY HOUSE

Constructed from Sydney sandstone, the simple but elegant Elizabeth Bay House was built between 1835 and 1839. The house's most important feature is its oval-shaped saloon and winding staircase, regarded as Australia's finest. Rooms are open to the public and are furnished in Regency style.

✚ ciii; L6 ✉ 7 Onslow Avenue, Elizabeth Bay ☎ 9356 3022 ⏰ Tue–Sun 10–4:30 🍴 Nearby 🚇 Kings Cross 💲 Moderate

Victoria Barracks' impressive sandstone facade

HOMEBUSH BAY OLYMPIC SITE

Visitors are now able to view the high-tech buildings of Sydney's 2000 Oympics site on a guided bus tour. The environment-friendly development, built between 1996 and 2000, includes the spectacular new Stadium Australia. Tours also take in the state's Hall of Champions and the wetlands of Bicentennial Park.

🚹 Off map to west ☎ 9735 4306 🕐 Tours Mon–Fri 9:30, 10:30, 12:30 🍴 Various 🚇 Olympic Park 🎟 Inexpensive

PADDINGTON HOUSES

Paddington's terraced houses, with their iron lacework fences and balconies, are delightful. Built in the 19th century as housing for workers, most have been carefully restored to create a charming suburb, listed as a conservation area by the National Trust.

🚹 L7–M7 ✉ ➤ 17 🍴 Nearby 🚌 378, 380, 382 🎟 Free

STATE PARLIAMENT HOUSE

Originally part of the Rum Hospital, Parliament House (built in 1816), with its shady verandas, is a fine example of early colonial architecture. You can take a tour of the building, but it is advisable to make a reservation.

🚹 iii; K5 ✉ Macquarie Street ☎ Tours 9230 2460 🕐 Tours Mon–Fri 9–5 🍴 Nearby 🚇 Martin Place 🎟 Free

VICTORIA BARRACKS

This imposing National Trust-listed 1840s building was constructed by soldiers and convicts, and boasts a 610 foot-long sandstone facade. Guided tours include a band performance, the military museum, and other sections of the historic base, which is still occupied by the Australian Army.

🚹 L7 ✉ Oxford Street, Paddington ☎ 9339 3268 🕐 Tours Thu 10AM. Museum Sun 10–3:30 🍴 Nearby 🚌 378, 380, 382 🎟 Free

Exquisite lacework balconies in Paddington

Mosman

Mosman, with magificent harbor views, is one of Sydney's most affluent suburbs. It lies on the northern side of the Harbour Bridge, just a few minutes by ferry from Circular Quay. Architecturally, the homes are a mix of 19th-century mansions, California- and Federation-style homes, and modern apartments. Military Road, the suburb's main thoroughfare, is the preserve of designer-clothing boutiques, antique galleries, fine food stores, and cafés. Nearby Balmoral has one of the harbor's prettiest beaches, a number of waterfront restaurants and a (take-out) fish store, Bottom-of-the-Harbour, so good that people line up for its excellent seafood.

OTHER ATTRACTIONS

See Top 25 Sights for
AQUARIUM, IMAX THEATRE & SEGA WORLD
 (► 29)
AUSTRALIAN MUSEUM (► 41)
OCEANWORLD (► 35)
POWERHOUSE MUSEUM (► 34)
TARONGA ZOO (► 36)

Australian wildlife

Australia's unique wildlife is irresistible, and the wildlife parks and zoos detailed here offer the chance to cuddle koalas, meet kangaroos and other marsupials, and see a variety of incredibly colorful birds. You will also be able to observe the strange egg-laying monotremes, the platypus and echidna. A word of advice: the easiest way to reach most of these suburban parks is on an organized tour (► 19).

AUSTRALIA'S WONDERLAND

In Australia's largest theme park, rides and displays are based on the "International Village," "Goldrush," and "The Beach." There are also musical shows, the Australian Wildlife Park and The Outback Woolshed, where sheep are shorn.
🚼 Off map ✉ Wallgrove Road, Eastern Creek ☎ 24-hour infoline 9830 9100 🕐 Daily 10–5 🍴 Cafés and picnic areas 🚆 Rooty Hill, then a special bus service 🎟 Expensive

FEATHERDALE WILDLIFE PARK

Encounters with cuddly and not-so-cuddly creatures are both fun and educational in this bush setting. Meet kangaroos, wallabies, koalas, wombats, and saltwater crocodiles, as well as a variety of native birds.
🚼 Off map to west ✉ 217–29 Kildare Road, Doonside ☎ 9622 1644 🕐 Daily 9–5. Closed Dec 25 🍴 Café and picnic areas 🚆 Blacktown, then bus 725 🎟 Moderate

HMAV *BOUNTY*

Sail around the harbor on a full-scale replica of Captain Bligh's 18th-century vessel, complete with authentic rigging and sails, and a crew dressed in period style.
🚼 bi; J4 ✉ Sails from Campbells Cove, The Rocks ☎ 9247 1789 🕐 Sailings daily; ring for information 🍴 Coffee, lunch, and dinner cruises 🚆 Circular Quay 🎟 Expensive

KOALA PARK SANCTUARY

In this famous private koala sanctuary, in operation since 1930, you can cuddle koalas, hand-feed kangaroos, and see traditional bush activities such as sheep shearing and boomerang throwing.
🚼 Off map to northwest ✉ 84 Castle Hill Road, West Pennant Hills ☎ 9484 3141 🕐 Daily 9–5. Closed Dec 25 🍴 Kiosk and picnic/barbecue area 🚆 Pennant Hills, then buses 651–5 🎟 Moderate

KATOOMBA SCENIC SKYWAY & RAILWAY

Rides on either the Scenic Skyway, which straddles precipitous Jamieson Valley, or the fast-plunging Scenic Railway combine heart-in-the-mouth thrills and glorious bushland vistas to keep everyone in the family happy.
🚼 Off map to west ✉ Corner of Cliff Drive and Violet Street, Katoomba, Blue Mountains ☎ 4782 2699 🕐 Daily 🍴 Restaurant, picnic/barbecue areas nearby 🚆 Katoomba 🎟 Inexpensive

SYDNEY HARBOUR CRUISES

Unwind on a fine day and learn about the harbor, its bays and waterways on a variety of cruises. Depart from Circular Quay (➤ 27).

J5 ✉ Captain Cook Cruises, No. 6 Jetty, Circular Quay NSW 2000 ☎ 9206 1111 🕐 Daily from 9:30AM 🍴 Coffee and dinner cruises 🚇 Circular Quay 💲 Moderate

WARATAH PARK

Waratah Park, the closest wildlife park to the city, features koalas, emus, birds, kangaroos, and other native fauna. The bushland setting can be appreciated from the short Bush Railroad ride.

➕ Off map to north ✉ Namba Road, Duffy's Forest ☎ 9450 2377 🕐 Daily 10–5. Closed Dec 25 🍴 Snack bar and barbecues 🚇 Chatswood, then a special bus service 💲 Moderate

Beaches for kids

Most of Sydney's surf beaches are not suitable for younger children, so if you are visiting in summer, head for sheltered spots such as Camp Cove at Watsons Bay, Nielsen Park (Vaucluse) and, north of the harbor, Balmoral or Shelly Beach at Manly. Bronte, although a surf beach, also has an ocean pool, a large park, and a good playground area.

The koala is a marsupial, not a bear

VIEWS

See Top 25 Sights for
AMP CENTREPOINT TOWER (▶ 31)
MRS MACQUARIES POINT (▶ 42)
SYDNEY HARBOUR BRIDGE (▶ 25)
SYDNEY HARBOUR FROM A HARBOR FERRY
  OR CRUISE (▶ 26)

The best views in town

To appreciate Sydney's spectacular harbor, the city skyline, and the Opera House from a great perspective, the three-hour BridgeClimb makes for an unusual tour of Harbour Bridge. Professional guides accompany you on day and night climbs. Bookings (☎ 9252 0077) are essential. Red Baron Scenic Flights (☎ 9791 0643), operating out of Rose Bay, include aerobatics over the harbor in their open-cockpit biplane.

CREMORNE POINT
Take a ferry ride to the north shore and enjoy the views of Sydney Harbour and the city skyline. Walk to Robertsons Point, or to Cremorne Point Reserve (▶ 50) and MacCallum Pool.
➕ L3 ✉ Cremorne 🚢 Cremorne Point 💷 Free

HORIZON COCKTAIL BAR
This aptly named cocktail bar, on the 36th floor of the ANA, has fantastic views.
➕ aii; J5 ✉ ANA Hotel, 176 Cumberland Street, The Rocks ☎ 9250 6000 🍴 Restaurants in hotel 🚉 Circular Quay 💷 The cost of a drink

MACKENZIES POINT
This promontory gives you wonderful views of the beach at Bondi, out to the Pacific Ocean and south down the rugged coast.
➕ Off map to east ✉ South of Bondi Beach 🚌 380, 382 💷 Free

MCKELL PARK
This pleasant reserve is great for picnics and for admiring the harbor. You can explore Darling Point and continue to Rushcutters Bay and its marina.
➕ M5 ✉ Darling Point Road, Darling Point 🕐 Daily during daylight hours 🚢 Darling Point 💷 Free

NEW SOUTH HEAD ROAD, ROSE BAY
The hill north of Rose Bay offers one of the best harbor panoramas in Sydney.
➕ Off map to east ✉ Near the junction with Vaucluse Road 🚌 324, 325 💷 Free

Rushcutters Bay, near Kings Cross

INTERESTING SUBURBS

See Top 25 Sights for
BONDI BEACH (► 30)
MANLY (► 35)
VAUCLUSE (► 47)

GLEBE
Glebe offers offbeat shopping, a Saturday market, and good-value restaurants, while the University of Sydney (established in 1850 and Australia's oldest university), features grand buildings and the superb Nicholson Museum with its famous archeological collection.

⊞ G7–G8 ⊠ Museum 9351 2812 🕓 Museum Mon–Fri 10–4:30. Closed 25 Dec–Jan 🍴 Many cafés and restaurants 🚌 431 🎫 Free

HUNTERS HILL
An attractive suburb worth visiting for the ferry ride west of the Harbour Bridge, and for a look at 1871 Vienna Cottage. This fine example of a small stone tradesman's house also has a small museum. Hunters Hill is a designated conservation area, so sample its refined atmosphere on the walk from the wharf.

⊞ D2 ⊠ Vienna Cottage, 38 Alexandra Street ☎ 9817 2240 🕓 Sat 2–4; Sun 11–4 ⛴ Valentia Street 🎫 Free. Vienna Cottage inexpensive

KINGS CROSS AND POTTS POINT
Once Sydney's most Bohemian district, Kings Cross is now rather seedy, but it's still interesting and *the* place for late nightlife. Potts Point (Macleay and Victoria streets in particular) is full of cafés and old houses.

⊞ L6 🍴 Many cafés and restaurants 🚉 Kings Cross 🎫 Free

WOOLLOOMOOLOO
This inner-city address, with its extraordinary Aboriginal name, offers quaint terraced houses and a few other attractions. On Cowper Wharf Road you will find the historic Finger Wharf that juts far out into the bay, ships of the Australian Navy's fleet, and Artspace, a gallery of contemporary art.

⊞ diii; K6 ⊠ Artspace, 43–51 Cowper Wharf Road ☎ 9368 1899 🕓 Mon–Sat 11–6. Closed hols 🍴 Nearby 🚌 311 🎫 Free

Harborside suburbs

Waterfront suburbs that are great for walks and picnics are Darling Point, Rose Bay, historic Watsons Bay (► 51), and Cremorne on the north side (► 58), all reached by ferry from Circular Quay. You can also shop until you drop at north shore Mosman (► 55) and at Double Bay in the eastern suburbs.

Hunters Hill, an expensive and fashionable Sydney suburb

WHAT'S FREE

Government House

As the move towards an Australian Republic gathered pace (although the change was rejected in the 1999 referendum), buildings like Government House, at the lower end of Macquarie Street, were opened to the public. Built between 1837 and 1845, it is considered the most sophisticated example of a Gothic Revival building in the state.

☎ Infoline 9931 5200

🕓 Fri–Sun 10–3

Darling Harbour has some of Sydney's most stimulating new buildings

---

See Top 25 Sights for
AROUND SYDNEY OPERA HOUSE (➤ 24) &
**   CIRCULAR QUAY (➤ 27)**
ART GALLERY OF NEW SOUTH WALES (➤ 43)
CENTENNIAL PARK (➤ 46)
THE ROCKS (➤ 28)
ROYAL BOTANIC GARDENS &
**   THE DOMAIN (➤ 42)**

DARLING HARBOUR

As well as offering major attractions such as Sydney Aquarium and the National Maritime Museum, Darling Harbour is great for free music and other entertainment, particularly around the Harbourside shopping complex or in Tumbalong Park.

➕ H6–J6 ☎ 1900 260 568 🍴 Many cafés and restaurants
🚝 Monorail to Harbourside 💲 Free

HYDE PARK

This CBD haven has been a park since 1810 and is a favorite lunchtime spot for city workers. You can wander among formal gardens and tree-lined paths, and visit the Anzac War Memorial (➤ 54).

➕ biv–civ; J6 ✉ Off Elizabeth Street 🕓 Daily 🍴 Nearby
🚉 St. James 💲 Free

MARTIN PLACE

Martin Place, the city's largest pedestrian area, offers free entertainment during weekday lunchtimes—try the amphitheater near Castlereagh Street.

➕ biii; J5 ✉ Between Macquarie and George streets 🍴 Several cafés 🚉 Martin Place 💲 Free

STATE LIBRARY OF NEW SOUTH WALES

More than just a library, this large complex has a good shop, free movies, exhibitions (a small charge for some), and tours. You can also browse among the vast collection of books and other material on Australia.

➕ ciii; K5 ✉ Macquarie Street ☎ 9273 1414 🕓 Mon–Fri 9–9; Sat–Sun 11–5. Closed 1 Jan, Good Fri, Easter Sun, Dec 25–26
🍴 Licensed café 🚉 Martin Place 💲 Free

SYDNEY OPEN MUSEUM

The many statues, fountains, and outdoor monuments under the care of Sydney City Council have been declared the "Sydney Open Museum"—a free attraction which provides you with a good excuse to wander the streets. Starting from Hyde Park, the trail takes you to Circular Quay and The Rocks before returning to the city center. An informative leaflet and map are available from the council's One-Stop Shop on the corner of Kent and Druitt streets.

➕ J6–J4 ✉ Start in Hyde Park South ☎ 9265 9775
🍴 Many cafés en route 🚉 St. James/Museum 💲 Free

SYDNEY
where to...

MODERN AUSTRALIAN RESTAURANTS

Prices

Expect to pay per person, excluding drinks and tips:

$	up to A$25
$$	up to A$45
$$$	more than A$45

Eating out in Sydney

Sydney restaurants range from super-inexpensive to the totally indulgent, while cuisines from all over the world are represented. Australian wines are a wonderful accompaniment to meals, and a large proportion of restaurants are BYO (bring your own alcohol)—a small corkage fee is usually charged. Reserving is generally recommended, but many brasserie-style establishments do not accept reservations. Most restaurants have a no-smoking area and some have now completely banned the practice—check when reserving.

BATHERS RESTAURANT ($$$)
Former Bathers Pavilion now refurbished with three separate dining areas, including a function room.
✚ N1 ✉ 4 The Esplanade, Balmoral Beach ☎ 9969 5050 🕐 Daily lunch, dinner

BEL MONDO ($$$)
Stefano Manfredi's newest venture. Streamlined and slick with two dining areas. Flavors of northern Italy tweaked with Australian produce.
✚ J5 ✉ Level 3, The Argyle, 24 Argyle Street, The Rocks ☎ 9241 3700 🕐 Daily lunch; Mon–Sat dinner; Sun noon–6; Anti Bar 🚊 Circular Quay

BILLS ($)
A popular breakfast and lunch spot for those on the run.
✚ K7 ✉ 433 Liverpool Street, Darlinghurst ☎ 9360 9631 🕐 Mon–Sat breakfast, lunch

BISTRO MONCUR ($$–$$$)
Highly rated, innovative food in a trendy eastern suburbs pub. Rather noisy.
✚ M8 ✉ Woollahra Hotel, 116 Queen Street, Woollahra ☎ 9363 2782 🕐 Daily lunch, dinner 🚊 389

BISTRO PAVE ($$$)
Diners are rarely disappointed here with wonderful food, the best wines, and superb service.
✚ J2 ✉ 181 Miller Street, North Sydney ☎ 9956 8583 🕐 Mon–Fri lunch; Thu–Sat dinner 🚊 North Sydney

CATALINA ($$$)
One of Sydney's best; diners come here to be seen and to relish the Japanese-inspired dishes with a touch of Mediterranean influence. The sushi is a specialty.
✚ Off map to east ✉ Lyne Park, Rose Bay ☎ 9371 0555 🕐 Daily lunch, dinner 🚊 324, 325

CLAUDE'S ($$$)
The fixed-price menu is expensive, but an advantage is that Claude's is BYO (see panel). The cuisine is classical, with an Australian flavor.
✚ L8 ✉ 10 Oxford Street, Woollahra ☎ 9331 2325 🕐 Tue–Sat dinner 🚊 378, 380, 382

DARLING MILLS ($$$)
Set in an atmospheric 19th-century cottage, Darling Mills features cross-cultural seafood, meat, and vegetarian dishes.
✚ G7 ✉ 134 Glebe Point Road, Glebe ☎ 9660 5666 🕐 Wed–Fri lunch; Thu–Sun dinner 🚊 431, 433

EDNA'S TABLE ($$–$$$)
Striking Aboriginal decor and the use of indigenous herbs and oils are highlights here. Try kangaroo, emu, or buffalo, plus other Australian dishes.
✚ G7 ✉ 204 Clarence Street, Sydney ☎ 9267 3933 🕐 Mon–Fri lunch; Tue–Sat dinner 🚊 Martin Place

FORTY ONE ($$$)
Panoramic views and inventive cuisine make

this one of the hottest
dining spots in town.
Reserve ahead.
➕ biii; J5 ✉ Level 41, Chifley
Tower, Chifley Square ☎ 9221
2500 🕐 Mon–Fri lunch;
Mon–Sat dinner 🚇 Martin Place

GALILEO ($$$)
This traditional
restaurant offers a
variety of Italian-
influenced dishes and a
top-of-the-range wine
menu.
➕ biii; J5 ✉ Observatory
Hotel, 89–113 Kent Street
☎ 9256 2215 🕐 Mon–Fri
lunch; daily dinner 🚇 Circular
Quay

MANLY PIER ($$)
East-West food
combinations just a ferry
ride across the harbor at
Manly. Licensed and
BYO.
➕ Off map to northeast
✉ Commonwealth Parade,
Manly Cove ☎ 9949 1994
🕐 Tue–Sun lunch, dinner
🚢 Manly

MG GARAGE ($$$)
Amazingly, this place
doubles as a car
showroom. Come here
for the fine seafood and
exotic dishes presented
with great style.
➕ K7 ✉ 490 Crown Street,
Surry Hills ☎ 9383 9383
🕐 Mon–Fri lunch; Mon–Sat
dinner 🚌 380, 390

PARAMOUNT ($$$)
Always a top culinary
experience from this
fine Sydney restaurant,
where Chinese, Thai,
and Middle Eastern
influences meet the
traditional skills of chef
Christine Manfield.
➕ L6 ✉ 73 Macleay Street,
Potts Point ☎ 9358 1652
🕐 Daily dinner 🚇 Kings Cross

QUAY ($$$)
Seafood is a specialty
here. Wonderful views
of the Opera House and
harbor.
➕ bi; J4 ✉ Upper level,
Overseas Passenger Terminal
Circular Quay West ☎ 9251
5600 🕐 Mon–Fri lunch; daily
dinner 🚇 Circular Quay

RAVESI'S ($$)
Another great brasserie,
in the boutique style,
Ravesi's Hotel over-
looks Bondi Beach.
➕ Off map to east ✉ 118
Campbell Parade, Bondi Beach
☎ 9365 4422 🕐 Daily
breakfast, lunch, and dinner
🚌 380, 382

TETSUYA'S ($$$)
Japanese cuisine
transformed to an
Australian art form by
one of Sydney's top
chefs.
➕ E5 ✉ 729 Darling Street,
Rozelle (corner of Cambridge
Street) ☎ 9555 1017
🕐 Wed–Sat lunch; Tue–Sat
dinner 🚌 440

WATERMARK ($$$)
A comfortable cab ride
from downtown Sydney
to possibly the harbor's
most beautiful venue.
The yuppies love it.
➕ N1 ✉ 2a The Esplanade,
Balmoral Beach ☎ 9968 3433
🕐 Daily lunch, dinner; Sat, Sun
breakfast 🚢 Taronga Zoo
Wharf, then bus 238

Modern Australian cuisine

Not so long ago, Australian
cooking revolved around meat
and three soggy vegetables, plus
"sophisticated" dishes like
shrimp cocktail and stroganoff.
An exciting new Australian
cuisine has emerged, however,
influenced by the eating habits
of migrant Italians, Thais,
Chinese, and others. This
experimental cooking might
blend French and Thai styles, or
local fish with Lebanese
ingredients, to create a great
dining experience. Bush
tucker—such as kangaroo,
crocodile, and native plants—is
another interesting addition to
the Sydney restaurant scene.

SEAFOOD RESTAURANTS

Australian seafood

It is not surprising that seafood is so popular in this oceanside city. Local specialties include Sydney rock oysters, while kingfish, enormous shrimps, Tasmanian scallops, and smoked salmon, South Australian tuna, and northern fish such as the delicious barramundi grace menus all over town. Appropriately, many seafood restaurants have waterfront locations and you can also enjoy excellent take-out fish-and-chips —Bondi, Balmoral, and Manly are particularly good spots for such alfresco eating.

BALKAN SEAFOOD ($$)

Chargrilled octopus, calamari, and fish. BYO.
🕂 K7 ✉ 215 Oxford Street, Darlinghurst ☎ 9331 7670 🕘 Tue–Sun dinner ✉ 380

DOYLES ON THE BEACH ($$–$$$)

Sydney's most famous seafood restaurant, with great food and wonderful harbor views. There is another Doyles in the Overseas Passenger Terminal at Circular Quay ☎ 9252 3400.
🕂 Off map to east ✉ 11 Marine Parade, Watsons Bay ☎ 9337 2007 🕘 Daily lunch, dinner ✉ 324, 325 🚢 Watsons Bay

FISH AT THE ROCKS ($$)

In the heart of The Rocks, with an excellent menu and good wine list, this family-owned seafood restaurant is sure to please.
🕂 bi; J5 ✉ 29 Kent Street, The Rocks ☎ 9252 4614 🕘 Mon–Fri lunch; daily dinner 🚆 Circular Quay

GOLDEN CENTURY ($$)

This busy Chinese restaurant, in the heart of Chinatown, specializes in the freshest seafood.
🕂 J7 ✉ 393–9 Sussex Street, Haymarket ☎ 9212 3901 🕘 Daily lunch, dinner 🚆 Central (Railway Square exit)

JORDONS SEAFOOD RESTAURANT ($$)

On the water at Darling Harbour. Serves everything from Atlantic salmon carpaccio to seafood platters.
🕂 H6 ✉ Harbourside, Darling Harbour ☎ 9281 3711
🕘 Daily lunch and dinner 🚆 Monorail to Harbourside

PIER ($$$)

Seared rare, yellow-fin tuna and Queensland reef fish poached in green curry are some of chef Greg Doyle's signature dishes. Superb location.
🕂 Off map to east ✉ 594 New South Head Road, Rose Bay ☎ 9327 4187 🕘 Daily lunch, dinner ✉ 324, 325 🚢 Rose Bay

ROCKPOOL ($$–$$$)

Continues its reign as Sydney's best seafood restaurant, chef Neil Perry presenting his signature dishes with flair. The bar serves oysters and other light meals.
🕂 bi; J5 ✉ 107 George Street, The Rocks ☎ 9252 1888 🕘 Mon–Fri lunch; Mon–Sat dinner 🚆 Circular Quay

SYDNEY COVE OYSTER BAR ($$)

Light and tasty seafood and oysters on the harbor near the Opera House, with panoramic views. Most seating is outdoors.
🕂 ci; K5 ✉ 1 Circular Quay East ☎ 9247 2937 🕘 Daily snacks, lunch, and dinner 🚆 Circular Quay

WATERFRONT ($$$)

Seafood in its many guises at a restaurant overlooking Sydney Harbour. Housed in a historic sandstone warehouse.
🕂 bi; J4 ✉ 27 Circular Quay West, The Rocks ☎ 9252 2228 🕘 Daily lunch and dinner 🚆 Circular Quay

THAI RESTAURANTS

ARUN THAI ($$)

One of Sydney's most reliable Thai restaurants, with a large outdoor dining area. It has a wine license, but you can also BYO.

➕ L6 ✉ 13/39 Elizabeth Bay Road, Elizabeth Bay ☎ 9357 7414 🕐 Tue–Sun lunch; daily dinner 🚇 Kings Cross

BAN THAI ($–$$)

Inner-west Newtown is packed with reasonably priced restaurants, and this is no exception. The menu includes good vegetarian dishes. Licensed and BYO.

➕ G8 ✉ 115 King Street, Newtown ☎ 9519 5330 🕐 Daily lunch, dinner 🚇 Newtown

DARLEY STREET THAI ($$$)

Most of Sydney's Thai restaurants are in the low-cost bracket, but this is a trend-setter in both decor and food. Cuisine is a balance between hot, sour, salty, and sweet.

➕ L6 ✉ 30a Bayswater Road, Kings Cross ☎ 9358 6530 🕐 Tue–Sun lunch; daily dinner 🚇 Kings Cross

LIME & LEMONGRASS ($$–$$$)

An unusual Thai eatery: stylish and noisy with ultra-modern interior, an outdoor terrace, and piquant curries. Thai with a difference.

➕ L6 ✉ 42 Kellett Street, Kings Cross ☎ 9358 5577 🕐 Daily dinner 🚇 Kings Cross

NARAI THAI ($$)

One of Sydney's longest-running and busiest Thai restaurants, with reliable food and a lively atmosphere. Licensed and BYO.

➕ K7 ✉ 346 Victoria Street, Darlinghurst ☎ 9331 1390 🕐 Tue–Fri lunch; daily dinner 🚇 Kings Cross

PRASIT TRADITIONAL ($$–$$$)

Rich green, yellow, and duck curries are some of the specialties of this sophisticated northside restaurant. BYO.

➕ L1 ✉ Shop 12/7, Waters Road, Neutral Bay ☎ 9953 2653 🕐 Wed–Sat dinner 🚌 178, 180, 182, 247

THAI FLORA ($–$$)

Fairly basic, but the food is great and prices reasonable. BYO.

➕ Off map to east ✉ 46 Hall Street, Bondi Beach ☎ 9130 2751 🕐 Tue–Sun dinner 🚌 378, 380, 382

THAI INTRA ($$)

One of a very popular group of Thai restaurants. This Thai Intra is on the main street of inner-city Darlinghurst—the others are at Neutral Bay and Glebe.

➕ K7 ✉ 217 Oxford Street, Darlinghurst ☎ 9331 3118 🕐 Daily lunch, dinner 🚌 378, 380, 382

TUM TUM'S THAI TAKEAWAY ($)

This bustling take-out establishment also has a small eating-in area, and produces fresh, delicious food. BYO— if you can find a seat.

➕ K6 ✉ 199 Darlinghurst Road, Darlinghurst ☎ 9331 5390 🕐 Daily noon–11 🚇 Kings Cross

Thai cuisine

Sydney is fortunate in that it is positively oversupplied with this wonderful cuisine. Thai food is light and extraordinarily delicious—the combination of very fresh vegetables, meats, and seafood with delicate spices and herbs is irresistible. Try the soup known as *tom yum goong*— shirmps flavoured with coriander, lemongrass, and chilli: a taste sensation.

OTHER ASIAN RESTAURANTS

Sydney's Asian restaurants

Multiculturalism has laid the foundation for an array of Asian restaurants in Sydney. The eating places listed here, from Chinese to Indonesian, are just a sample, but you will also find Singaporean, Nepalese, Burmese, Taiwanese, Javanese, Korean, and Laotian. Most Asian restaurants are reasonably priced and many are BYO.

BOROBUDUR ($)

This excellent, long-established Indonesian eatery offers delicious food. An outdoor courtyard is used in summer. BYO.
✚ G7 ✉ 123–5 Glebe Point Road, Glebe ☎ 9660 5611 🕐 Tue–Sun dinner 🚌 431

CHINATOWN CENTRE ($)

Sydney has many such inexpensive self-service food halls—choose from excellent Chinese, Malaysian, Thai, and others. Licensed.
✚ J7 ✉ 25 Dixon Street, Haymarket ☎ 9212 3335 🕐 Daily 10–10 🚇 Town Hall

EDOSEI ($$–$$$)

This is a very popular Japanese restaurant near Kings Cross. The sushi is highly recommended. Fixed-price dinners are the best value.
✚ L6 ✉ 22 Rockwall Crescent, Potts Point ☎ 9326 9108 🕐 Daily dinner 🚇 Kings Cross

FLAVOUR OF INDIA ($$)

Sydney isn't renowned for its Indian food, but this is definitely one of the best. Another outlet at Glebe. Licensed and BYO.
✚ M7 ✉ 120–8 New South Head Road, Edgecliff ☎ 9326 2659 🕐 Daily dinner 🚇 Edgecliff

IMPERIAL HARBOURSIDE ($$$)

One of Sydney's best Chinese restaurants, with harbor views. Emphasis on seafood.
✚ bi; J4 ✉ 15 Circular Quay West, The Rocks ☎ 9247 7073 🕐 Daily lunch, dinner 🚇 Circular Quay

MALAYA ($–$$)

One of the longest-established and best Asian restaurants in town, serving a tempting array of Indonesian, Malaysian, and Chinese.
✚ J7 ✉ 761 George Street ☎ 9211 4659 🕐 Daily lunch, dinner 🚇 Central

OH! CALCUTTA ($$)

This compact restaurant has long been regarded as the home of Sydney's top Indian dishes.
✚ K7 ✉ 251 Victoria Street, Darlinghurst ☎ 9360 3650 🕐 Fri lunch; Mon–Fri dinner 🚌 378, 380

OLD SAIGON ($–$$)

Excellent Vietnamese and Thai food. Cosy atmosphere. Licensed and BYO.
✚ G8 ✉ 107 King Street, Newtown ☎ 9519 5931 🕐 Wed–Fri lunch; Tue–Sun dinner 🚇 Newtown

ORIGAMI ($$)

This award-winning Japanese restaurant offers unusual, always good dishes. BYO.
✚ K7 ✉ 150 Liverpool Street, Darlinghurst ☎ 9331 3733 🕐 Mon–Fri lunch; daily dinner 🚇 Museum

RANGOON RACQUET CLUB ($$)

The Indian and Sri Lankan food. Excellent tandoori dishes. The decor is straight out of the British Raj.
✚ H1 ✉ 7/70 Alexander Street, Crows Nest ☎ 9906 4091 🕐 Mon–Fri lunch; daily dinner 🚌 263

EUROPEAN CUISINE

AMPERSAND ($$$)

Top dining at this trendy establishment, where contemporary French cuisine meets Japanese influences.

🗺 J6 ✉ Cockle Bay Wharf, Darling Park, 201 Sussex Street, Pyrmont ☎ 9264 6666 🕐 Mon–Fri lunch; Mon–Sat dinner 🚇 Town Hall

BEPPI'S ($$–$$$)

Of all Sydney's wonderful Italian restaurants, it is hard to beat Beppi's. One of the originals still attracting the faithful and the connoisseurs.

🗺 K6 ✉ Corner of Yurong and Stanley streets, East Sydney ☎ 9360 4558 🕐 Mon–Fri lunch; Mon–Sat dinner 🚌 389

BENNELONG ($$$)

Overlooking Sydney Harbour at the Opera House, this prestigious venue offers formal dining, plus a bar area serving light meals for theatergoers.

🗺 K4 ✉ Sydney Opera House ☎ 9250 7548 🕐 Fri lunch; Mon–Sat 5:30–11 🚢 Circular Quay

BISTRO MARS ($$)

Part of a new hotel and ideally located next to Rushcutters Bay Park. It's French bistro style here, plus a seafood café.

🗺 L6 ✉ 100 Bayswater Road, Rushcutters Bay ☎ 9361 3000 🕐 Daily breakfast, lunch, and dinner 🚌 324, 325, 365

BONDI TRATT ($$)

A café/restaurant, which provides tempting Italian food and views over Bondi Beach.

🗺 Off map to east ✉ 34b Campbell Parade, Bondi Beach ☎ 9365 4303 🕐 Daily 7AM–midnight 🚌 380, 382

CAPITAN TORRES ($$)

A popular city-center establishment with great Spanish dishes, sangria, and a lively atmosphere.

🗺 J6 ✉ 73 Liverpool Street ☎ 9264 5574 🕐 Daily lunch, dinner 🚇 Town Hall

GELATO BAR ($–$$)

Central and Eastern European food is served at this Bondi institution.

🗺 Off map to east ✉ 140 Campbell Parade, Bondi Beach ☎ 9130 4033 🕐 Daily 8AM–midnight 🚌 380, 382

LUCIO'S ($$$)

Top service and top Italian dishes are the trademark of this long-established restaurant.

🗺 L7 ✉ 47 Windsor Street, Paddington ☎ 9380 5991 🕐 Mon–Sat lunch, dinner 🚌 389

ROSSINI'S ($)

Front row position at Circular Quay. True Italian style: pay first, then choose your food from the display.

🗺 bi; J5 ✉ Shop W5, Circular Quay ☎ 9247 8026 🕐 Daily breakfast, lunch, and dinner 🚢 Circular Quay

UN MOMENTO ($$–$$$)

Funky, ultra chic, and one of the northside's best eateries, with a large selection from all regions of Italy.

🗺 H1 ✉ 407 Pacific Highway, Crows Nest ☎ 9966 8555 🕐 Tue–Fri lunch; daily dinner 🚉 St. Leonards

Australian wines

Australian wines have taken the world by storm and are, for many, an integral part of dining out. There have been vineyards in New South Wales and other regions since the 1820s, these producing fine varieties such as Cabernet Sauvignon, Shiraz, Chardonnay, and Chablis. There are hundreds of labels, but good winemakers to look for include Lindemans, Rosemount Estate, Houghtons, Wyndham Estate, Henschke, Tyrrells, Penfolds, and Wolf Blass.

CAFÉS

Sydney's café scene

A favorite Sydney occupation is hanging out in a café. The drinks, snacks, and meals are generally good value, but many establishments offer far more. Outdoor seating, or a view over Bronte Beach, the Opera House, or harbor are some of the bonuses, while other cafés are in lively areas like The Rocks, Bondi, or inner-city Darlinghurst. Sydney's coffee, thanks to European (particularly Italian) influences, is usually excellent.

BRONTE CAFÉ ($)
With views of the ocean and Bronte Beach, this café's specialties are its chicken and mushroom pies and its delicious baked-on-the-premises cakes. The sidewalk tables are popular.
✚ Off map to southeast ✉ 467 Bronte Road, Bronte ☎ 9387 4011 ⏰ Wed–Sun 8–5:30 (later in summer) 🚌 378

CAFFE TROPPO ($–$$)
This bright and cheerful café serves good soups, pasta, and snacks, and totally decadent cakes and desserts. BYO.
✚ G7 ✉ 175 Glebe Point Road, Glebe ☎ 9552 1233 ⏰ Daily snacks, lunch, and dinner 🚌 431

BAR COLUZZI ($)
This tiny café, with its alfresco seating, is deservedly popular. The coffee is some of the best around.
✚ K6 ✉ 322 Victoria Street, Darlinghurst ☎ 9380 5420 ⏰ Daily 6AM–8PM 🚆 Kings Cross

GOLDEN DOG ($$)
One of Paddington's trendiest cafés. Modern decor, inventive meals, and desserts. It's often difficult to get a seat.
✚ L8 ✉ 388 Oxford Street, Paddington ☎ 9360 7700 ⏰ Daily breakfast, lunch, and dinner 🚌 378, 380, 382

GUMNUT TEA GARDEN ($–$$)
Situated in a tiny cottage, this is one of the nicest places in The Rocks for a break. The all-day menu includes cakes, focaccia, scones, and home-made pies.
✚ bi; J5 ✉ 28 Harrington Street, The Rocks ☎ 9247 9591 ⏰ Daily to 5PM 🚆 Circular Quay

HYDE PARK BARRACKS CAFÉ ($$)
Eat inside or in the courtyard at this café, which incorporates the original convict confinement area.
✚ ciii; K6 ✉ Queens Square, Macquarie Street ☎ 9223 1155 ⏰ Mon–Fri 10–4; Sat, Sun 11–4 🚆 Martin Place

JACKIE'S ($$)
At the quieter end of Bondi Beach, Jackie's is relaxed and has good water views. Serves snacks and more substantial meals.
✚ Off map to east ✉ 132 Warners Avenue, Bondi Beach ☎ 9300 9812 ⏰ Daily breakfast, lunch, and dinner 🚌 378, 380, 382, 389

L'OTEL CAFÉ ($$)
Yummy breakfasts, aromatic coffee, and a wide range of meals at a trendy Darlinghurst hotel, bar, and café.
✚ K6 ✉ 114 Darlinghurst Road, Darlinghurst ☎ 9360 6868 ⏰ Daily 7AM–midnight 🚆 Kings Cross

MCA FISH CAFÉ ($$)
Excellent light meals, coffee, and tea for museum visitors or passers-by. There are great views of the Opera House and harbor from the terrace.
✚ bi; J5 ✉ MCA, Circular Quay West ☎ 9241 4253 ⏰ Mon–Fri 11–5:30; Sat, Sun 9–5:30 🚆 Circular Quay

MISCELLANEOUS

STEAKS & BURGERS

BOURBON & BEEFSTEAK BAR ($$)

A Kings Cross institution offering hearty American-style breakfasts to late night/early morning diners in one of the liveliest parts of town.

✛ L6　✉ 24 Darlinghurst Road, Kings Cross
☎ 9358 1144　⏱ 24 hours
🚉 Kings Cross

DANIELS ($$–$$$)

This is probably the city's best steak restaurant: the elegant yet friendly atmosphere makes this place a sure winner with patrons.

✛ J5　✉ 1 Bent Street, City
☎ 9251 6977　⏱ Mon–Fri lunch, dinner　🚉 Wynyard

HARD ROCK CAFÉ ($$)

Extremely noisy, but fun, and the rock 'n' roll memorabilia is fascinating. Serves American fare such as hamburgers and French fries.

✛ K6　✉ 121–9 Crown Street, East Sydney　☎ 9331 1116
⏱ Daily noon–midnight
🚌 324, 325, 389

NOVELTY

THE ARGYLE ($$)

This all-you-can-eat theater restaurant, which is aimed squarely at tourists, serves traditional Aussie food. The price of the dinner includes a sheepshearing demonstration.

✛ bi; J5　✉ 18 Argyle Street, The Rocks　☎ 9247 7782
⏱ Daily dinner and show
🚉 Circular Quay

SYDNEY TOWER ($$–$$$)

A revolving restaurant. Two levels of à la carte dining right in the heart of the CBD, with ever-changing views of the city.

✛ J6　✉ Gallery Level, 100 Market Street, Centrepoint
☎ 8223 3800　⏱ Daily lunch, dinner　🚉 Town Hall

PRE-THEATER

THE HARBOUR RESTAURANT ($$$)

This excellent restaurant appropriately specializes in seafood dishes. Dinner is served early, pre-theater. Superb harbor views.

✛ ci; K4　✉ Sydney Opera House, Bennelong Point　☎ 9250 7577　⏱ Daily lunch; Mon–Sat dinner　🚉 Circular Quay

BAR/PUB FOOD

WATSONS BAY HOTEL ($)

This pub offers barbecued seafood and the same harbor outlook as its more expensive neighbor, Doyles (► 64).

✛ Off map to east　✉ 1 Military Road, Watsons Bay
☎ 9337 4299　⏱ Daily lunch
🚌 324, 325　⛴ Watsons Bay

VEGETARIAN

ROY'S FAMOUS ($$)

A good vegetarian eatery, offering inventive, tasty, and filling meals. BYO and licensed.

✛ div; L6　✉ 176 Victoria Street, Potts Point　☎ 9357 3579　⏱ Daily breakfast, lunch, and dinner　🚉 Kings Cross

Food afloat

There is no better way to experience the harbor's magic than by dining on the water. Although the cuisine of these floating restaurants rarely reaches gourmet standards, lunch or dinner cruises are understandably popular. Operators include Captain Cook Cruises (lunches and dinners ☎ 9206 1111), Matilda Cruises (lunchtime barbecues ☎ 9264 7377), and the *Bounty* is a replica of the original 18th-century ship offering a lunch cruise with a difference (► 56).

SHOPPING CENTERS & DEPARTMENT STORES

Upmarket shopping

If you're after international designer labels, the best places to visit are Castlereagh Street (names such as Chanel and Louis Vuitton), the MLC Centre, the glossy David Jones Elizabeth Street store, and the suburb of Double Bay (see opposite). Other international stores include Emporio Armani on Martin Place and the Chifley Plaza shops, while you could also splash out on superb jewelry crafted from Australian gold, pearls, opals, and diamonds (▶ 73).

CHIFLEY PLAZA
Designer shops in wonderful surroundings that include marble and terrazzo walkways. The complex also features two fine restaurants and a food court.
⊞ biii; J5 ✉ Chifley Square ☎ 9221 4500 🚇 Martin Place

DAVID JONES
"DJs," Sydney's best department store, occupies two vast buildings. Elizabeth Street is a masterpiece of glass, marble, and chrome; Market Street has a wonderful food hall (▶ 76).
⊞ biv; J6 ✉ Elizabeth Street and Market Street ☎ 9266 5544 🚇 St. James

GREENWOOD PLAZA
The northside's most glamorous shopping centre is beautifully appointed, and includes exclusive clothing stores and a food court.
⊞ J2 ✉ Miller and Blue streets ☎ 9954 0296 🚇 North Sydney

MLC CENTRE
The MLC features everything from a food court to some of Sydney's most exclusive shops—international labels such as Gucci and Cartier are represented here, as are some of the top Australian designers.
⊞ biii; J6 ✉ Corner of King and Castlereagh streets ☎ 9224 8333 🚇 Martin Place

QUEEN VICTORIA BUILDING
This imposing 1898 building occupies an entire city block and is a delightful environment of stained glass, tiled floors, and beautifully appointed stores and cafés (▶ 33).
⊞ biv; J6 ✉ Corner of George, York, Market and Druitt streets ☎ 9264 9209 🚇 Town Hall

THE ROCKS CENTRE
A well-designed new complex in The Rocks, specializing in Australiana, Aboriginal items, and souvenirs.
⊞ bi; J5 ✉ Argyle Street ☎ 9255 1788 🚇 Circular Quay

SKYGARDEN
A stylish building that's a pleasure to shop in. Upmarket shopping and the top-level Skydining café and restaurant area, all contained under a spectacular dome.
⊞ biii; J6 ✉ 77 Castlereagh Street and Pitt Street Mall ☎ 9231 1811 🚇 St. James

THE STRAND ARCADE
This rebuilt historic arcade, originally dating from 1892, contains shops on three levels, surrounded by decorative wrought ironwork and stained-glass windows.
⊞ biii; J6 ✉ Pitt Street Mall and 412 George Street ☎ 9232 4199 🚇 St. James

SYDNEY PLAZA
Stunning new complex incorporating the old Grace Bros. department store and several levels of specialty shops.
⊞ biv; J6 ✉ Pitt Street Mall and 436 George Street ☎ 9238 9111 🚇 Town Hall

SHOPPING AREAS & SUBURBS

CASTLEREAGH STREET
This city-center street offers Louis Vuitton, Hermes, Chanel, Christian Lacroix, and other designer labels, as well as the chic MLC Centre opposite.
➕ biii; J6 ✉ Around where Castlereagh Street intersects with King Street 🚇 Martin Place

CHINATOWN AND HAYMARKET
In addition to the weekend Paddy's Markets (▶ 74), this area is home to many Asian food shops, dozens of cafés and restaurants, and inexpensive clothes stores. Lively and cosmopolitan.
➕ J7 ✉ South of Goulburn Street 🚇 Central

DOUBLE BAY
This harborside suburb is a must for Australian and overseas designer shopping—expensive clothes, shoes, and leather goods—as well as antiques, books, and jewelry. Don't miss heritage-listed Transvaal Avenue, with its interesting boutiques.
➕ M6–M7 ☎ Infoline 9388 8205 🚌 324, 325

HARBOURSIDE DARLING HARBOUR
Darling Harbour's shopping complex is vast—more than 150 stores, selling fashion items, souvenirs, CDs and tapes, jewelry, and many other goods.
➕ H6 ✉ Darling Harbour ☎ Infoline 0055 20261 🚝 Monorail to Harbourside

OXFORD STREET, DARLINGHURST
Lower Oxford Street is a weird and wonderful place. The province of the gay community and inner-city grunge, the area has some fascinating stores. Check out Cash Palace (No. 42) and Nelson Leong (No. 72) for women's clothes, and the strip between South Dowling Street and Victoria Barracks for books, jewelry, and more clothes.
➕ K7 ✉ From Hyde Park to Victoria Barracks 🚇 Museum

OXFORD STREET, PADDINGTON
The north end of colorful Oxford Street is the best source for the most fashionable clothing for men and women, as well as for books, homeware, artworks, and records (at the excellent Folkways, No. 282). Paddington Bazaar (▶ 74), held here on Saturdays, is well worth a visit.
➕ L7–L8 ✉ From Ormond Street to Queen Street 🚌 378, 380, 382

THE ROCKS
The area that's a highlight of any visit to Sydney has many fun souvenir shops, particularly in the Rocks Centre and on George Street. You can buy artwork and souvenirs here, as well as opals, jewelry, and Australian crafts (▶ 73 and 72).
➕ bi; J4–J5 ✉ The Rocks Heritage and Visitor's Centre 9255 1788 🚇 Circular Quay

Shopping tours
If you want to shop in the right areas with the aid of local knowledge, or find the best bargains, consider joining a shopping tour. Bargain Buyers Tours (☎ 9310 1088) and Shopping Spree Tours (☎ 9360 6220) specialize in warehouse shopping for clothing and other goods at wholesale prices, while Sydney Guided Tours (☎ 9660 7157) offers a more personalized and upmarket touring service.

AUSTRALIANA & SOUVENIRS

Shopping hours

Shopping hours are generally 9–5:30 on weekdays and 9–4 on Saturdays, but many stores, particularly in tourist areas, are open daily. It is always best to check by phoning beforehand.

Australiana

If you are looking for souvenirs to take home, go for high-quality Australiana. You will find everything from colorful beachwear to sheepskin products, books on every aspect of Australia, Aboriginal crafts, and superb gemstones and jewelry (▶ 73).

AUSFURS

Australian sheepskins are an excellent purchase, and Ausfurs is the best place for coats, vests, footwear, cuddly toys, and floor rugs.
✚ bi; J5 ✉ Clocktower Square, 55 Harrington Street, The Rocks ☎ 9247 3160 🚇 Circular Quay

AUSTRALIAN CRAFTWORKS

This collection of craft shops sells high-quality ceramics, textiles, jewelry, leather goods, and other Australian-made products.
✚ bi; J5 ✉ 127 George Street, The Rocks ☎ 9247 7156 🚇 Circular Quay

THE AUSTRALIAN GEOGRAPHIC SHOP

Operated by a popular magazine, this store sells unusual and environmentally friendly Australian books, gifts, and outdoor clothing.
✚ biv; J6 ✉ Shop 34, Centrepoint, Pitt Street Mall ☎ 9231 5055 🚇 St. James

BLUE GUM DESIGNS

A general Australiana shop with souvenirs and clothing, but specializing in Aboriginal items such as didgeridoos (lessons are available).
✚ biv; J6 ✉ Shop 32, Queen Victoria Building, George Street ☎ 9264 8070 🚇 Town Hall

COO-EE ABORIGINAL ART

One of the best outlets in Sydney for good quality Aboriginal paintings, crafts, fabrics, basketware, and clothing. It also sells limited-edition lithographs and etchings.
✚ K7 ✉ 98 Oxford Street, Paddington ☎ 9332 1544 🚍 378, 380, 382

DONE ART & DESIGN

Ken Done's "art to wear" has become a vibrant Australian symbol, and this shop stocks his popular resortwear and homeware. The nearby Ken Done Gallery, at 1 Hickson Road, sells his paintings.
✚ bi; J5 ✉ 123 George Street, The Rocks ☎ Freephone 1800 818 132 🚇 Circular Quay

R.M. WILLIAMS

The legendary Bushman's Outfitters sells Australian country clothing, including moleskin pants, leather boots, and Drizabone oilskin coats.
✚ biii; J6 ✉ 389 George Street ☎ 9262 2228 🚇 Town Hall

SOUNDS AUSTRALIAN

A specialist shop offering Australian classical, folk, jazz, and Aboriginal music in the form of CDs, tapes, and sheet music, as well as books on music.
✚ bi; J5 ✉ The Rocks Centre, 10–26 Playfair Street, The Rocks ☎ 9247 7290 🚇 Circular Quay

WEISS ART

Distinctive black and white line-drawings of Aussie animals decorate clothing, homeware, and other goods.
✚ bi; J5 ✉ 85 George Street, The Rocks ☎ 9241 3819 🚇 Circular Quay

OPALS, GEMS & JEWELRY

AUSTRALIAN GOLD SHOP
This wonderful shop sells Australian gold, platinum, and silver in the form of collectors' coins, bullion bars, gold nuggets, and jewelry.
⊞ aiv; J6 ✉ Corner of York and Druitt streets ☎ 9267 7481 🚇 Town Hall

DINOSAUR DESIGNS
Silver and semi-precious stones are used in offbeat and modern designs in this city-center jewelry shop.
⊞ biii; J6 ✉ Shop 73, Strand Arcade, Pitt Street Mall ☎ 9223 2953 🚇 St. James

THE FAMILY JEWELS
Beautifully designed contemporary gold, silver, and other jewelry, set with semi-precious stones such as amethyst and turquoise.
⊞ K7 ✉ 46 Oxford Street, Paddington ☎ 9331 6647 🚌 378, 380, 382

FLAME OPALS
One of Sydney's many opal stockists, selling everything from the white milk variety to black Lightning Ridge opals from the remote New South Wales town of that name. The stones are also sold set in gold or silver.
⊞ bi; J5 ✉ 119 George Street, The Rocks ☎ 9247 3446 🚇 Circular Quay

HARDY BROTHERS
An Australian gem specialist, featuring exquisite Broome South Sea pearls, Argyle diamonds, and fine opals. You will also find the best silverware, china, and other items here.
⊞ biii; J6 ✉ Skygarden, 77 Castlereagh Street ☎ 9232 2422 🚇 St. James

MAKERS MARK
Beautifully crafted Australian jewelry and other objects, including an extensive range of Argyle diamonds. Buy ready-made pieces or design your own.
⊞ biii; J5 ✉ Chifley Tower, Chifley Square ☎ 9231 6800 🚇 Martin Place

OPAL FIELDS
Sydney's largest opal specialist also sells unusual gifts. An opal museum is on the premises.
⊞ bi; J5 ✉ 151 George Street, The Rocks ☎ 9247 6800 🚇 Circular Quay

PASPALEY PEARLS
Sydney's South Sea pearl specialist, with outlets in Paris and New York. Paspaley's northern Australian pearling company is regarded as the source of the finest pearls in the world.
⊞ biii; J6 ✉ 142 King Street ☎ 9232 7633 🚇 Martin Place

PERRI JEWELLERS
Another good quality establishment, selling jewelry crafted from gold, pearls, opals, diamonds, and other stones. The company has won prestigious De Beers design awards.
⊞ biii; J6 ✉ Shop 708, MLC Centre, corner of King and Castlereagh streets ☎ 9231 1088 🚇 Martin Place

Australian gems and jewelry
The local jewelry, featuring opals, South Sea pearls, and exquisite Argyle diamonds in white, pink, and champagne colors, is superb. You can also buy loose stones, especially colorful opals—Australian varieties are of a particularly high quality. Visitors can purchase such stones and jewelry tax-free, which cuts the cost by around 30 percent. Sydney's more offbeat, contemporary jewelry is also of a very high standard.

MARKETS

Bargain shopping

The best shopping bargains are found at sales times—after Christmas and into January, and again at the end of winter in July and August. You can shop for budget clothing at any time in Surry Hills, Sydney's rag trade area, and at Redfern, where designer outfits and other clothes are very reasonably priced. Inner-west Newtown (especially King Street) offers bargains in secondhand clothing and many other items. In the city, be sure to check out Market City near Chinatown for bargains galore from the hundreds of stand operators who trade here.

BALMAIN MARKETS

With shoppers ranging from punks to ageing hippies, this market (held in the grounds of an old church) has a pleasant community feel. Come and browse for arts and crafts, and, in the church hall, try the vegetarian food.

➕ G4 ✉ Corner of Darling Street and Curtis Road, Balmain ☎ 9818 2674 🕐 Sat 8:30–4 🚌 433, 442 🚢 Darling Street

BONDI MARKETS

One of Sydney's newer markets, the outdoor Bondi sells arts and crafts, clothing, and an interesting range of secondhand goods.

➕ Off map to east ✉ Corner of Campbell Parade and Warners Avenue, Bondi Beach ☎ 9398 5486 🕐 Sun 9–4 🚌 380, 382

GLEBE MARKETS

Around 200 outdoor stands with plenty of clothing and fashion items, crafts, and collectibles. Many interesting shops and some great cafés are nearby.

➕ H7 ✉ Glebe Public School, Glebe Point Road, Glebe ☎ 9660 6667 🕐 Sat 9–4 🚌 431, 433

PADDINGTON BAZAAR

This is the trendiest market in town. Mostly clothes, arts, crafts, and jewelry. The street performers are often very entertaining.

➕ L8 ✉ Corner of Oxford and Newcombe streets, Paddington ☎ 1900 260 622 🕐 Sat 10–4 🚌 378, 380, 382

PADDY'S MARKETS

Sydney's biggest and oldest market, with more than 1,000 stands under cover, selling everything from clothes and books to jewelry and vegetables.

➕ J7 ✉ Corner of Thomas and Hay streets, Haymarket ☎ 1900 957 202 🕐 Fri–Sun 9–4:30 🚉 Central (Railway Square exit)

THE ROCKS MARKET

More than 150 stands sell gifts, homeware, antiques, and jewelry in The Rocks; there are also plenty of streetside cafés, as well as free entertainment.

➕ bi; J4 ✉ George Street, The Rocks ☎ 9255 1717 🕐 Sat, Sun 10–5 🚉 Circular Quay

THE SYDNEY ANTIQUE CENTRE

Not so much a market as a treasure trove of antiques. Around 60 shops sell jewelry, furniture, glassware, prints, books, and many other items.

➕ K8 ✉ 531 South Dowling Street, Surry Hills ☎ 9361 3244 🕐 Daily 10–6 🚌 373, 374, 394 to Anzac Parade

SYDNEY FISH MARKET

Come to admire (and buy if you are going to a barbecue!) the extraordinary range of fresh seafood and to sample the great fish and French fries. Fruit, vegetables, and deli items are also on sale.

➕ H6 ✉ Blackwattle Bay, Pyrmont ☎ 9660 1611 🕐 Daily 7–4 🚌 441

BOOKS

ARIEL BOOKSELLERS
This stylish establishment is a delightful place to shop. There is a particularly good photography and art section.
🞢 K7 ✉ 42 Oxford Street, Paddington ☎ 9332 4581
🕐 Daily until midnight
🚌 378, 380, 382

BERKELOUW BOOKDEALERS
Mostly secondhand and rare books. Has a good coffee bar upstairs.
🞢 K7 ✉ 19 Oxford Street, Paddington ☎ 9360 3200
🕐 Daily until midnight
🚌 378, 380, 382

COLLINS BOOKSELLERS
A mega store whose stock includes a comprehensive collection of Australian fiction and non-fiction.
🞢 H7 ✉ The Broadway Shopping Centre, Glebe
☎ 9566 1095 🚊 Central

DYMOCKS
Sydney's largest bookstore stocks books on every imaginable topic. The Australian section near the entrance is very good.
🞢 biv; J6 ✉ 424–30 George Street ☎ 9235 0155
🚊 Town Hall

GLEEBOOKS
An excellent and long-established bookstore in the inner-west suburb of Glebe, close to the University of Sydney. Great for browsing.
🞢 G7 ✉ 49 Glebe Point Road, Glebe ☎ 9660 2333 🚌 431
✉ Also at 191 Glebe Point Road (see next entry)

GLEEBOOKS
This branch specializes in secondhand and children's books.
🞢 G7 ✉ 191 Glebe Point Road, Glebe ☎ 9552 2526
🚌 431

LESLEY MCKAY'S BOOKSHOP
This beautifully laid-out store has varied Australian topics. A children's bookstore is across the road and the Nicholas Pounder shop (devoted to modern first editions) is upstairs.
🞢 M7 ✉ 346 New South Head Road, Double Bay
☎ 9327 1354 🚌 324, 325

NEW EDITION BOOKSHOP
This small Paddington shop contains particularly good Australian and New Age and self-help sections.
🞢 L7 ✉ 328 Oxford Street, Paddington ☎ 9360 6913
🚌 378, 380, 382

STATE LIBRARY OF NSW
If you are particularly interested in Australian history or literature, this is your best bet.
🞢 ciii; K5 ✉ Macquarie Street
☎ 9273 1414 🚊 Martin Place

THE TRAVEL BOOKSHOP
If you need maps, books, or travel literature on virtually any destination in the world, including Australia itself, a visit to this fine shop, with its well-informed staff, is a must.
🞢 J6 ✉ 175 Liverpool Street
☎ 9261 8200 🚊 Museum

Books on Australia
If you are looking for a worthwhile souvenir of your visit, there are dozens of high-quality photographic books on Sydney and Australia in the city's many bookstores. For a well-written, no-holds-barred account of the nation's early history, *The Fatal Shore* by Robert Hughes is unbeatable. Another interesting historical book is *The Road to Botany Bay* by Paul Carter, while visitors can learn much about Aboriginal Australia by reading any of Jennifer Isaacs' beautifully illustrated books.

FOOD & WINE

Australian delicacies

While in Sydney, don't fail to sample some Australian delicacies. Cheeses, particularly those from Tasmania, are wonderful—try King Island cheddar and camembert. Seafood is relatively inexpensive and incredibly varied—everything from Sydney rock oysters to Tasmanian smoked salmon—and most fish stores will cook your selection. Exotic Aussie-grown fruits and vegetables such as mangoes, bananas, avocados, and pineapples are plentiful. Other Australian specialties are macadamia nuts, Tasmanian honey, and wines.

THE AUSTRALIAN WINE CENTRE
Choose from more than 1,000 Australian wines, including a good range of vintages. The center will deliver to your hotel, or arrange overseas delivery.
⊞ bii; J5 ✉ Goldfields House, 3/1 Alfred Street ☎ 9247 2755 🚊 Circular Quay

DAVID JONES FOOD HALL
The lower level of this store is the city's most exclusive food shop. You will find wonderful produce here, including delicatessen lines, Australian wines, beers, cheeses, meats, seafood, fruit, and vegetables.
⊞ biv; J6 ✉ Market Street store, corner of Market and Castlereagh streets ☎ 9266 5544 🚊 St. James

ODDBINS
This city-center wine, beer, and spirits shop offers an excellent range (especially of Australian wines), good service, and very well-informed staff.
⊞ aiii; J6 ✉ 46 York Street ☎ 9299 5075 🚊 Town Hall

PARIS CAKE SHOP
Wonderfully fresh cakes and pastries, including French specialties such as brioche, *pain au chocolat*, and croissants.
⊞ Off map to east ✉ 91 Bondi Road, Bondi ☎ 9387 2496 🚌 380, 382

PARISI'S OF ROSE BAY
This fruit and vegetable store is an attraction in its own right. Along with the beautifully displayed produce, Parisi's sells delectable take-out salads and homemade *gelato*.
⊞ Off map to east ✉ 15 Dover Road, Rose Bay ☎ 9371 0870 🚌 324, 325

THE QUAFFER'S CHOICE—DOUBLE BAY CELLARS
One of the city's best package stores (Australians call them bottle shops), with a high-quality range of Australian and imported wines, beers, and spirits.
⊞ M7 ✉ 396 New South Head Road, Double Bay ☎ 9327 1333 🚌 324, 325

RUSSELL'S NATURAL FOODS
A large food store in inner-west Glebe with a good selection of natural products. Russell's has branches in several other suburbs.
⊞ H7 ✉ 55 Glebe Point Road, Glebe ☎ 9660 8144 🚌 431

SWEET WILLIAM CHOCOLATES
This tiny shop, just off Paddington's Oxford Street, sells exquisite handmade chocolates.
⊞ L7 ✉ 4 William Street, Paddington ☎ 9331 5468 🚌 378, 380, 382

THAI-KEE SUPERMARKET
An Asian supermarket in Chinatown, featuring exotic fruit and vegetables, a butcher's section, and every kind of spice and ingredient for Chinese, Malaysian, Thai, and Vietnamese cooking.
⊞ J7 ✉ 393 Sussex Street ☎ 9281 2202 🚊 Central

OTHER SHOPS

THE ABC SHOP

Operated by the Australian Broadcasting Corporation, this shop offers books, videos, music and audio cassettes, CDs, toys, and clothes relating to Australian TV, and radio programs.

✚ biv; J6 ✉ Shop 48, First Floor, Queen Victoria Building, George Street ☎ 9331 1635 🚇 Town Hall

ADRIENNE & MISS BONNEY

The finest of the fine at this exclusive baby boutique. Exquisite handmade clothes, nursery gifts, soft toys, and boudoir garments. Tom Cruise and Nicole Kidman used to shop here.

✚ M7 ✉ 20 Cross Street, Double Bay ☎ 9363 1723 🚌 324, 325

BONDI SURF CO.

Everything for the surfer. You can rent surfboards and boogie boards to try out in the Bondi surf, and buy beachwear, including the popular Billabong, Rip Curl, and Hot Tuna brands.

✚ Off map to east ✉ Shop 2, 72–6 Campbell Parade, Bondi Beach ☎ 9365 0870 🚌 9380, 382

COUNTRY ROAD

An Australian international success story, Country Road also has branches in the Queen Victoria Building and the Skygarden Centre (as well as overseas). Countrified his and hers casual clothes and home furnishings. Favored by bush and city dwellers alike.

✚ J6 ✉ Corner of Pitt and King streets ☎ 9394 1818 🚇 Martin Place

FOLKWAYS

One of Sydney's finest tape and CD stores, selling everything from classical to comedy, but with a particularly good selection of Australian, Aboriginal, blues, and world music.

✚ L7 ✉ 282 Oxford Street, Paddington ☎ 9361 3980 🚌 378, 380, 382

LEFT-HANDED PRODUCTS

This unusual shop sells an imaginative array of products and gadgets for left-handed people.

✚ bi; J5 ✉ Playfair Street, The Rocks ☎ 9247 3674 🚇 Circular Quay

SANCTUM

Wonderful Australian-made New Age beauty products, cosmetics, essential oils, and health drinks in a simple but elegant shop in trendy Paddington.

✚ L8 ✉ 446–8 Oxford Street, Paddington ☎ 9360 3895 🚌 378, 380, 382

STRAND HATTERS

President Clinton has one, Greg Norman plays golf in his, and Australian cattlemen wouldn't be seen without one—the genuine Akubra rabbit-skin hat. Strand Hatters has the best range.

✚ biii; J6 ✉ Shop 8, Strand Arcade, 412 George Street ☎ 9231 6884 🚇 St. James

Sydney lifestyle

For a taste of Sydney's diverse lifestyle, combine a harbor crossing (➤ 19) with a visit to the northern beaches' premier shopping center, Warringah Mall (✉ Pittwater Road, Brookvale 🕐 Mon–Wed, Fri 9–5:30; Thu 9–9; Sat 9–4; Sun 10–4). Just 30 minutes from the city by JetCat and bus, and 10 minutes from Manly (➤ 35) are its 170 specialist shops, plus branches of the department stores David Jones and Grace Bros (➤ 70), as well as relaxed outdoor and indoor shopping with garden courtyards, open-air cafés, movie theaters, restaurants, and free entertainment.

THEATERS & CLASSICAL PERFORMANCES

Classical Sydney

Sydney offers an excellent array of opera, ballet, and classical music. Don't miss seeing a performance at the Sydney Opera House (see entry this page)—the Sydney Symphony Orchestra, Australian Chamber Orchestra, Sydney Philharmonia, the Australian Ballet, and Australian Opera all perform regularly. The Sydney Theatre Company and Sydney Dance Company can often be seen at the Opera House Drama Theatre, while the complex's Playhouse offers a variety of theater shows. Classical music concerts also take place at the Town Hall and the Conservatorium of Music on Macquarie Street.

CAPITOL THEATRE
Refurbishment has made the historic 2,000-seat Capitol, dating from 1928, Sydney's most glorious performance space. This is the home of musicals and major theatrical events.
✚ J7 ✉ 13 Campbell Street, Haymarket ☎ 9266 4800 for performance information ⬛ Central (Railway Square exit)

HER MAJESTY'S THEATRE
This modern theater is one of Sydney's main performance venues, and features musicals such as *Cats* and other major productions.
✚ J7 ✉ 107 Quay Street, Haymarket ☎ 9212 3411 for performance information ⬛ Central (Railway Square exit)

LYRIC THEATRE
Managed by Andrew Lloyd Webber's company, this new theater presents a variety of internationally acclaimed theatrical performances.
✚ H6 ✉ 20–80 Pyrmont Street, Pyrmont ☎ 9265 4800 for performance information ⬛ Star City

SEYMOUR THEATRE CENTRE
There are three theaters here—for drama, dance, and chamber music—plus good restaurant and bar facilities.
✚ H8 ✉ Corner of Cleveland Street and City Road, Chippendale ☎ 9364 9400 for performance information ⬛ 422–428

STATE THEATRE
This ornate 2,000-seat theater is the venue for musicals, ballet, the Sydney Film Festival, and performances of live music. The State dates from 1929 and is National Trust-classified because of its splendid Art Deco interior.
✚ biv; J6 ✉ 49 Market Street ☎ 13 6100 for performance information ⬛ Town Hall

SYDNEY OPERA HOUSE
Despite its name, this famous building is not just a home for operatic productions. It contains four main performance spaces, including the 2,690-seat concert hall and the smaller opera theater (see panel).
✚ ci; K4 ✉ Bennelong Point ☎ Events information 9250 7209. Box office 9250 7777 ⏲ Daily. Closed Good Fri, Dec 25 ⬛ Circular Quay

THEATRE ROYAL
This modern, well-appointed, city-center theater specializes in putting on long-running musicals.
✚ biii; J6 ✉ MLC Centre, King Street ☎ 13 6166 for performance information ⬛ Martin Place

WHARF THEATRE
The home of the excellent Sydney Theatre Company, this intimate theater also features performances by the Sydney Dance Company. The popular restaurant has wonderful harbor views.
✚ J4 ✉ Pier 4, Hickson Road, Walsh Bay ☎ 9250 1777 ⏲ Shows Mon–Sat ⬛ Circular Quay

MODERN LIVE MUSIC

ANNANDALE HOTEL
Pub rock has been an important part of the local music scene for more than 30 years, and this lively hotel is one of the many good places to sample some of Australia's up-and-coming bands.

🕇 F8 ✉ 17 Parramatta Road, Annandale ☎ 9519 1078 🕒 Daily 🚌 461, 480, 483

THE BASEMENT
This famous, long-established club is the city's best venue for live blues, jazz, and funk at reasonable prices. The atmosphere is great and the good value restaurant serves nice food.

🕇 biii; J5 ✉ 29 Reiby Place, Circular Quay ☎ 9251 2797 🕒 Daily 🚉 Circular Quay

HARBOURSIDE BRASSERIE
This is one of Sydney's favorite venues for blues, jazz, and world music and, occasionally, stand-up comedy. The waterfront Harbourside gets very crowded but there is definitely a good atmosphere.

🕇 J4 ✉ Pier 1, Hickson Road, Walsh Bay ☎ 9252 3000 🕒 Nightly 🚉 Circular Quay

MARBLE BAR
Good jazz and similar music is what's on offer here. The magnificent High Victorian bar dates from 1893.

🕇 biv; J6 ✉ Basement, Sydney Hilton Hotel, 259 Pitt Street ☎ 9266 0610 🕒 Bar daily. Music Wed–Sat evenings 🚉 Town Hall

METRO THEATRE
The Metro, which is in the same complex as the excellent Dendy Cinema (► 83 panel), is a great venue to catch local rock, folk, and other types of bands. Dance, comedy, and other performances also feature occasionally.

🕇 J6 ✉ 624 George Street ☎ 9264 2666 for performance information 🚉 Town Hall

ROUND MIDNIGHT
This sophisticated, intimate, and very trendy venue puts on top-quality blues and jazz. Located in the heart of the Kings Cross night scene.

🕇 L6 ✉ 2 Roslyn Street, Kings Cross ☎ 9356 4045 🕒 Nightly 8PM–3AM 🚉 Kings Cross

SOUP PLUS
A moderately priced restaurant with good soups, snacks, and pasta, plus free jazz. Great value.

🕇 biii; J6 ✉ 383 George Street ☎ 9299 7728 🕒 Mon–Sat from lunchtime 🚉 Town Hall, Wynyard

SYDNEY ENTERTAINMENT CENTRE
Sydney's largest entertainment venue hosts everything from concerts by touring international rock groups to indoor tennis and basketball matches.

🕇 J7 ✉ Harbour Street, Haymarket ☎ 9211 2222. Recorded show information 11582 🚌 Performances most days 🚈 Monorail to Haymarket

Buying a ticket
There are several ways of obtaining tickets for theater, live music, and other events. You can visit the box offices, purchase via credit card from the ticketing agencies Ticketek (☎ 9266 4800) and First Call (☎ 9320 9000), or buy discounted tickets from Halftix (☎ Infoline 0055 26655). This half-price service operates from a booth in Martin Place (near Elizabeth Street); discounted tickets are sold only on the day of performance 🕒 Mon–Sat noon–6.

WHERE TO BE ENTERTAINED

HOTELS & BARS

Sydney watering holes

Drinking is a very popular pastime in Sydney and there are countless bars and pubs to visit. In addition to the well-known Foster's and Swan beers, there are more unusual brands such as Redback, Hahn, and Coopers. Australia's local spirit is Bundaberg rum "Bundy," available in underproof and the lethal overproof varieties. Beer is generally served in "middies" (10fl oz/ 284ml glasses) and larger "schooners." Bars and pubs, some of which are located in hotels, are licensed to trade for varying hours each day but are generally open until at least 11PM, while nightclubs and discos stay open longer.

BROOKLYN HOTEL
The Brooklyn is one of the city center's best and trendiest hotels, with contemporary decor and a good dining room.
✚ bii; J5 ✉ Corner of Grosvenor and George streets ☎ 9247 6744 ⏰ Daily 🚇 Wynyard

BURDEKIN HOTEL
This popular hotel in Darlinghurst has a large bar on the Oxford Street side and the more intimate, expensive Dugout Bar on Liverpool Street.
✚ K7 ✉ 2 Oxford Street, Darlinghurst ☎ 9331 3066 ⏰ Daily 🚇 Museum

CORTILE BAR
This first-floor hotel bar and lounge is surrounded by the imposing facade of the 1851 Treasury Building. Although it's expensive, the youthful business crowd makes it one of Sydney's most pleasant bars.
✚ cii; K5 ✉ Hotel Inter-Continental, 117 Macquarie Street ☎ 9230 0200 ⏰ Daily 🚇 Circular Quay

THE FOUR IN HAND
Mobile phones and beautiful people abound in this trendy, noisy, and vibrant Paddington pub. The food in the long-established restaurant is great.
✚ M7 ✉ Corner of Elizabeth and Sutherland streets, Paddington ☎ 9326 2254 ⏰ Daily 🚌 389

THE HORIZON
This pricey 36th-floor cocktail bar in one of the city's top hotels provides astounding views of the harbor.
✚ aii; J5 ✉ ANA Hotel, 176 Cumberland Street, The Rocks ☎ 9250 6000 ⏰ Daily 🚇 Circular Quay

LORD DUDLEY
A very popular English-style pub which (unusually for Sydney) serves beer in pint and half-pint tankards. The downstairs eating area is worth a visit, too.
✚ M7 ✉ 236 Jersey Road, Woollahra ☎ 9327 5399 ⏰ Daily 🚌 389

LORD NELSON BREWERY HOTEL
A visit to Sydney's oldest pub is a must—drinks have been served in this sandstone building since 1842, and the atmosphere is wonderful. The counter meals are also good.
✚ ai; J4 ✉ 19 Kent Street, Millers Point ☎ 9251 4044 ⏰ Daily 🚌 431, 432, 433

MERCANTILE HOTEL
Established in 1915, this colorful Rocks hotel is famous for its Art Deco wall tiles, Irish music, and draft Guinness.
✚ bi; J4 ✉ 25 George Street, The Rocks ☎ 9247 3570 ⏰ Daily 🚇 Circular Quay

PUMPHOUSE BREWERY AND TAVERN
This popular pub, sited in an historic 1891 pumphouse building, brews its own fine beer.
✚ J7 ✉ 17 Little Pier Street, Darling Harbour ☎ 9281 3967 ⏰ Daily 🚝 Monorail to Haymarket

DISCOS & NIGHTCLUBS

THE CAULDRON
A legend of the Sydney night scene, The Cauldron expects you to be hip and dress for success—or no admission! Good food and music, and it is always great for a late-night bop.

✚ K6 ✉ 207 Darlinghurst Road, Darlinghurst
☎ 9331 1523 🕐 Tue–Sat
🚇 Kings Cross

GLOBE
One of the best clubs in the CBD. A variety of music can be heard here, and it is the place to go to catch hot new bands-about-town.

✚ J6 ✉ 60 Park Street, Sydney ☎ 9264 4844
🕐 Nightly 🚇 Town Hall

GRAND PACIFIC BLUE ROOM
Trendy favorite of the young, with a variety of music. It is one of Sydney's most popular night spots.

✚ K7 ✉ Corner of South Dowling Street and Oxford Street, Paddington ☎ 9331 7108
🕐 Mon–Sat 🚌 380, 382

ICEBOX
A mix of rhythm and blues, hip hop, and funk, with different raves on different nights. The Milkbar offers a retro atmosphere and has a camp following.

✚ L6 ✉ 2 Kellet Street, Kings Cross ☎ 9331 0058
🕐 Wed–Sun 🚇 Kings Cross

KINSELAS
There is a broad spectrum of entertainment at Kinselas—a café/bar area, swanky cocktail bar, pool tables, live music, and even theater shows.

✚ K7 ✉ 383 Bourke Street, Taylor Square ☎ 9331 2699 or 331 3299 🕐 Nightly
🚌 373, 374, 380, 382

MIDNIGHT SHIFT
One of Sydney's most popular gay bars and discos. Not for everyone, but a great place to visit if the gay scene interests you (see panel).

✚ K7 ✉ 85 Oxford Street, Darlinghurst ☎ 9360 4463
🕐 Nightly 🚇 Museum

MR GOODBAR
Formerly The Freezer and Hip Hop Club—loud, packed, and hyper-hip. Free Monday and Wednesday. Thursday is jazz night, Friday the music is canned, Saturday is the hip icebox, and on Sunday it is soul.

✚ K7 ✉ 11 Oxford Street, Paddington ☎ 9360 6759
🕐 Nightly 🚌 373, 374, 380, 382

PALLADIUM
Located at the old Les Girls site, this sophisticated two-level club offers surprise and variety.

✚ L6 ✉ Roslyn Street, Kings Cross ☎ 9331 0127
🕐 Thu–Sun 🚇 Kings Cross

SOHO
For the serious clubber who likes to dress up to dance. Polar cool is needed to get past the doorman.

✚ L6 ✉ 171 Victoria Street, Potts Point ☎ 9358 6511
🕐 Nightly 🚇 Kings Cross

Gay and lesbian Sydney
Sydney is the home of the world's largest gay and lesbian parade—the Mardi Gras—that takes place each February/March. The area around lower Oxford Street (sometimes referred to as The Great Gay Way) is the heart of this alternative scene. Many hotels, bars, and clubs here cater to gays and lesbians; popular venues include the Midnight Shift (see entry this page), the Albury Hotel (✉ 6 Oxford Street, Paddington), and the Beresford Hotel (✉ 354 Bourke Street, Surry Hills).

SPORTS

Watersports

Sydney's location offers unlimited opportunities for watersports. You can windsurf from Rose Bay (☎ 9371 7036), go diving at Coogee (☎ 9665 6333), or sail with the Northside Sailing School (☎ 9969 3972). Weekend surf carnivals, where lifesavers from opposing clubs compete, are held at beaches such as Bondi and Manly from October to March, and you can watch competitive sailing on the harbor. The most exciting races, between 19ft-long skiffs, are held on Saturday afternoons from mid-September to April—full details are available from the Sydney Flying Squadron (☎ 9955 8350).

CENTENNIAL PARK

The perfect venue for cycling, horse riding, walking, rollerblading, and jogging. Horses and equipment can be hired (▶ 46).
✚ M8 ⊠ Off Oxford Street, Woollahra ☎ 9331 5056
🕐 Daily during daylight hours 🚌 378, 380, 382

COOPER PARK TENNIS COURTS

Scenically, there is no better place for tennis than this bushland spot between Bondi Junction and Double Bay.
✚ N8 ⊠ Suttie Road, Double Bay ☎ 9389 9259
🕐 Daily 🚌 Bondi Junction, then bus 330

MOORE PARK GOLF CLUB

An easily accessible golf club that offers an 18-hole course, a day and night driving range, and all the normal facilities for very reasonable rates.
✚ K9 ⊠ Cleveland Street, Moore Park ☎ 9663 1064
🕐 Daily (driving range until 8PM) 🚌 373, 374, 377, 394

NORTH SYDNEY OLYMPIC POOL

This harborside pool has views of the Harbour Bridge and Opera House. Open air in summer, but covered by a "bubble" in cooler months.
✚ J3 ⊠ Alfred Street, Milsons Point ☎ 9955 2309
🕐 Mon–Fri 6AM–9PM; Sat, Sun 7–7 🚊 Milsons Point

RANDWICK RACECOURSE

This famous eastern suburbs racecourse offers more than 50 horse-racing meetings each year.
✚ L10 ⊠ Alison Road, Randwick ☎ 9663 8425
🚌 372, 373, 374, 377

SYDNEY CRICKET GROUND

The famed SCG is the home of first class cricket in New South Wales. Test and one-day matches are played in summer, or you can visit the stadium and its Cricket Museum on a tour—contact Sportspace Tours (☎ 9380 0383).
✚ L8 ⊠ Driver Avenue, Moore Park ☎ 9360 6601, match information 0055 63132
🕐 Tours Mon–Sat 🚌 372, 373, 377, 393, 394, 396

SYDNEY ENTERTAINMENT CENTRE

The home of Sydney basketball, whose season runs from April to September.
✚ J7 ⊠ Harbour Street, Haymarket ☎ 9320 4200. Recorded events information 11582 🕐 Apr–Sep usually Fri and Sat 🚝 Monorail to Haymarket

SYDNEY FOOTBALL STADIUM

Rugby league, rugby union, and soccer are played in this ultra-modern stadium. You can watch a match during winter, or join a guided tour (see Sydney Cricket Ground, above).
✚ L8 ⊠ Driver Avenue, Moore Park ☎ 9360 6601, match information 0055 63133
🕐 Tours Mon–Sat 🚌 372, 373, 377, 393, 394, 396

OTHER ENTERTAINMENT

See also Architecture & Interiors (➤ 54–55), Free Attractions (➤ 60) Sydney Harbour dinner cruises (➤ 69 panel).

CITY FARM

This is a great place for the family to share some experiences of bush life, including shearing sheep, tractor rides, and milking demonstrations.

✚ Off map to southeast
✉ 31 Darling Street, Abbotsbury
☎ 9823 3222 ◷ Daily 9–5
🚉 Fairfield

CLOUD 9 BALLOON FLIGHTS

An adventurous way to view Sydney is from the air. Take a hot-air balloon flight and follow it with a champagne breakfast.

✚ Off map to northeast
✉ Parramatta Park
☎ 9686 7777 ◷ Daily at dawn 🚉 Parramatta

THE COMEDY STORE

Sydney's original comedy venue puts on two shows each night and features stand-up comedians, the hilarious improvised comedy contest, and similar acts of lunacy.

✚ E8 ✉ Corner of Parramatta Road and Crystal Street, Leichhardt
☎ 9564 3900 ◷ Shows nightly 🚌 461, 480, 483

DON BURROWS SUPPER CLUB

Mellow out on a Friday evening at dinner in Gilberts Restaurant, in the seaside suburb of Manly, listening to the sounds of legendary Australian jazz musician Don Burrows and his quartet.

✚ Off map to northeast
✉ Manly Pacific Parkroyal, 55 North Steyne, Manly
☎ 9977 7666 ◷ Fri night
⛴ Manly

HAROLD PARK HOTEL

This inner-city pub has a long tradition of comedy nights, as well as writers', poets', and other interesting evenings. Come along if you'd welcome an unusual night out.

✚ G7 ✉ 115 Wigram Road, Glebe ☎ 9692 0564
◷ Nightly 🚌 432, 433, 434

HAYDEN ORPHEUM PICTURE PALACE

Far more than just a movie theater, the Orpheum is worth a visit for its wonderful Art Deco interior and old-fashioned touches—such as Wurlitzer organ music at some movie sessions.

✚ L1 ✉ 380 Military Road, Cremorne ☎ 9908 4344
◷ Daily 🚌 178, 180, 182, 247

OLD SYDNEY TOWN

Although this is an hour's car ride from the city, the Central Coast area's Old Sydney Town is well worth a visit. The state's largest heritage park is a re-creation of harsh life in Sydney 200 years ago, complete with soldiers, convicts, mock floggings, and craftsmen.

✚ Off map to northeast
✉ Pacific Highway, Somersby
☎ 4340 1104 ◷ Wed–Sun (daily during school hols) 10–4. Closed Dec 25 🚉 Gosford, then a connecting bus

The movie scene

The main complexes are on George Street, south of Bathurst Street, and at 232 Pitt Street. Alternative movie theaters include the Dendy at Martin Place and 624 George Street; both have bars, while the Martin Place venue offers a bistro and specialist movie-buff shop. Less mainstream foreign and offbeat movies are also screened at the Academy Twin, 3a Oxford Street, Paddington. For movie details, see the *Sydney Morning Herald*.

Fox Studios Backlot

Located on the site of the old Sydney Showgrounds, this behind-the-scenes look at Twentieth Century Fox's Australian studio offers a great day out for all. The emphasis here is on fun-packed discovery, so be prepared to join in with film experiences such as *Titanic* and *Babe* and find out how TV shows are made. There are also restaurants, cafés, and stores and the colorful Show Ring Markets on weekends.

✚ L8 ✉ Driver Avenue, Moore Park ☎ 1300 369 849
◷ Daily 10–6. Closed 25 Dec
🚌 372, 377, 390, 399

LUXURY HOTELS

Prices

You may expect to pay the following prices per room per night regardless of single or double occupancy:

Luxury   more than A$240

Mid-range   up to A$170

Budget   up to A$90

It is always worth asking when you make your reservation whether any special deals are available. There are also many economical self-catering serviced apartments, while reasonably priced guesthouses and hostels are plentiful. Sydney's major hotel areas are The Rocks, the city center, Kings Cross, and North Sydney.

ANA HOTEL SYDNEY

The ANA is one of Sydney's newest hotels, offering wonderful views over the harbor. There are 10 dining and entertainment facilities, and the cocktail bar offers superb panoramic views for just the price of a drink.

✚ aii; J5 ✉ 176 Cumberland Street, The Rocks ☎ 9250 6000 🚇 Circular Quay

HOTEL INTER-CONTINENTAL SYDNEY

Close to the Botanic Gardens and The Rocks, this hotel is centered on the historic 1851 Treasury Building, the imposing facade of which remains in place.

✚ cii; K5 ✉ 117 Macquarie Street ☎ 9230 0200 🚇 Circular Quay

HOTEL NIKKO DARLING HARBOUR SYDNEY

A glossy, deluxe hotel overlooking Darling Harbour. It blends modern design with historic buildings, including the 1850s Dundee Arms Pub.

✚ aiii; J6 ✉ Corner of Sussex and King streets ☎ 9299 1231 🚇 Monorail to Darling Park

PARK HYATT SYDNEY

In terms of harborside location, this hotel has it all, plus plenty of style and direct views to the Harbour Bridge and Opera House. Languish in the elegant No. 7 At The Park restaurant.

✚ J4 ✉ 7 Hickson Road, The Rocks ☎ 9241 1234 🚇 Circular Quay

THE REGENT OF SYDNEY

Situated between the city center and The Rocks, the Regent is one of Australia's better hotels, with the city's largest hotel pool. Its Kable's restaurant offers fine dining.

✚ bii; J5 ✉ 199 George Street ☎ 9238 0000 🚇 Circular Quay

THE RITZ-CARLTON, SYDNEY

With just 100 or so rooms, this European-style hotel is one of Sydney's most intimate. On Macquarie Street, with sweeping Botanic Garden and harbor views, it is close to harbor ferry terminals and the Opera House.

✚ cii; K5 ✉ 93 Macquarie Street ☎ 9252 4600 🚇 Circular Quay

SEBEL TOWN HOUSE HOTEL

Long the favorite Sydney address of celebrities, the Sebel is in Kings Cross and is famous for its privacy and impeccable service.

✚ L6 ✉ 23 Elizabeth Bay Road, Elizabeth Bay ☎ 9358 3244 🚇 Kings Cross

SHERATON ON THE PARK

One of the Sheraton group's élite Luxury Collection, this magnificent city-center hotel has a grand three-story lobby and a fine restaurant. Rooms have excellent views.

✚ biv; J6 ✉ 161 Elizabeth Street ☎ 9286 6000 🚇 St. James

MID-RANGE HOTELS & APARTMENTS

BAYSIDE HOTEL

This is in a quiet location overlooking Rushcutters Park and the harbor, and close to Kings Cross and the shopping center of Double Bay, yet the hotel is just 1.5 miles from the city center.

➕ L6 ✉ 85 New South Head Road, Rushcutters Bay ☎ 9327 8511 🚇 Kings Cross/Edgecliff

THE CASTLEREAGH INN

Very central and good value. The Castlereagh features a magnificently restored traditional dining room. All rooms have private bathrooms, and continental breakfast is included.

➕ biv; J6 ✉ 169 Castlereagh Street ☎ 9264 2281 🚇 Town Hall

MANHATTAN HOTEL

The long-established and friendly Manhattan Hotel lies just a short walk from Kings Cross station. Tasteful modernization has made this Art Deco property even better value than it already was.

➕ L6 ✉ 8 Greenknowe Avenue, Elizabeth Bay ☎ 9358 1288 🚇 Kings Cross

OAKFORD APARTMENTS

These comfortable self-contained apartments offer fully equipped kitchens, private balconies, and pleasant water views. There is also a swimming pool.

➕ L5 ✉ 10 Wylde Street, Potts Point ☎ 9358 4544 🚇 Kings Cross

RAVESI'S ON BONDI BEACH

This boutique hotel has just 16 rooms and suites, overlooking Bondi Beach. The restaurant and cocktail bar are excellent, and the hotel is tastefully decorated and furnished.

➕ Off map to east ✉ 118 Campbell Parade, Bondi Beach ☎ 9365 4422 🚌 380, 382

REGENTS COURT

A good, moderately priced hotel, with spacious apartment-style suites, kitchens, and designer furnishings. This long-established, friendly, family-owned hotel is set in a quiet Kings Cross street.

➕ L6 ✉ 18 Springfield Avenue, Potts Point ☎ 9358 1533 🚇 Kings Cross

SAVOY SERVICED APARTMENTS

Located near Darling Harbour, these comfortable one-bedroom apartments with maid service have kitchens, balconies, and separate dining room.

➕ aiii; J6 ✉ Corner of King and Kent streets ☎ 9267 9211 🚇 Wynyard

VICTORIA COURT

This charming 1881-built Victorian guesthouse, pleasantly situated on a leafy avenue in Potts Point, is a member of the Historic Hotels of Australia network. Very comfortable and atmospheric.

➕ div; L6 ✉ 122 Victoria Street, Potts Point ☎ 9357 3200 🚇 Kings Cross

Apartments

Apartment-style hotels in Sydney generally fall into the mid-range price category. These so-called serviced apartments vary from one to three bedrooms, with separate dining areas and kitchens or kitchenettes. Many are large enough for families or small groups.

BUDGET HOTELS & GUESTHOUSES

Budget accommodations

In addition to these budget hotels, Sydney has dozens of backpackers' lodges. Prices start at A$15 per night and many establishments offer reduced rates for long stays.

Accommodations vary from private rooms to dormitories, and the best backpacker areas are Kings Cross, inner-west Glebe, and beach suburbs such as Bondi and Coogee. Another budget option is staying in a "hotel." In Australia, the word hotel, confusingly, has two meanings: the conventional hotel and a pub with a few bedrooms. More details can be obtained from the NSW Travel Centre (☎ 9231 4444).

AARONS HOTEL
Better-than-average accommodations near Darling Harbour, with 24-hour reception services and a licensed restaurant and bar.
✚ J7 ✉ 37 Ultimo Road, Haymarket ☎ 9281 5555
🚊 Central

AUSTRALIAN SUNRISE LODGE
Good choice of single or double rooms, most with private balcony and bathrooms. Well located in the vibrant suburb of Newtown.
✚ Off map to west ✉ 485 King Street, Newtown ☎ 9550 4999 🚌 422 🚊 Newtown

CREMORNE POINT MANOR
Located on the north shore a few minutes by ferry from the city, this 30-room on-the-harbor manor house provides kitchens, laundry service, and a continental breakfast on request.
✚ L3 ✉ 6 Cremorne Road, Cremorne Point ☎ 9953 7899 ⛴ Cremorne Point

KINGSVIEW MOTEL
In the heart of the Kings Cross bustle, the Kingsview Motel has a variety of suites.
✚ L6 ✉ 30 Darlinghurst Road, Kings Cross ☎ 9358 5599 🚊 Kings Cross

KIRKETON HOTEL
A true budget hotel with its own restaurant and a range of rooms, from those with private facilities to bunk rooms. Very close to Kings Cross station.
✚ K6 ✉ 229 Darlinghurst

Road, Kings Cross ☎ 9360 4333 🚊 Kings Cross

THE LODGE MOTEL
Studios include kitchenettes and air-conditioning. Laundry facilities.
✚ L6 ✉ 44 New South Head Road, Rushcutters Bay ☎ 9328 0666 🚊 Kings Cross/Edgecliff

MANLY BEACH RESORT
This resort offers double, twin, and family rooms, a swimming pool, and good facilities. A scenic ferry ride away from the city.
✚ Off map to northeast
✉ 6 Carlton Street, Manly
☎ 9977 4188 ⛴ Manly

METRO MOTOR INN KINGS CROSS
A comfortable apartment-style hotel in a quieter part of Kings Cross. Good facilities for those on a budget.
✚ L6 ✉ 40 Bayswater Road, Kings Cross ☎ 9356 3511
🚊 Kings Cross

SYDNEY CENTRAL YHA
An excellent place near Central station for backpackers. There is also motel-style accommodation and you don't need a hostel card to stay here.
✚ J7 ✉ Corner of Pitt Street and Rawson Place
☎ 9281 9111 🚊 Central

THELELLEN LODGE
Small building offering 14 rooms. Conveniently located close to the beach and stores.
✚ Off map to east ✉ 11a Consett Avenue, Bondi Beach
☎ 9130 5333 🚌 380, 382

SYDNEY's
travel facts

ARRIVING & DEPARTING

Before you go

- All visitors require a valid passport and an electronic travel authority (ETA), which has replaced the traditional visa.
- A Tourist ETA is valid for multiple travel within one year (or the expiry date of your passport, if sooner) on three-month visits. An ETA is available through most travel agents as well as overseas Australian diplomatic offices.
- Vaccination certificates are not normally required.
- Check your insurance coverage before you leave home and buy a supplementary policy if necessary.
- Australian Tourist Commission offices: ⊠ 25th Floor, 100 Park Avenue, New York, NY 10017 ☎ 212/687–6300. ⊠ 2049 Century Park East Suite 1920, Los Angeles, CA 90067 ☎ 310/552–1988

When to go

- Sydney has warm to very hot summers, which can also be humid and rather wet. Semi-tropical summer thunderstorms are common.
- In summer (December to February) take light cotton clothing, sandals, a broad-brimmed hat, sunglasses, and other summer-weight items, plus an umbrella.
- In winter (June to August) take a raincoat and/or medium-weight coat, plus clothing suitable for a temperature range of 37–41°F.
- Most rain falls March to July.
- The best months for a visit are generally October to April.

Arriving by air

- Sydney International Airport is the main port of entry for the majority of airlines.
- The airport is 7 miles from Sydney's center. There are taxis and inexpensive bus services into the city (see Airport Express below), as well as car-rental outlets.
- Green and yellow Airport Express buses run between the airport and: the city (route 300), city and Kings Cross (route 350), Coogee and Bondi Beaches (route 351), and Darling Harbour/Glebe (route 352) every 10–20 minutes daily, and are the cheapest way of getting into the city on arrival.

Traveling from Sydney

- There are numerous daily flights, buses, and train services to all major towns and cities throughout Australia.

Customs and quarantine regulations

- Visitors aged 18 or over may bring in 250 cigarettes or 250g of tobacco or cigars; 1.125 liters of alcoholic liquor; plus other dutiable goods to the value of A$400 per person.
- There is no limit on money imported for personal use, although amounts in excess of A$5,000 or its equivalent must be declared on arrival.
- All animals are subject to quarantine, and all goods of plant or animal origin must be declared on arrival—anything suspect will be confiscated. It is forbidden to bring in food.
- The smuggling of all drugs is treated harshly in Australia, and the importing of firearms and items such as ivory or other products from endangered species is illegal or restricted.

Departure tax

- A departure tax of A$27, plus A$3.40 noise tax, is collected by the travel agent when you purchase your airline ticket.

ESSENTIAL FACTS

Electricity
- The electricity supply in Australia is 230–250 volts AC. Three-flat-pin plugs are the standard—you will need to bring an adapter.
- Hotels provide standard 110-volt and 240-volt shaver sockets.

Etiquette
- Smoking is prohibited on public transportation (including all domestic flights and inside airport terminals), in movie theaters, theaters, and most stores and shopping centers. Many restaurants provide no-smoking areas.
- Dress is generally smart-casual except for the most formal occasions. Beach-style clothing for women and shorts for men are commonplace in summer, even in the city center.
- Tipping (normally 10 percent) is expected only in restaurants where service charges are not added to bills. Tipping taxi-drivers and hotel staff is optional.

Money matters
- The Australian unit of currency is the Australian dollar ($), comprising 100 cents. Banknotes come in A$100, $50, $20, $10, and $5 denominations. Coins come in 5¢, 10¢, 20¢, and 50¢ (silver), and A$1 and $2 (gold colored).
- Currency exchanges where you can cash travelers' checks and most currencies at hotels, some stores, tourist centers, and outlets such as American Express and Thomas Cook are open outside banking hours. International airport exchange facilities are open daily 5:30AM–11PM. You can obtain cash from 24-hour ATMs throughout the city and country.

- Major credit cards (American Express, Visa, and MasterCard) are widely accepted.

Opening hours
- Stores: generally Mon–Fri 9–5:30; Sat 9–4. Late-night shopping until 9 on Thu. Large stores open Sun until 4. Suburban corner shops often open daily 8–8 or later.
- Post offices: generally Mon–Fri 9–5. Sydney General Post Office hours are Mon–Fri 8:15–5:30; Sat 8:30–noon.
- Banks: Mon–Thu 9:30–4; Fri 9:30–5. City head-office banks open Mon–Fri 8:15–5.
- Hotels (bars/pubs): licensing hours are generally 10AM–11PM.
- Museums and galleries: generally daily 10–5. Some close one day in the week.
- Offices: Mon–Fri 9–5 (or 5:30).
- Restaurants: some close on Sun or Mon; phone beforehand.

Places of worship
- Anglican: St. Andrew's Cathedral ✉ Sydney Square, George Street
- Roman Catholic: St. Mary's Cathedral ✉ College Street
- Presbyterian: Scots Church ✉ 44 Margaret Street
- Baptist: Central Baptist Church ✉ 619 George Street
- Interdenominational: Wayside Chapel ✉ 29 Hughes Street, Kings Cross
- Jewish: The Great Synagogue ✉ 166 Castlereagh Street
- Buddhist: Buddhist Centre ☎ 9929 8643
- Muslim: Sydney Mosque ✉ 13 John Street, Erskineville

Public holidays
- Jan 1, Jan 26 (Australia Day), Good Fri, Easter Mon, Apr 25 (Anzac Day), 2nd Mon in Jun (Queen's birthday), 1st Mon in Aug (NSW; banks only), 1st Mon

in Oct (Labor Day: NSW state holiday), Dec 25–26.

- School summer holidays are mid-December to late January—transportation, accommodations, and tourist facilities are heavily reserved at this time.

Restrooms

- Free restrooms are found in parks, public places, galleries and museums, department stores, and bus and train stations.

Student travelers

- International Student Cards are *not* usually recognized by movie theaters, theaters, or transportation authorities, but you may be able to get concessions on bus travel.
- There are many backpackers' lodges, Youth Hostel Association (YHA) establishments, and hostels in Sydney. YHA card-holders *may* obtain discounts.

Time differences

- Australia has three time zones, with Sydney and other eastern cities on Eastern Standard Time (EST), 10 hours ahead of GMT.
- Daylight saving Summer Time operates from late October to March. Sydney is then 11 hours ahead of GMT.

Tourist information

- Useful phone information services:
  Tourist Information Service
  ☎ 9669 5111
  Sydney Information Line
  ☎ 9911 7700
- Sydney's State Travel Centre (🕐 Mon–Fri 9–5) offers information, advice, maps and details of accommodations, and will make travel and hotel reservations.
- New South Wales Travel Centre
  ✉ 19 Castlereagh Street ☎ 9231 4444

Freephone outside Sydney 008 817 987

- Australian Tourist Commission offices outside Australia:
  U.S.A. ✉ 2049 Century Park East Suite 1920, Los Angeles, CA 90067 ☎ 310/229–4870
  U.K. ✉ 10–18 Putney Hill, London, SW15 6AA ☎ 020 8780 1496

PUBLIC TRANSPORTATION

- For all timetable and ticket inquiries (buses, ferries, and Cityrail trains) ☎ 13 1500
  🕐 Daily 6AM–10PM
- Monorail information ☎ 9552 2288
- Countrylink (out of town) train information ☎ 13 2232

Buses

- Sydney's buses are usually blue and white, except the Airport Express and Explorer buses.
- The most important bus terminals are Circular Quay (to Bondi Beach, the eastern suburbs, the south, and some inner-west areas) and Wynyard (over Harbour Bridge).
- Ordinary tickets can be bought on board, but special passes (see below) should be bought from the driver or State Transit sales outlets.

Ferries

- Ferry services operate from four wharves on Circular Quay to 28 places around the harbor, and upriver towards Parramatta.
- Buy tickets from the Circular Quay counters (opposite Wharf 4).
- Ferries and the high-speed Manly JetCats run daily 6AM–midnight.

Monorail

- The privately run monorail runs in a loop above the city, Darling Harbour and the Chinatown area. Use it for the Sydney Aquarium, National Maritime Museum, and Powerhouse Museum.

- The monorail runs every few minutes Mon–Thu 7AM–10PM; Fri, Sat 7AM–midnight; Sun 8AM–10PM. You can buy an economical all-day pass.

Taxis and water taxis

- Taxis are meter-operated and conspicuously marked with a "Taxi" sign on top of the vehicle. There is a minimum flagfall charge and the remainder of the fare is calculated on a distance/time-of-rental basis, with a small additional service charge for taxis ordered by phone.
- Cabs are abundant and fares are reasonable by world standards.
- Main operators include: Legion Cabs ☎ 13 1451; Taxis Combined Services ☎ 8332 8888; Premier Cabs ☎ 13 1017; RSL Cabs ☎ 13 2211
- Taxis for people with disabilities ☎ 9339 0200
- Water taxis operate to and from virtually anywhere on the harbor that has steps or a wharf. Call Taxis Afloat ☎ 9955 3222 or Aboat Taxis ☎ 9955 1155

Trains

- Sydney's inner-city rail services include the City Circle (Central, Town Hall, Wynyard, Circular Quay, St. James, and Museum) and the Eastern Suburbs Line, which runs from Central to Town Hall, Martin Place, Kings Cross, Edgecliff, and Bondi Junction.
- Buy tickets from booths or machines, and enter platforms via the automatic barriers.
- Trains generally operate 4:30AM–midnight.

Trams

- A 15-minute light rail service connects Central Station to Chinatown, the University of Technology, Darling Harbour,

Star City Casino, the Sydney Fish Market, and Wentworth Park.

Transportation maps and tickets

- Free maps are available from bus, ferry, and train offices at Circular Quay, Wynyard bus station, Town Hall train station, and other public transportation offices.
- The Sydneypass, valid for three, five, or seven days, includes the Airport Express bus, cruises, the Explorer buses, and unlimited travel on the regular state-operated bus and ferry services.
- Train: off-peak tickets (for travel at weekends and after 9AM at weekdays) represent a 45 percent saving. A Cityhopper pass allows travel on the inner-city rail service all day for a very reasonable price. Other Travelpasses include rail, bus, and ferry travel.
- Buses: Bustripper passes allow unlimited travel all day on the bus network; a budget Travelten ticket is valid for 10 journeys. The red Sydney Explorer and blue Bondi & Bay Explorer services operate to the city's most important sights at regular intervals daily 9AM–6PM. Tickets offer all day travel and the option of leaving and reboarding the buses at will.
- Ferries: A Ferrytravel+ ticket offers a considerable saving for 10 journeys. Travelpasses also permit combined bus and ferry travel, or a combination of bus, ferry, and train. There are also special ferry travel/entrance passes to attractions such as Taronga Zoo, the Aquarium, and Oceanworld.

DRIVING & CAR RENTAL

Driving

- Driving is on the left and overtaking traffic (which has the

right of way) is on the right. This,
however, may not be immediately
obvious on multi-lane highways
where the preference seems to be
to stay in the right-hand lane. On
some stretches of winding roads,
lay-bys are provided to be used by
by slow traffic to enable other
drivers to overtake.

• Take special care when driving on
unsurfaced roads; they are best
avoided. Also, avoid driving in the
country at night; and beware of
stray animals on motorways at
dawn and dusk.

• Some road signs are peculiar to
Australia, but most will be
immediately understandable to
visitors; they may involve tortuous
wordage rather than symbols.

• Full details of Australia's road
rules are available from the AAA
in Canberra ☎ 02 6247 7311

• Speed limits are 30/35mph in
urban areas and 60/65mph
elsewhere unless indicated.

• Seatbelts must be worn in front
and back seats.

• Gasoline (unleaded and leaded) is
sold by the liter; gas stations are
numerous but may have restricted
weekend opening hours.

• The legal limit for alcohol is 0.05
percent blood alcohol level.

Car rental

• Renting a car may be necessary
for some of the out-of-town trips
within this book. You must be
over 21. Compulsory third-party
insurance is included in rental
prices, which are on average
A$60–$80 per day. Visitors must
have an international driving
license or a valid overseas driving
license (with a translation if it is
not in English).

• Major Sydney car-hire companies:
Avis ☎ 9357 2000; Budget ☎ 13 2727;
Hertz ☎ 13 3039

MEDIA & COMMUNICATIONS

International newsdealers

• U.S. and U.K. newspapers, and
many foreign-language papers are
available from large newsdealers
and at the following outlets: TNT
Express Worldwide ✉ The Atrium, 33
Pitt Street; World News Centre ✉ 402
Harbourside, Darling Harbour; City Library
✉ Town Hall House, Sydney Square

Newspapers & magazines

• The main national newspaper is
The Australian; read *The Australian
Financial Review* for business news.

• The major city newspaper is the
Sydney Morning Herald.

• The weekly *Bulletin Newsweek* is
Australia's answer to *Time*.

Postal services

• Larger post offices provide
services such as aerograms, fax
facilities, and e-mail. (► 89 for
post office opening times.)

• Stamps can also be purchased
from hotels, and from some
newsstands and souvenir shops.

• Postage inquiries ☎ 13 1317

Radio & television

• Radio: Sydney has 25 major
stations, from FM rock music
broadcasters such as 2 DAY-FM,
Triple J-FM, and Triple M-FM to
ABC Radio National and ABC 2
BL. There are also many AM
music, chat, and news stations.

• Television: Channel 2 has no
commercials. Channels 7, 9, 10,
and SBS are commercial and there
are two cable networks.

Telephones

• Public telephones are found at
phone booths, post offices, hotels,
service stations, stores, railroad
and bus stations, and cafés. There

is a 24-hour telephone center ✉ **100 King Street**. Local calls cost 40¢ for unlimited time (20¢ and 10¢ coins can be used).

- Long-distance calls within Australia, known as STD, vary considerably in price, but you should have a good supply of 50¢ and A$1 coins. Calls are cheaper after 6PM and all day Sunday.
- Operator assistance ☎ **012 (0176 from payphones)**
- Reverse-charge calls ☎ **011**
- Phonecards come in values of A$2 to $20; credit cards can also be used from some (silver) phones.
- For international (IDD) calls (can be made from some public phones) dial 0011 followed by the country codes: U.S.A. and Canada 1; U.K. 44; France 33; Germany 49.
- International inquiries (such as time differences and costs) ☎ **0102**. To reserve an operator-connected call ☎ **0101**
- To call a Sydney number from outside the metropolitan area, use the prefix 02.

EMERGENCIES

Consulates
- Canada ☎ **9364 3000**
- France ☎ **9261 5779**
- Germany ☎ **9328 7733**
- U.K. ☎ **9247 7521**
- U.S.A. ☎ **9373 9200**

Emergency phone numbers
- Police, ambulance or fire ☎ **000** (24 hours). Calls are free.
- Dental, pharmaceutical, personal, or other: see the front of the A–K volume of the Sydney White Pages telephone book.

Medical treatment
- Medical, dental, and ambulance services are excellent but costly.
- Doctors and dentists are readily

available and there are many medical centers where appointments are not necessary.
- Hotel Doctor Service ☎ **9962 6000** ⓒ **Daily 7AM–11PM (applies only to CBD hotels)**

Medicines
- You may bring in prescribed medications. Keep them in the original containers and bring a copy of your physician's prescription to avoid problems at customs.

Sensible precautions
- Report theft or any other incident to your hotel and/or the police as soon as possible. If your travelers' checks are stolen, advise the relevant organization.
- The non-emergency, police enquiries number is ☎ **9281 0000**
- Sydney's police wear blue uniforms and a peaked cap. They are generally helpful and polite.
- Tap water is safe to drink; the only medical problems you are likely to experience are sunburn and mosquito bites.
- If you burn easily, generously apply sun block SPF15+, wear sunglasses, a broad-brimmed hat, and long sleeves, and avoid the summer sun from 11 to 3.
- Dangerous currents and marine stingers can cause problems in the sea in summer, so take notice of lifeguards and any beach signs.
- Women are generally safe in Sydney, but walking alone in parks or on beaches at night and traveling alone on out-of-city-center trains is not recommended.

INDEX

Citypack
Sydney

AUTHOR *Anne Matthews*
REVISED BY *Rod Ritchie, Julia Walkden* COPY EDITOR *Karen Bold*
COVER DESIGN *Tigist Getachew, Fabrizio La Rocca*
COVER PICTURES *AA Photo Library*

Copyright   ©Automobile Association Developments Limited 2001
Maps copyright ©Automobile Association Developments Limited 1996, 2000
Fold-out map: © RV Reise- und Verkehrsverlag Munich · Stuttgart
               © Cartography: GeoData

ISBN 0–679–00842–X
Second Edition

Acknowledgments

The Automobile Association wishes to thank the following photographers, libraries and
associations for their assistance in the preparation of this book: The Art Gallery of New
South Wales 43b; Asiafoto 33; Australian Museum 41b; Australian National Maritime
Museum 37; Australian Tourist Commission 7, 22, 24b, 34b, 40b, 55; Customs House,
Sydney 27b; Mary Evans Picture Library 12; Historic Houses Trust of New South Wales
47, 52, 53; International Photobank 17, 20, 27a, 50; Lone Pine Sanctuary 57; Anne
Matthews 28, 42; Museum of Contemporary Art 40a; Museum of Sydney 44a, 44b;
Pictures Colour Library 87a; The Stock Market Photo Agency Inc F/Cover; Sydney Star
Casino 39. All remaining pictures are held in the Association's own library (AA Photo
Library) with contributions from A Baker 18, 25a, 29a, 29b, 32, 36, 38, 46a, 46b, 60, 61a,
61b; P Kenward F/Cover inset, 1, 5a, 5b, 6, 13a, 13b, 15, 16, 19, 21, 23a, 23b, 24a, 25b,
26, 30a, 30b, 31, 34a, 35a, 35b, 41a, 43a, 45, 48, 49a, 49b,54, 58, 59, 87b.

Important tip

Time inevitably brings changes, so always confirm prices, travel facts, and other perishable
information when it matters. Although Fodor's cannot accept responsibility for errors, you can
use this guide in the confidence that we have taken every care to ensure its accuracy.

Special sales

Fodor's Travel Publications are available at special discounts for bulk purchases
(100 copies or more) for sales promotions or premiums. Special editions, including
personalized covers, excerpts of existing guides, and corporate imprints, can be created
in large quantities for special needs. For more information, contact your local bookseller
or write to Special Markets, Fodor's Travel Publications, 280 Park Avenue, New York,
NY 10017. Inquiries from Canada should be directed to your local Canadian bookseller
or sent to Random House of Canada, Ltd., Marketing Department, 2775 Matheson
Blvd. East, Mississauga, Ontario L4W 4P7.

Color separation by Daylight Colour Art Pte Ltd, Singapore
Manufactured by Dai Nippon Printing Co. (Hong Kong) Ltd
10 9 8 7 6 5 4 3 2 1

Titles in the Citypack series
- Amsterdam ● Barcelona ● Beijing ● Berlin ● Boston ● Brussels & Bruges ●
- Chicago ● Dublin ● Florence ● Hong Kong ● Lisbon ● London ●Los Angeles ●
- Madrid ● Melbourne ● Miami ● Montreal ● Munich ● New York ● Paris ●
- Prague ● Rome ● San Francisco ● Seattle ● Shanghai ● Singapore ● Sydney ●
- Tokyo ● Toronto ● Venice ● Vienna ● Washington, D.C. ●